AMERICAN PLANER, SHAPER and SLOTTER BUILDERS 1830 — 1910

AMERICAN PLANER, SHAPER and SLOTTER BUILDERS 1830 — 1910

Kenneth L. Cope

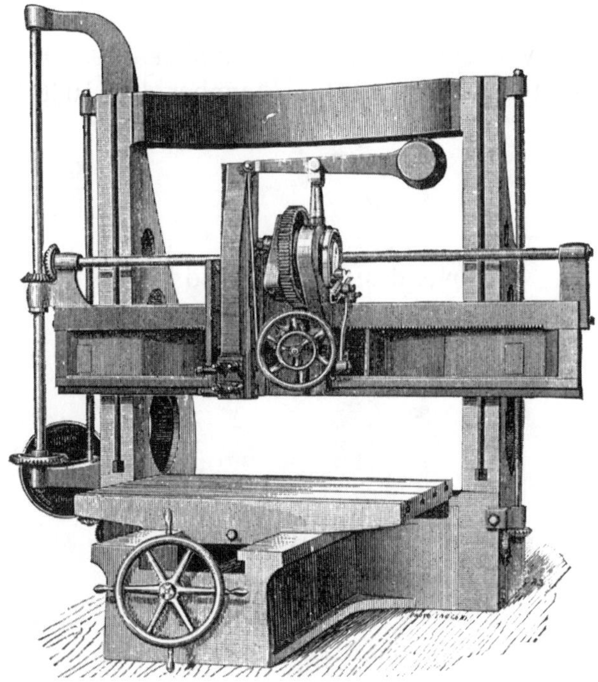

ASTRAGAL PRESS
Mendham New Jersey

Library of Congress Control Number 2002105250
International Standard Book Number 1-931626-04-9

Cover design by Donald Kahn

Published by
THE ASTRAGAL PRESS
5 Cold Hill Road, Suite 12
P.O. Box 239
Mendham NJ 07945-0239

Manufactured in the United States of America

DEDICATION

Dedicated to the men and women of the American machine tool industry. Often working under very difficult conditions, they made the tools that made the machines that made the United States the envy of the industrial world.

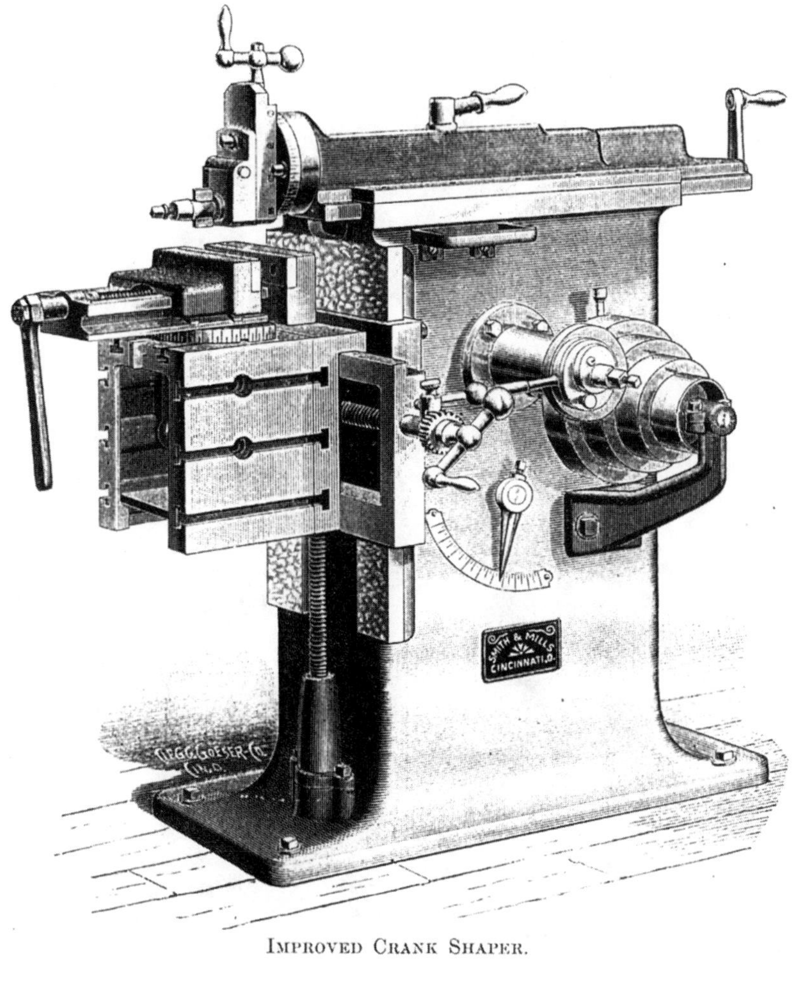

IMPROVED CRANK SHAPER.

ACKNOWLEDGMENTS

Heartfelt thanks are extended to all those who helped make this book as complete as it is. Many people sent material from catalogs, city directories, and contemporary magazines from their collections or from sources to which they had access.

Special thanks to:

- Ken Kranzusch whose machine tool catalog collection proved invaluable.

- Frank Morrison who scoured the Fitchburg, Massachusetts, Public Library and Fitchburg Historical Society.

- Phil Platt who did the same at Worcester, Massachusetts.

- Bob Vogel who tapped the machine tool catalog resources of the Smithsonian.

- The staff of the Milwaukee Public Library who never seemed to tire of hauling heavy, bound volumes of "American Machinist," "Machinery," "Iron Age," and other, more obscure, periodicals.

- Dozens of other librarians scattered across the United States who were unfailingly polite and helpful when I called.

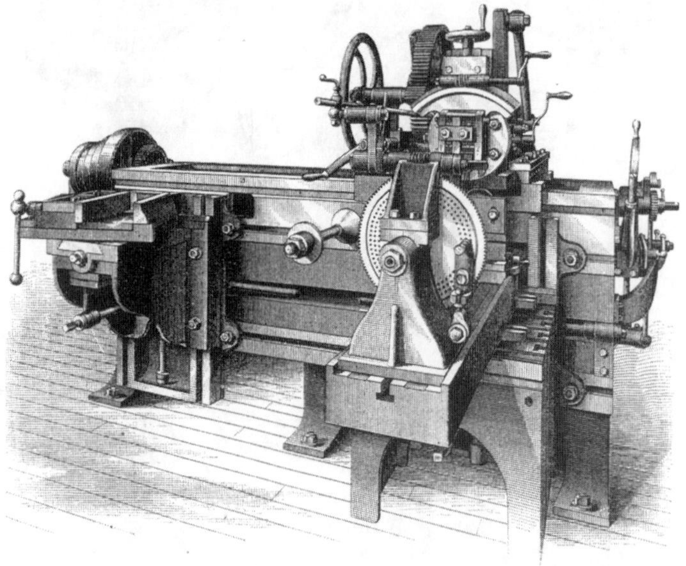

SHAPING-MACHINE FOR GUN-WORK, BUILT BY W. H. WARREN.

INTRODUCTION

Continuing the pattern set by *American Lathe Builders 1810-1910*, this book is not meant to be a history of planers, shapers and slotters. It is meant to bring to light the pioneer builders of the American planer, shaper and slotter and to illustrate, as far as possible, their products. Many of the builders listed are well known, and a very few are still operating; others are obscure, and some are known only from a single advertisement placed in a contemporary magazine. Information and illustrations have been gleaned from such sources as city directories, records of sales to the U.S. government, contemporary publications including *American Artisan, American Machinist, American Manufacturer, Iron Age, Machinery, Mechanics*, and *Scientific American* magazines, and a large number of catalogs issued by planer, shaper and slotter builders and dealers.

To put the entries into context, perhaps we need to start with short, late 19th century definitions of the machines as follows:

PLANER—A machine whose natural function is to produce a flat surface. This is accomplished by causing the work, which is fastened to a table that has a reciprocating motion, to pass back and forth under a cutting tool; the tool is fed across the work at right angles to the line of motion of the table.

SHAPER—The principal points of difference between the planer and shaper are found in the relation that the tool and work bear to each other, and in the method of obtaining the feed. In the shaper the work is stationary during the cut and the tool passes over it; the work feeds sideways during the return stroke of the tool.

SLOTTER—A modification of the shaper and similar to it in many respects. In the slotter, the ram moves vertically instead of horizontally. It is used for finishing flat or curved surfaces at right angles to a horizontal surface of the work. The name derives from the fact that it was originally intended for cutting slots or keyways in gears or pulleys.

The following list, with short descriptions, will help the reader wade through references to the various forms of planers, shapers, and slotters named in the text. Please note that all entries and descriptions apply to machines produced during the period 1830-1910. Many of these machine types were later abandoned, greatly modified, or became known by different names.

BACK GEARED SHAPER A shaper with a set of back gears, such as commonly found on engine lathes, which could be engaged to slow the speed of the ram and increase the cutting force available. Back gears were supplied on both crank shapers and geared shapers.

CHAIN DRIVE PLANER A planer driven by a heavy chain attached to the table and driven by sprockets at each end. This early drive was unsatisfactory due to the large amount of backlash inherent in chain drives. See GAY, SILVER & CO. entry for an illustration.

COLUMN SHAPER Also called pillar shapers, a column shaper is equipped with a ram which moves only in and out, with no side motion. This is one of two basic types of shapers, the other being the TRAVERSE or TRAVELING HEAD SHAPER.

CRANK PLANER A planer driven by a rotating crank which generates a reciprocating, linear motion. Crank drives are found only on very short stroke planers.

CRANK SHAPER The most common and simplest type of shaper, its reciprocating motion is generated by the operation of a rotating crank driven by a belt or motor. The crank may be mounted in a vertical or horizontal plane.

CYLINDER SHAPER Long stroke shaper designed to machine the inside of locomotive cylinders. See BEMENT, MILES & CO. entry for an illustration.

DRAW CUT SHAPER A shaper designed to cut on the return stroke of the ram, rather than the forward stroke. The feature was claimed to allow heavier cuts, since the cutting force was taken against the heavy structure of the machine rather than tending to push the table away from the column. This may have been true, but the draw cut shaper never achieved a large market share. See MORTON MFG. CO. entry for an illustration.

EXTENSION BASE SHAPER A shaper with the main column/base casting extended as far as the outer end of the table. This allow a brace to be installed from the table down to the base, better supporting the table during a heavy cut.

EXTENSION PLANER A planer with one stationary upright and one moveable upright, usually supported on an extension bed mounted at right angles to the main bed. The feature allowed the distance between uprights to be increased for larger workpieces or decreased for smaller one. Some designs allowed complete removal of the moveable upright, converting to an open-side planer. See DETRICK & HARVEY MACHINE CO. entry for an illustration.

FRICTION PLANER A planer designed to reverse table direction by the action of mechanically operated friction clutches.

FRICTION SHAPER A shaper designed to reverse ram direction by the action of mechanically operated friction clutches.

FROG & SWITCH PLANER A planer built for makers of frog and switch components for railway use. The machines were of simple and heavy construction and had less height under the crossrail than standard planers. See G.A. CRAY CO. entry for an illustration.

GEARED SHAPER A shaper driven by a rotating gear train meshing with a rack attached to the ram. Reciprocating motion is generated by reversing the direction of rotary motion, usually by shifting belts from a forward to a reverse pulley.

GEARED SLOTTER A slotter driven by a rotating gear train. Reciprocating motion is generated by reversing the direction of rotary motion, usually by shifting belts from a forward to a reverse pulley. Most large slotters were equipped with worm and wheel gear trains.

HAND PLANER A planer driven by a hand crank powered by the machine operator. Some planers were made to operate with either hand or belt power and were advertised as especially useful to shops with unreliable power, such as water wheels which often froze in the winter.

HAND SHAPER A shaper driven by a lever or crank powered by the machine operator.

LITHOGRAPHIC STONE PLANER A planer designed to plane the surfaces of lithographic stones used in printing. See G.A. GRAY CO. entry for an illustration.

LOCOMOTIVE FRAME SLOTTER A large slotter designed to machine openings in locomotive frames. Most were equipped with two heads. See WILLIAM SELLERS & CO. entry for an illustration.

OPEN SIDE PLANER A planer with only one extra heavy upright supporting the crossrail. This allowed machining of workpieces wider than the table. Such machines were often supplied with outriggers that supported the overhanging weight of the workpiece. See DETRICK & HARVEY entry for illustrations of open side machines.

OPEN SIDE SHAPER A shaper in which the ram moves in a slide support which extended over the table, but offset to one side. See FOX MACINE CO. entry for an illustration.

PILLAR SHAPER See COLUMN SHAPER

PLATE PLANER A machine designed to plane the edges of iron or steel plates before they were assembled. Not only were the edges planed straight but if the plate was formed into a cylinder, as when used in boilers, or otherwise formed after planing, a bevel was machined which allowed the edges to butt squarely after the plate was bent. See HILLES & JONES entry for an illustration.

RACK DRIVE PLANER A planer with a rack, fastened on the underside of the table, that converts rotary motion of a gear train to linear motion of the table.

ROD PLANER A planer designed to machine surfaces of locomotive connecting rods. The machine had much less height under the crossrail than standard planers. See WILLIAM SELLERS & CO. entry for an illustration.

ROTARY PLANER Technically not a planer, the machine is more accurately described as a milling machine. However, the industry called them planers so they are included. Rotary planers were equipped with large rotating discs in which a number of planing tools were mounted. They were used primarily to machine the ends of large, cast iron, architectural components popular in the last quarter of the 19th century. See NEWTON MACHINE TOOL WORKS entry for illustration.

SCREW DRIVE PLANER A planer driven by a lead screw that converts rotary motion of a belt or set of gears to linear motion of the table.

SCREW DRIVE SHAPER A shaper driven by a lead screw that converts rotary motion of a belt or set of gears to linear motion of the ram.

SELLER'S DRIVE PLANER A planer driven by a spiral worm gear that meshes with a rack fastened to the underside of the table. See WILLIAM SELLERS & CO. entry for a detailed description. This drive was patented by William Sellers in 1862 and was much copied after the patent expired.

SNAGGING SHAPER A shaper designed for very rough work on raw castings, it was built for ruggedness rather than accuracy, Finish cuts would be done on a separate machine. See PERKING MACHINE CO. entry for an illustration.

SPUR GEARED PLANER A planer driven by a set of spur gears transferring power from the input pulley to a rack fastened on the underside of the table. The largest diameter gear is called the Bull-Wheel or Bull-Gear and acts as a flywheel for smoother operation through variable cutting loads.

STONE PLANER A planer designed to plane stone, either to a flat surface or the shapes desired for moldings. See LINCOLN IRON WORKS entry for an illustration.

SUSPENSION SHAPER A shaper with the head suspended on a crossrail above a fixed platen on which the workpiece is mounted. See HENDEY MACHINE CO. entry for an illustration.

TRAVELING HEAD SHAPER A shaper with a ram and saddle mounted on a bed which allows longitudinal motion. Most such shapers were equipped with two tables to handle long parts mounted between them or to handle two parts, one of which could be loaded by the operator while the other was being machined. The machine was also called a Traverse Shaper.

TRAVELING HEAD SLOTTER A slotter with a ram and saddle mounted on a crossrail which allows left/right motion above a table with in/out motion. See WILLIAM SELLERS & CO. for an illustration.

TRAVERSE SHAPER See traveling head shaper.

VERTICAL and HORIZONTAL PLANER A planer with a tool head mounted on a compound slide giving both vertical and horizontal motion in front of a stationary workpiece. These were also called WALL PLANERS, since they were usually installed with the upright portion supported by a wall. See BEMENT, MILES & CO. entry for an illustration.

WALL PLANER See VERTICAL and HORIZONTAL PLANER

WIDENED PLANER A planer with one upright mounted on a separate bed placed at right angle to the main bed. This allowed more distance between uprights and thus machining of wider workpieces. See G.A. GRAY CO. entry for an illustration.

WORM DRIVE A form of gear drive used on both planers and shapers. It has the advantage of a high reduction ratio using only a worm and worm gear. See F.F. CHASE MACHINE WORKS entry for an illustration. See following section for identification of individual parts.

Identification of Parts

The major parts of a typical belt driven planer, below, are identified as follows:

A. Platen or Table
B. Housing or Upright
C. Cross-rail
D. Saddle
E. Planer Head
F. Down-feed Handle
G. Tool Clamps
H. Feed Screw Handle
I. Reversing Lever
J. Tappets or Dogs
K. Belt Shifting Lever
L. Driving Pulleys
M. Reversing Pulleys
N. Down-feed Adjustment
O. Bevel Gears for Raising and Lowering Cross-rail
P. Pulley for Raising and Lowering Cross-rail
Q. Bed
R. Shaft for Raising and Lowering Cross-rail
S. Cross-feed Handle
T. Rear Cross-feed Gear
U. Feed Rack
V. Down-feed Crank
W. Clapper Box

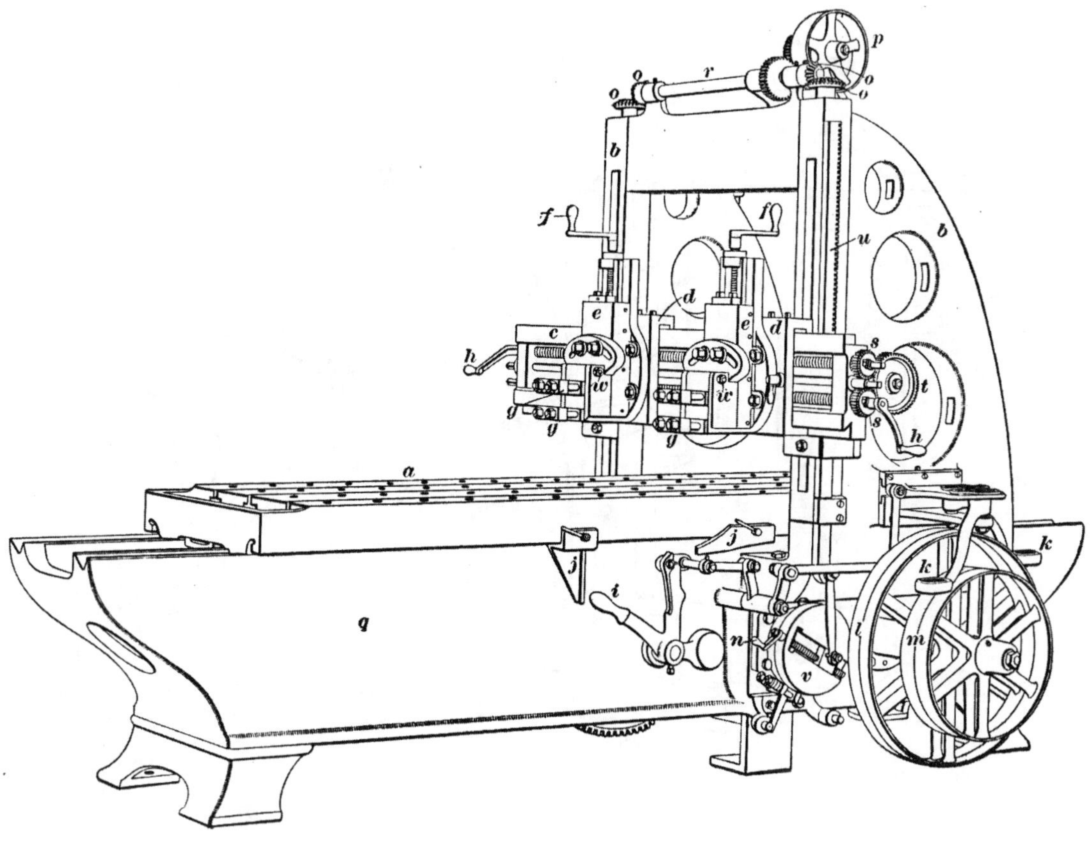

The major parts of a typical crank shaper, below, are identified as follows:

A. Column
B. Ram
C. Swivel
D. Shaper Head
E. Table
F. Vise
G. Vertical Slide
H. Tool Block
I. Cross Rail for Left/Right Motion
J. Step Pulley
K. Locknut
L. Locking Handle for Feed Adjustment
M. Saddle
N. Outboard Support Screw Jack

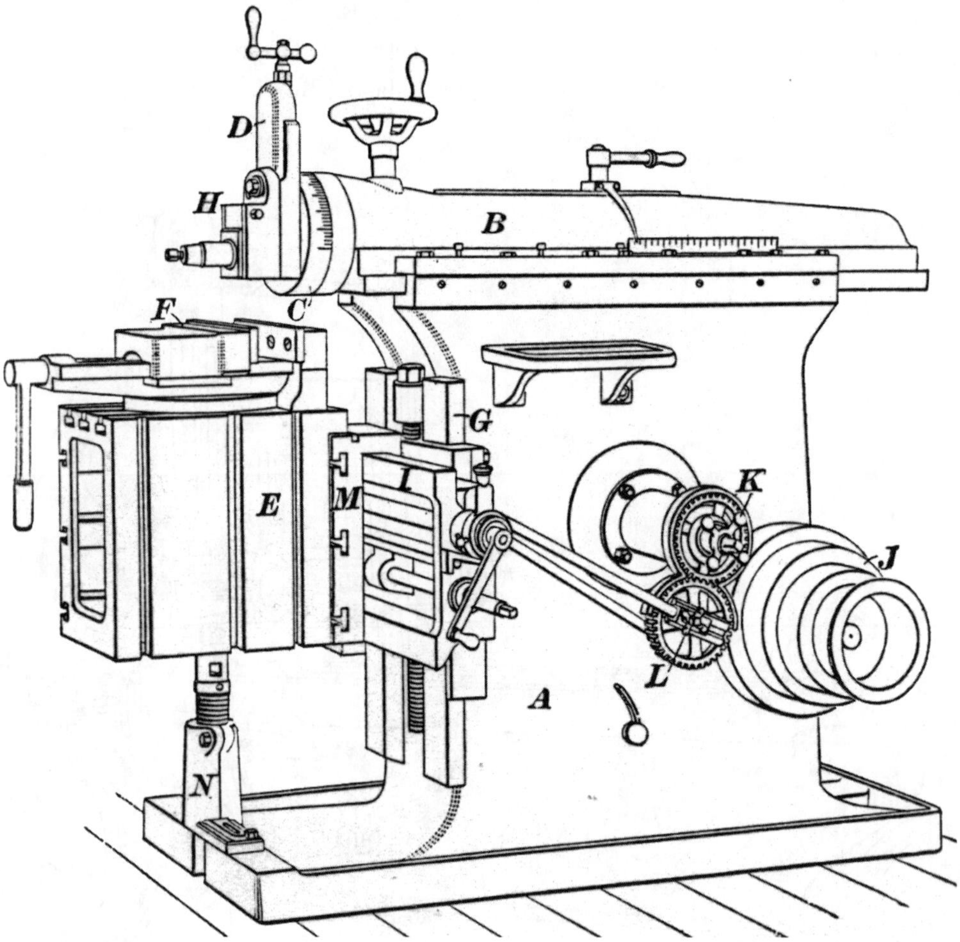

The major parts of a typical slotter, below, are identified as follows:

A. Ram
B. Crank-disk
C. Connecting Rod
D. Counterbalance Weight
E. Step Pulley
F. Platen or Table
G. Feed Rod and Telescoping Shaft
H. Handle for Rotating Table
I. Handle for Left/Right Motion
K. Crank Plate for Feed
L. Tool Head
M. Frame
N. Bull Gear
O. Link Pin
P. Pin for Adjusting Length of Stroke
Q. Worm Gear for Table Rotation

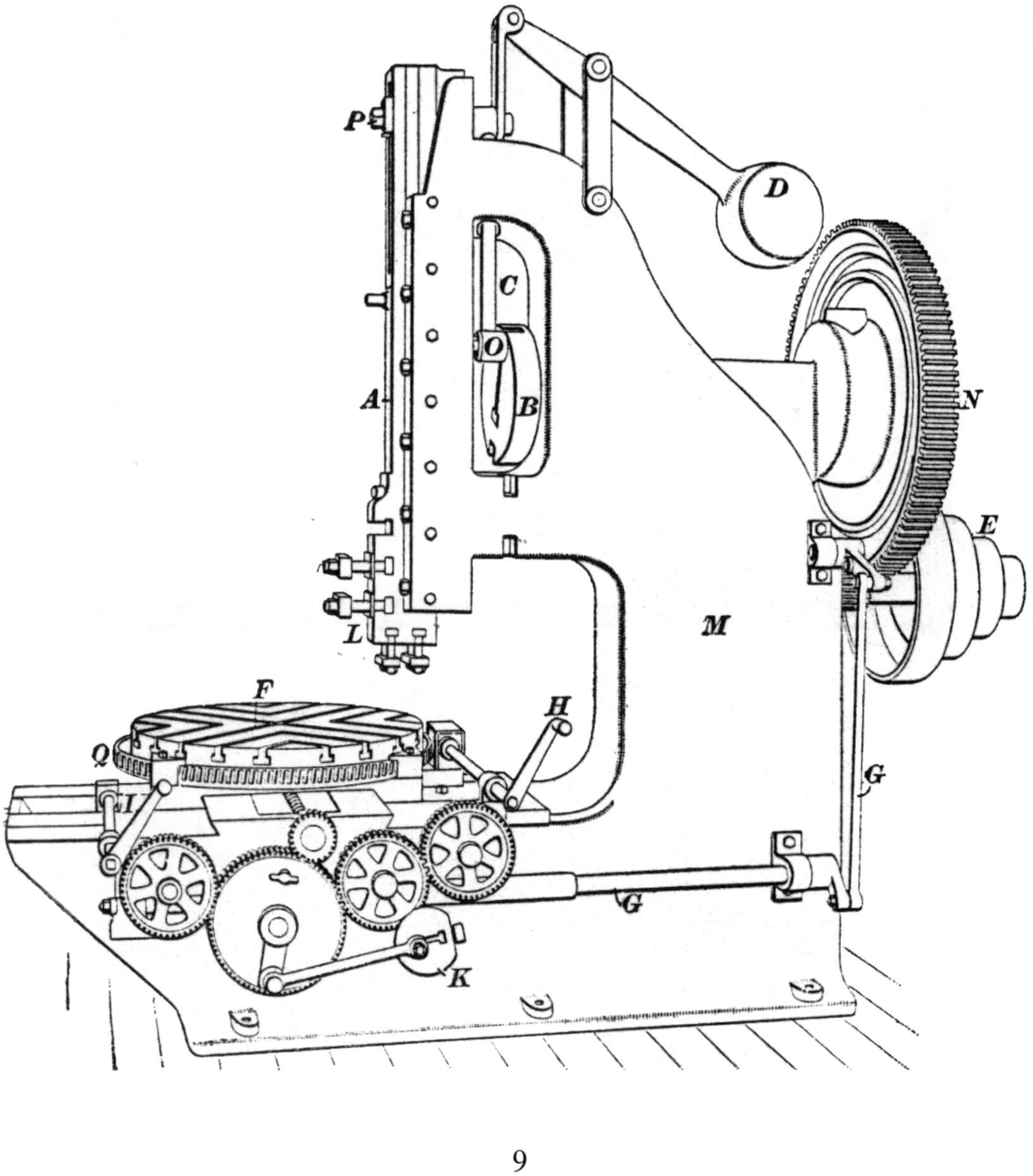

DIRECTORY OF MAKERS

ADAMS CO., Dubuque, IA

Formed in 1892 when Eugene Adams (1860-1952) and his brother Herbert Adams (1863-1945) bought and reorganized the Roberts & Langworth Iron Works. Eugene served as president; Herbert as secretary and treasurer.

In 1896, the firm introduced a milling attachment for planers, shown below, which could be mounted as a horizontal spindle or vertical spindle. They advised customers "do not plane surfaces that should be milled, or mill surfaces that should be planed." The attachment was made for 25 years or more.

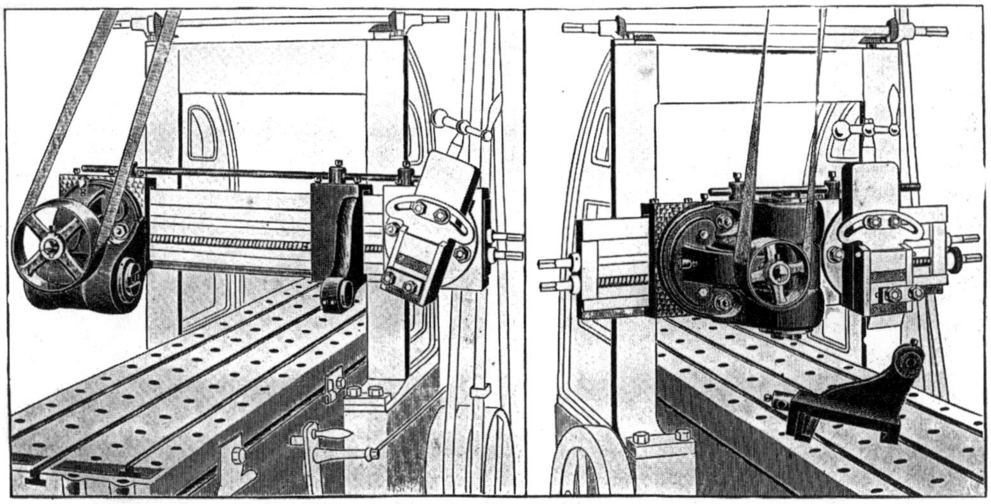

Fig. 1. Horizontal Spindle. MILLING ATTACHMENT TO PLANER. Fig. 2. Vertical Spindle.

ALCORN & SEXTON, Hartford, CT

A partnership of John S. Alcorn (1860-1938) and Joel B. Sexton formed about 1883 to build machine tools. Products included planers patented September 1, 1885 (see right). By 1898, Alcorn was a partner in Alcorn & Ames, which made small lathes and other machinery for the watch industry.

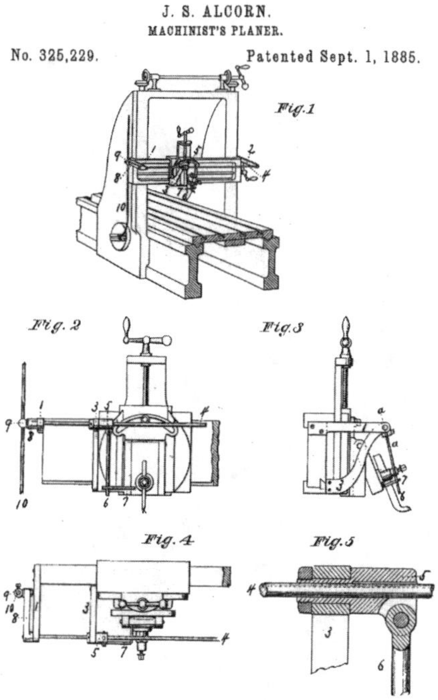

AMERICAN FOUNDRY & MACHINE CO., Hanover, PA

Builder, beginning in 1903, of open side planers made in 36" x 36" and 42" x 42" sizes. The design, shown at left, allowed removal of the beam to allow longer vertical travel of the side head.

In 1904, Detrick & Harvey Machine Co. filed a patent infringement suit, which appears to have halted further production.

AMERICAN MACHINE WORKS, Richmond, IN

Established in 1856 by Isaac Ringe to make steam engines. Ringe was joined by Luther B. Brady in 1857 and the firm shortly afterword added planers, lathes, screw cutters and boring mills to their line.

The partnership later became, successively, Brady & Son, J.M. Aiken & Co., and A.N. Hadley & company

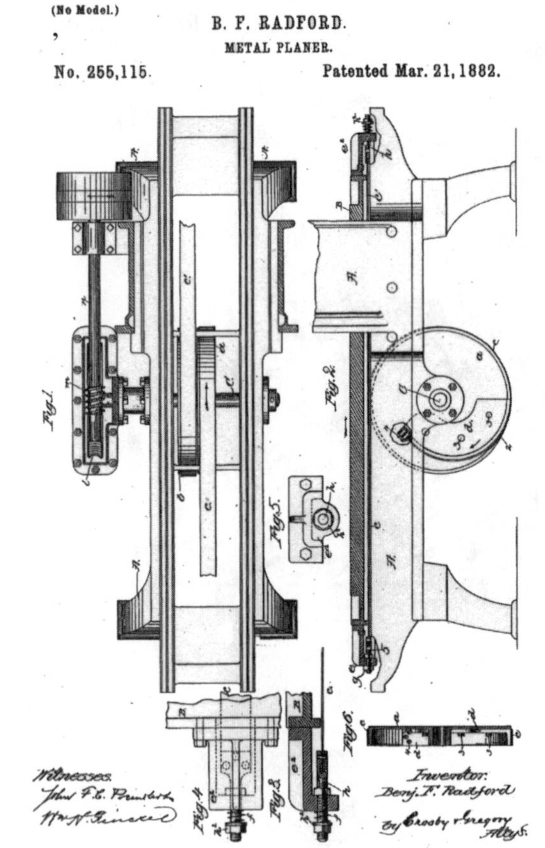

AMERICAN TOOL & MACHINE CO., Boston, MA

Formed in 1864 as the successor to G.H. Fox & Co., the firm was best known for production of brassworkers' lathes, including the FOX lathe invented by Joseph Nason. About 1882, however, American began building planers based on the Benjamin F. Radford patent of March 21, 1882. Radford had been the superintendent for some years. *(Illustration at left.)*

AMERICAN TOOL WORKS CO., Cincinnati, OH

Formed in 1898 by Franklin Alter (1831-1916), Albert B. Voorheis and Charles Davis (1853-1903) as a reorganization of the DAVIS & EGAN MACHINE TOOL CO. Capital was $1,000,000. The new firm continued production of Davis & Egan designs, including engine lathes, milling machines, drilling machines, shapers and planers. Production continued until the company went out of business in the 1970s.

Shaper production included a new back geared 16" model (Fig.1) introduced in 1900. A completely new line of shapers was introduced in 1902, after a fire had destroyed all their patterns. The new line (Fig.2) offered 16" plain crank shapers; 16", 18", 21", and 25" back geared crank shapers; and 26" and 30" triple geared shapers. Motor driven shapers (Fig.3) were introduced in 1903. A new, heavy duty line of back geared shapers, including a 21" model (Fig.4), was introduced in 1909.

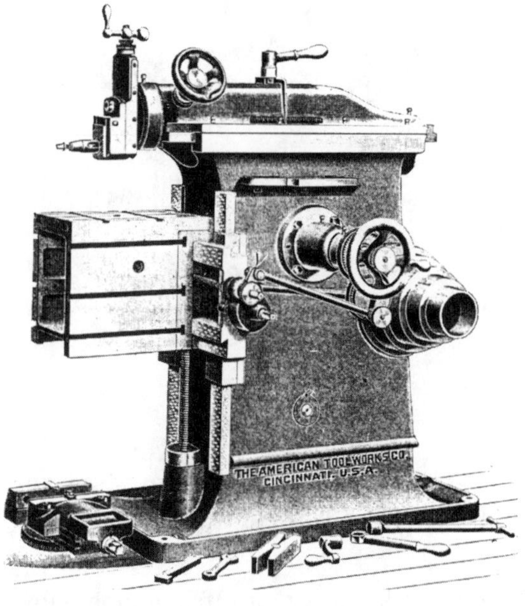

Fig.1

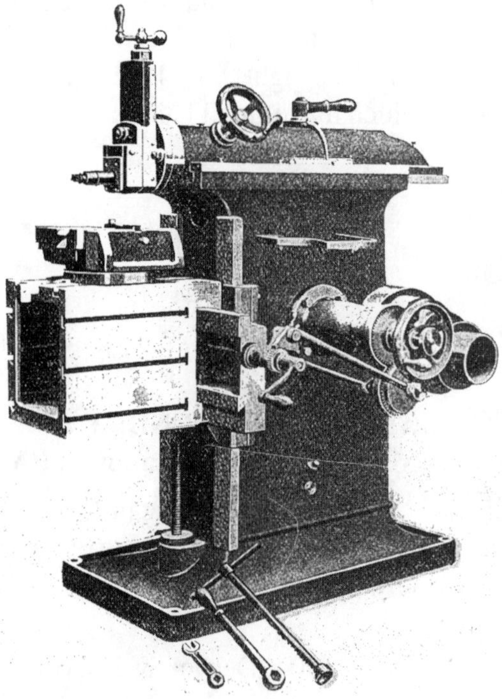
Fig.2

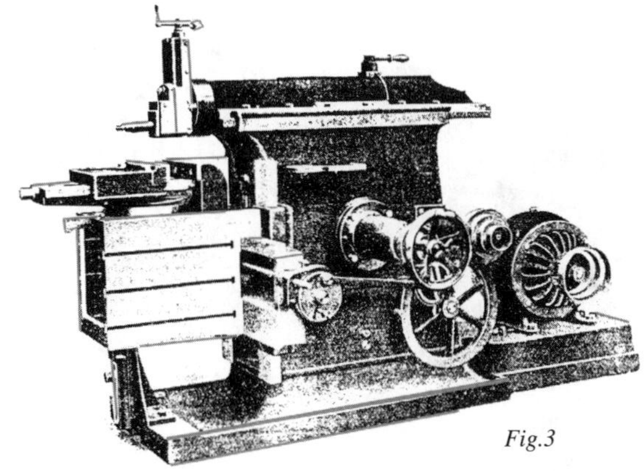

Fig.3

Fig.4

24 Inch Extra Heavy Planer.

Fig.5

Fig.6

A NEW AMERICAN 36-INCH PLANER.

Planer production started with the Davis & Egan style (Fig.5) offered in 1901. In 1903, American introduced a completely new line of heavy construction planers, from 22" to 48", which included 36" (Fig.6) and 48" (Fig.7) models. A motor driven, variable speed planer (Fig.8) was introduced in 1907.

Fig.8

Fig.7

AMES MFG. CO., Chicopee Falls, MA

Founded in 1834 by James T. Ames (1810-1883) and his brother Nathan P. Ames, Jr. (1803-1847) to build cotton machinery and machine tools. Ames was one of the first machine tool builders to build and market a standard line of machine tools. Machine tool production began as early as 1835 when a screw turning lathe and several milling machines were sold to Merrick, Agnew & Tyler, Philadelphia, PA.

From the 1850s through 1865 Ames was an important supplier of machine tools to the Springfield Armory. At the end of the Civil War, however, firearms, swords, sewing machines, etc. became important products. Machine tool production began to taper off and ceased soon after 1890. The firm was closed in 1898.

A combined drill and slotter (right) was offered in 1884 and was available in four sizes as shown in the table.

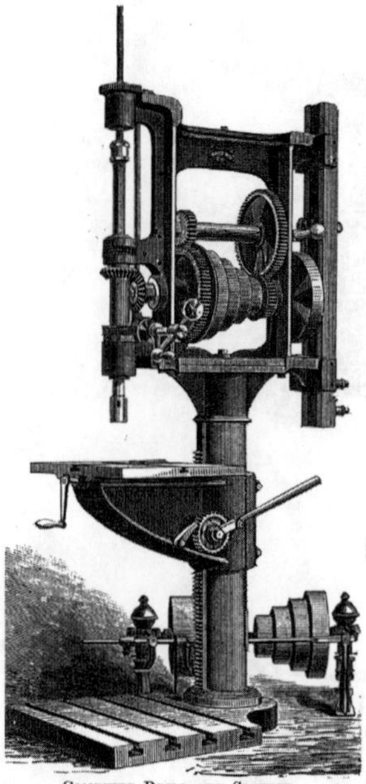

COMBINED DRILL AND SLOTTER.

—COMBINED DRILL AND SLOTTER.

Drill and Slot to Center of Circle.	Distance, end of Spindle to Drill Table.	Distance, end of Spindle to Base Plate.	Stroke of Slotter.	Weight.	Prices.
11 inch dia.	17¾ inches.	....	5 inches.	500 lbs.	$325 00
25 " "	24½ "	41 inches.	9½ "	2,300 "	675 00
44 " "	34 "	51 "	10 "	4,800 "	950 00
52 " "	43½ "	71½ "	18 "	9,500 "	......

AMOSKEAG CO., Manchester, NH

A large maker of textile machinery, the shops were erected in 1840. William A. Burke (1811-?) served as superintendent until leaving in 1845 to join the Lowell Machine Shop. The firm built a variety of machinery, including planers and large engine lathes. Both William B. Bement and Ira Gay were employed by Amoskeag early in their working lives.

BADGER & CO., A.M., Rochester, NY

Operated by Alfred M. Badger. Builder, in 1865, of "all kinds of machinists' tools" including a planer advertised to plane 20' long, 4' wide and 3'8" high. In 1869, his widow was advertising the business for sale.

BAIRD MACHINERY CO., U., Pittsburgh, PA

A large Pittsburgh machinery dealer, the firm offered a variety of lathes and planers under its own name but probably made by others.

BALDWIN, N.H., Lanconia, NH

Formed in 1868 when N.H. Baldwin, probably the son of S.K. Baldwin, took over S.K. Baldwin's foot lathe business. By 1896, Baldwin also offered two sizes of hand planers (Fig.1) a 22" stroke priced at $95 and a 40" priced at $115. By 1874, a larger planer (Fig.2), made for either hand or power operation, was offered in 36" and 48" strokes, both with 15 3/4" between uprights. The 1875 A.J. Wilkinson catalog offered a small Baldwin hand planer (Fig.3) to plane 6" wide, 6" high and 15" long, priced at $75. The small planer was also offered with a 20" stroke for $85. *(Illustrations continued next page)*

N.H. Baldwin

Fig.1

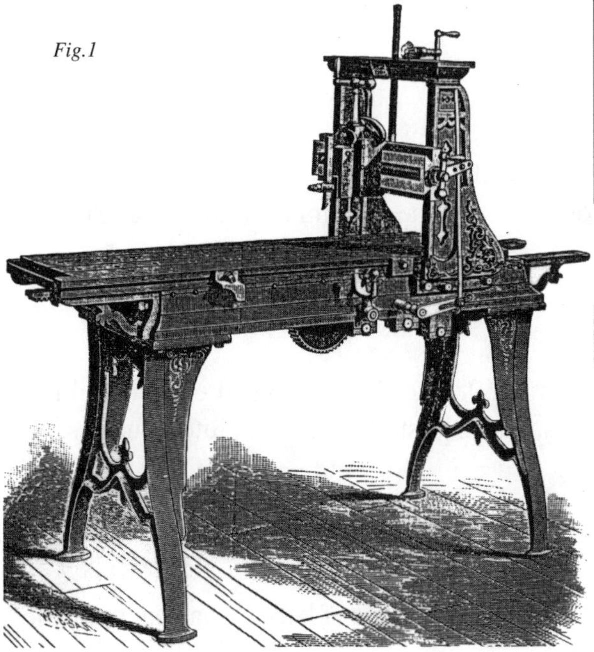

HAND PLANER.

Price, 22 inch,	$95.00
" 40 inch,	115.00
Tools, each	.40
Chuck for Planer,	12.00
Centres, with Index Plate,	12.00

Planes 22 and 40 In.; 7 1-2 by 7 in. Square.

This Planer has all the facilities for doing work that is needed. It runs very easily and is highly prized by those using them. The 40-inch Planer is designed for Gunsmiths to plane rifle barrels, or for anyone desirous of planing long work on centres or otherwise. The platen is supported at the ends of bed with brackets. It is a very nice arrangement, adding not much to the cost of 22-in. planer.

Fig.2

Fig.3

BALLARD & CO., C.H., Worcester, MA

Formed about 1873 by Charles H. Ballard (1822-1901), the firm made the Warren patent planer chuck, planer centers, and "hand lathes of several sizes, with and without foot power."

BANCROFT, EDWARD, Providence, RI

Credited with building the first iron planer in North America about 1830. By 1833 he was a partner in Bancroft & Poole, which reorganized as Fairbanks, Bancroft & Co. in 1837, becoming Bancroft, Nightingale & Co. in 1846.

In 1848 Bancroft moved to Philadelphia where he formed BANCROFT & SELLERS.

BANCROFT & SELLERS, Philadelphia, PA

A partnership of Edward Bancroft (?-1855) and his brothers-in-law William Sellers (1824-1905) and John Sellers, Jr. (1826-1906), formed in 1848 to build machine tools and power transmission components for the Philadelphia metalworking industries. The firm was reorganized as WILLIAM SELLERS & CO. when Bancroft died in 1855.

BANCROFT & SON, N.W., Worcester, MA, later
BANCROFT & SMITH, Worcester, MA, later
BANCROFT & CO., W.F., Worcester, MA

A partnership of Nathan W. Bancroft and his son William F. Bancroft formed about 1880. By 1883, the firm became BANCROFT & SMITH, a partnership of William F. Bancroft and Harvey H. Smith. In 1884, the firm reorganized as W.F. BANCROFT & CO.

All three firms made woolen machinery and a variety of machinists' tools, including 30" planers beginning in 1883.

BARKER & CHARD MACHINE TOOL CO., Cincinnati, OH

Founded in 1897 by William Barker (1853-1915), Nicholas D. Chard (1863-1942) and William H. Burtner. Burtner was also associated with the Davis & Egan Machine Tool Co. and the Cincinnati Planer Co. Products included 22" crank shapers made until the company closed in 1901.

BARKER & CO., T.L., Fitchburg, MA

A partnership of T.L. Barker and Abram Brigham, operating in 1869. The firm produced engine and hand lathes, shaping machines, Baldwin's automatic wood turning lathes, and Olmsted's friction clutch pulleys.

BARNETT, OSCAR, Newark, NJ

Operator of a gray iron foundry and machine shop in 1865, Barnett was a builder of lathes, shaping machines, and "drop, screw and foot presses for jewelers and hatters."

BARR & CO., ROBERT H., Wilmington, DE

Founded in 1860 by Robert H. Barr (1825-1897), the firm reorganized as R.H. BARR & CO. when William S. Hilles joined in 1862 and Henry C. Jones in 1863. In 1870 Barr sold out to his partners who then reorganized as the HILLES & JONES CO. Products offered in 1865 included radial drill presses, lathes, planers, etc.

BARTLETT, E.E., Boston, MA

Edwin E. Bartlett first appears in the Boston City Directory in 1886, listed as a mechanical engineer working for Charles F. Harlow. In 1899, he is shown as successor to Charles F. Harlow & Co. Bartlett's primary product, throughout his time in business, was the Greenard arbor press.

In 1900, Bartlett introduced the FEDERAL bench planer which could be operated by either hand or power. The first model (Fig.1) could plane 9" wide, 6" high and 24" long, weighed 300 pounds and sold for $135. In 1902, he introduced a new model (Fig.2) that planed 10" wide, 10" high and 30" long and weighed 475 pounds. *(continued on next page)*

Fig.1

Planer for Accurate Work.

In August, 1916, Bartlett announced that he was moving his business to Nashua, NH, where he would continue to make arbor presses. No mention was made of the FEDERAL bench planer.

Fig.2

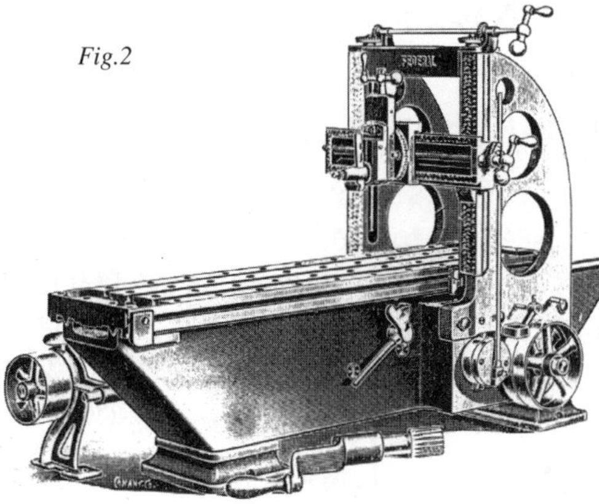

IMPROVED CRANK PLANER

Planes 16 inches high and wide, and has 12 inch stroke. It has power, cross and angular down feed as shown in cut, or cross feed only, if desired. Also, quick return motion and screw running whole length under bed. It is self-oiling in its ways.

R. A. BELDEN & CO.

Danbury, Conn.

BELDEN & CO., R.A., Danbury, CT

Founded in 1867 by Russell A. Belden ((1835-1899) to build "iron planers (patented September 11, 1869), crank planers and shaping machines, engine lathes, screw machines, milling machines and gun machinery." An improved crank planer, shown left, was offered in 1883 to plane 16" high and wide with 12" stroke.

The firm incorporated as the R.A. BELDEN CO. in 1885 and reorganized as the BELDEN MACHINE CO. in 1888. R.A. Belden remained president until his death in 1899.

BELLOWS & WHITCOMB, Worcester, MA

A partnership of Ephraim H. Bellows and Bryon Whitcomb, formed in 1865 and dissolved in 1868. The firm was primarily a steam engine builder but also made "lathes, planers, drills, and shaping machines."

BELMER-EAMES CO., Cincinnati, OH

Formed in 1899 by H. Belmer and G.T. Eames to build planers, as shown below. The machines were offered in sizes "36" and up." Short lived, the company reorganized as the BELMER MACHINE TOOL CO. by 1903, which was absorbed by the Hamilton Machine Tool Co. in 1905.

THE BELMER-EAMES PLANER.

BEMENT, COLBY, DOUGHERTY & CO., Philadelphia, PA, later
BEMENT, DOUGHERTY & THOMAS, Philadelphia, PA, later
BEMENT & DOUGHERTY, Philadelphia, PA

A partnership of William B. Bement (1817-1897), his nephew Gilbert H. Colby, and James Dougherty (1815-1900), formed in 1853 as a reorganization of MARSHALL, BEMENT & COLBY. The firm reorganized as BEMENT, DOUGHERTY & THOMAS when Colby was replaced by George Thomas in 1855 and again as BEMENT & DOUGHERTy in 1856. The firms operated as proprietors of the Industrial Works. Bement, who had been a noted designer of machine tools for the Lowell Machine Shop during 1845-1851, was the machine designer; Dougherty oversaw the shop.

Machine tool production included two-table traverse shapers much like those built at the Lowell Machine Shop; 12" slotters; No. 3, 12" crank shapers in two styles, one with a complex feed mechanism (Fig.1) and one with a very simple mechanism (Fig.2); and No. 3 1/2, 12" crank shapers (Fig.3) of heavier construction that incorporated features patented by Bement June 3, 1862. The No. 3 shaper with simple feed mechanism was photographed in 1923, still in operation; the No. 3 1/2 shaper in 1925, also still in operation. In 1868, the firm advertised: "Machinists' Tools and Equipment for Railroad, Iron Ship Building, and Gun shops."

Dougherty left the firm in 1870 when it reorganized as WILLIAM B. BEMENT & SON.

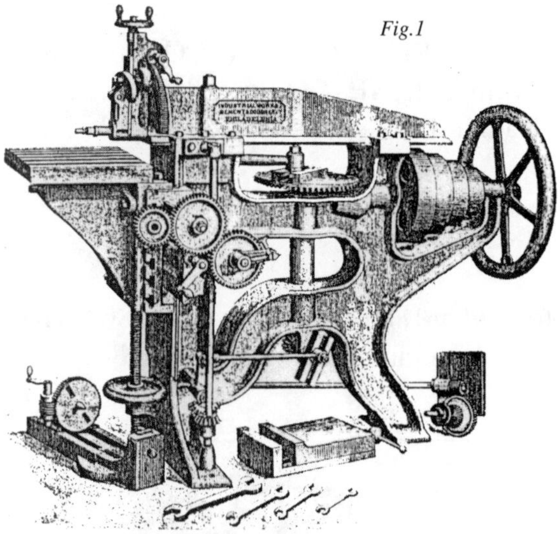

Fig.1

Fig.2

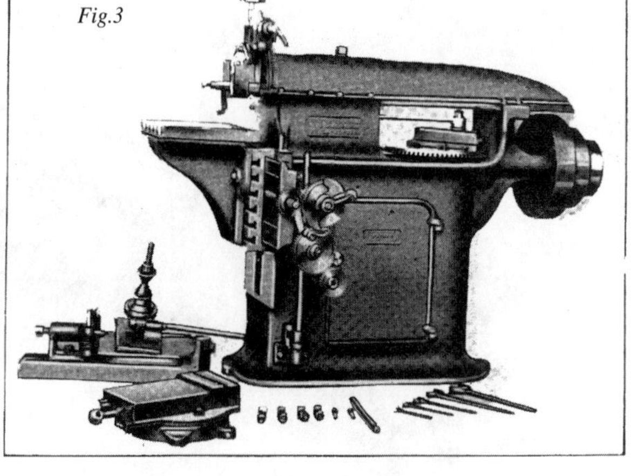

Fig.3

BEMENT & SON, WILLIAM B., Philadelphia, PA, later

BEMENT, MILES & CO., Philadelphia, PA

Formed in 1870 by William B. Bement (1817-1897) and his son Clarence S. Bement (1843-1923) as a reorganization of BEMENT & DOUGHERTY. The new firm continued to operate as proprietor of the Industrial Works, where it built machine tools designed by Bement.

1880 production included double head planers (Fig.1) to plane in both directions thus reduce machining time, 18" x 18" (Fig.2) and 25" x 25" (Fig.3) planers; 12" two-table, traverse shapers (Fig.4) that trace back to Bement's designs at the Lowell Machine Shop; 12" pillar shapers (Fig.5); and 8" slotters (Fig.6). A large, combined drill and slotter (Figs. 7-8-9) was offered in 1883 and 36" rotary planers (Fig.10) in 1884. *(continued on next seven pages)*

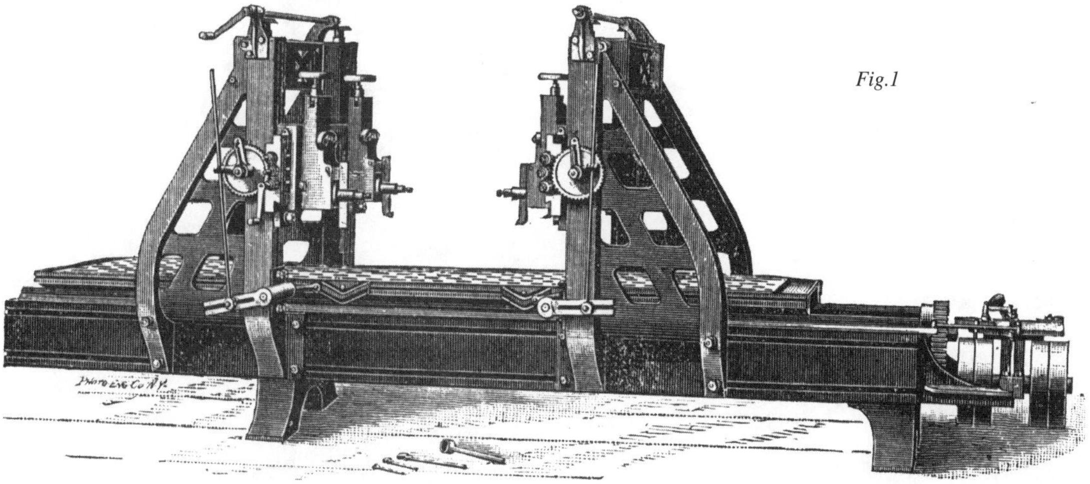

Fig.1

Fig.2

Fig.3

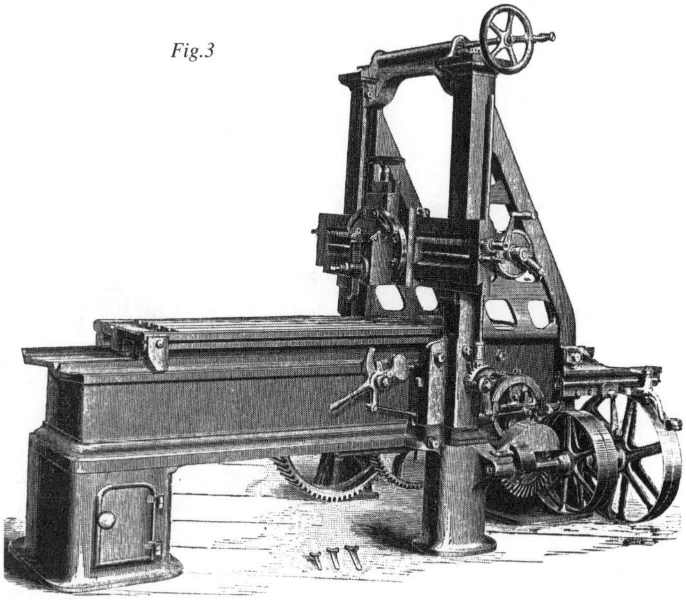

Fig.4

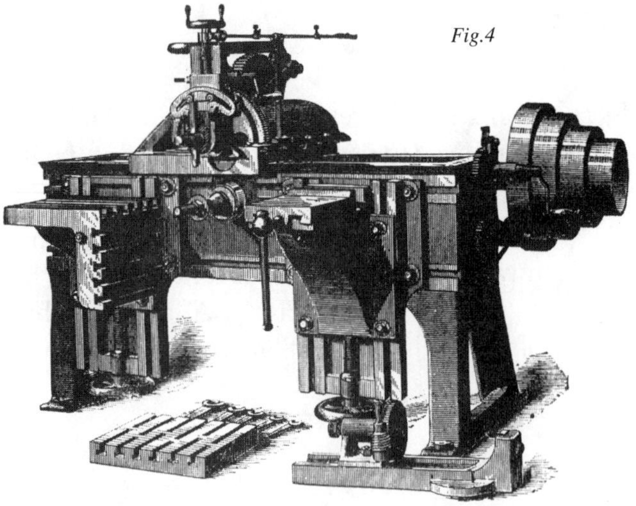

Fig.5

Fig.6

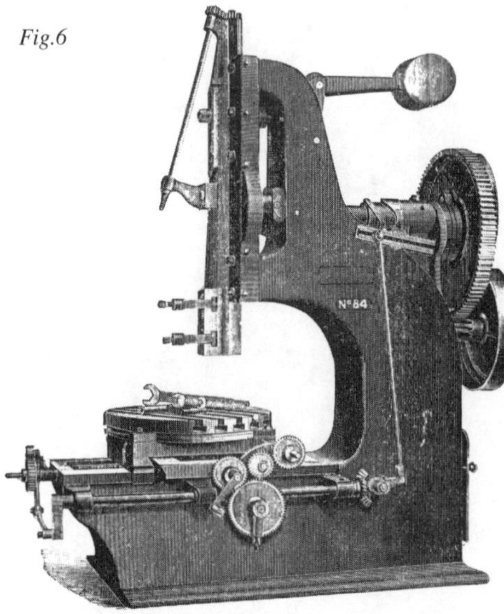

Fig.7

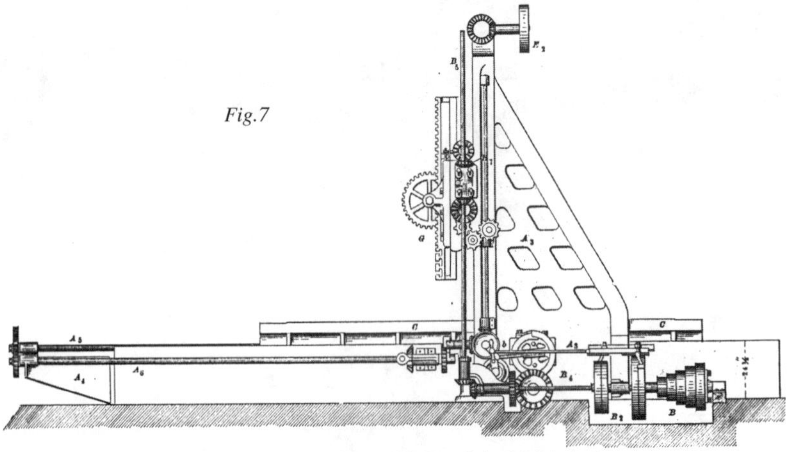

Combined Drill and Slotter.—Fig. 1.—Side View.—Scale, ¼ Inch to the Foot.

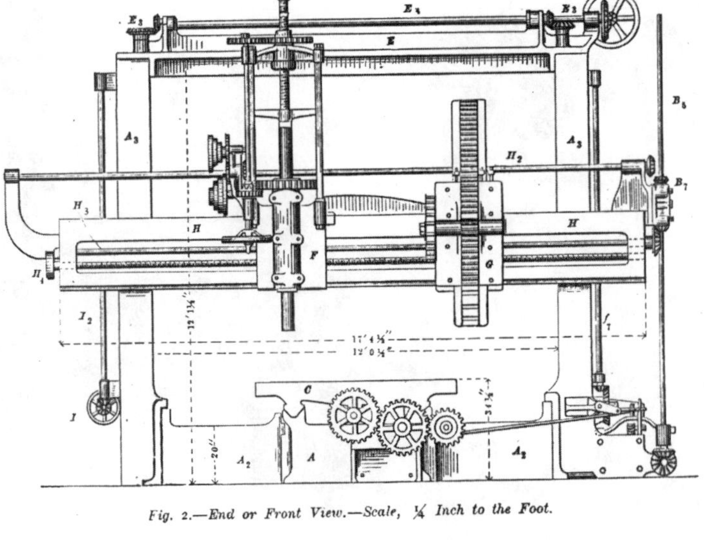

Fig. 2.—End or Front View.—Scale, ¼ Inch to the Foot.

Fig.8

Fig.9

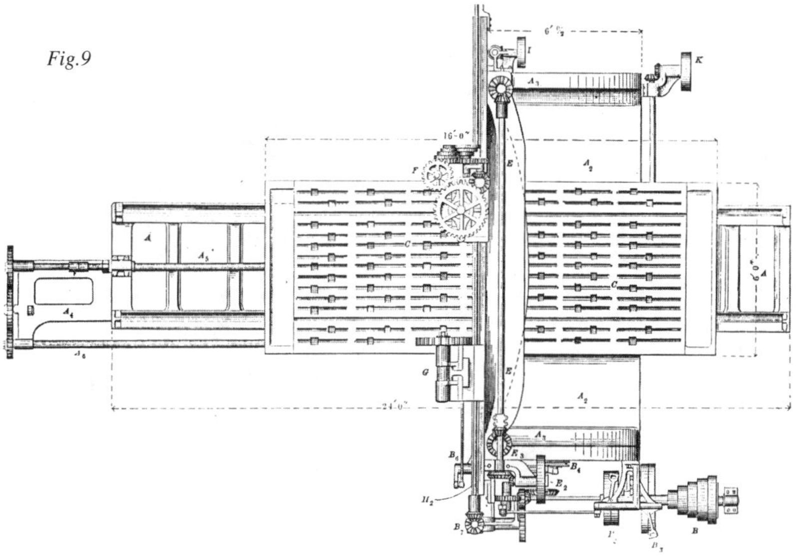

Combined Drill and Slotter.—Fig. 3.—Plan.—Scale, ¼-Inch to the Foot.

Fig.10

Fig.11

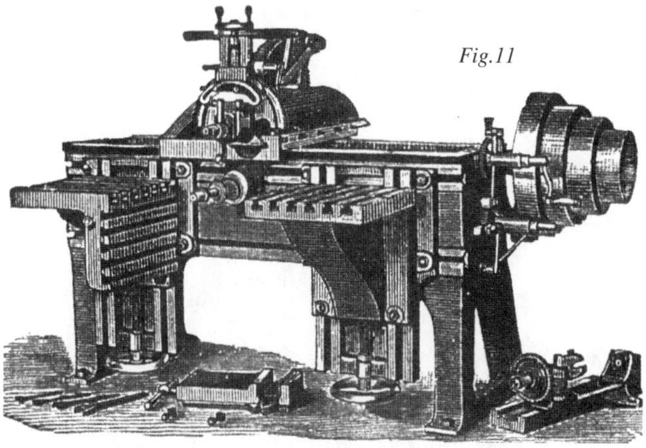

The firm reorganized as BEMENT, MILES & CO. May 1, 1885, when it merged with the MACHINE TOOL WORKS operated by Frederick B. Miles. William B. Bement retired in 1888, leaving management to Miles. By 1891, the company employed 1000 hands.

Products included 12" two-table, traverse shapers (Fig.11) offered in 1885, and a new line of planers (Fig.12) based on the designs of Frederick B. Miles. A 42" stroke shaper (Fig.13), designed for machining the inside of locomotive cylinders, was introduced in 1888 and a vertical/horizontal planer with 22' horizontal and 20' vertical travel (Fig.14) in 1892. New products offered in 1893 included an improved design 120" planer (Fig.15), and 48" slotter (Fig.16).

Fig.13

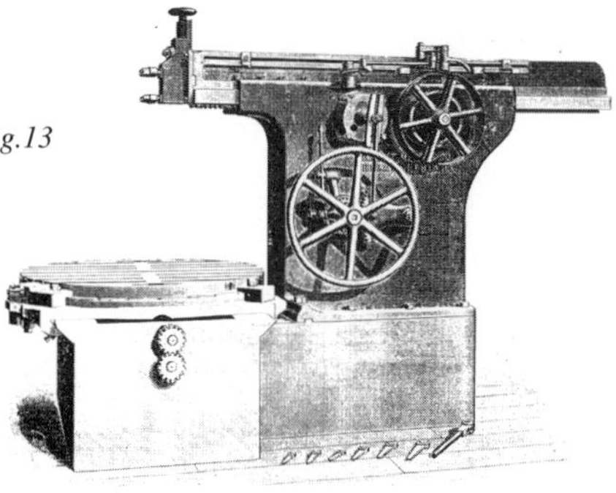

Fig.12

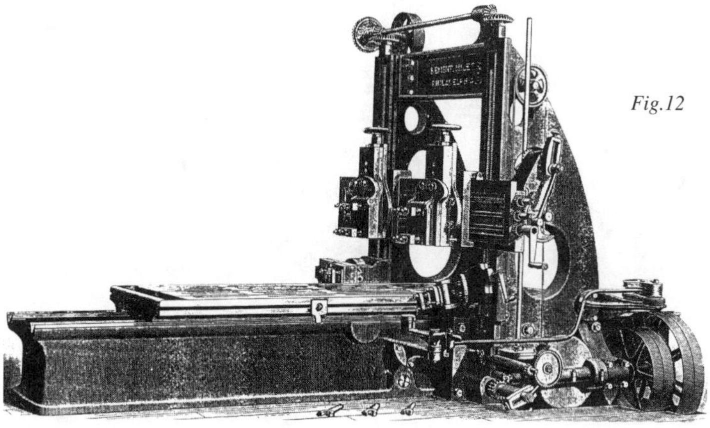

Fig.14

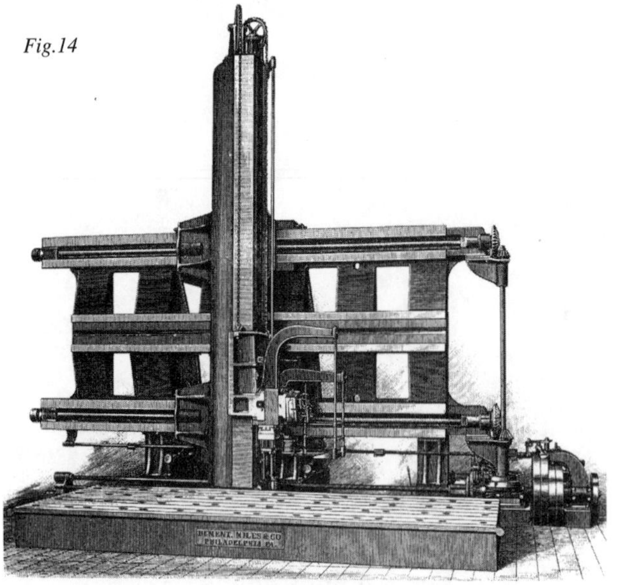

VERTICAL AND HORIZONTAL PLANING MACHINE.

Fig.15

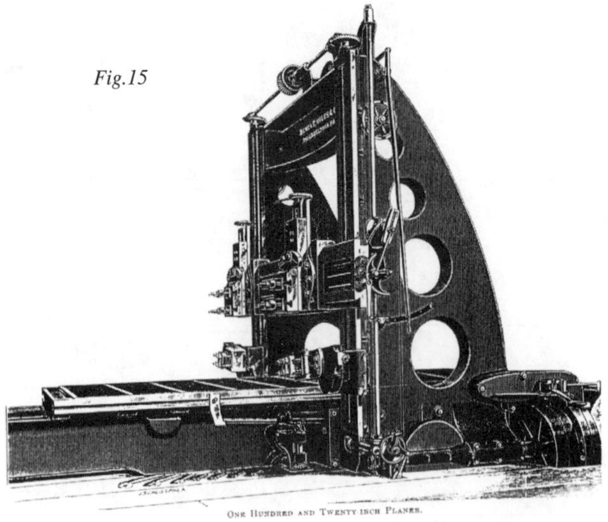

One Hundred and Twenty inch Planer.

Fig.16

Fig.17

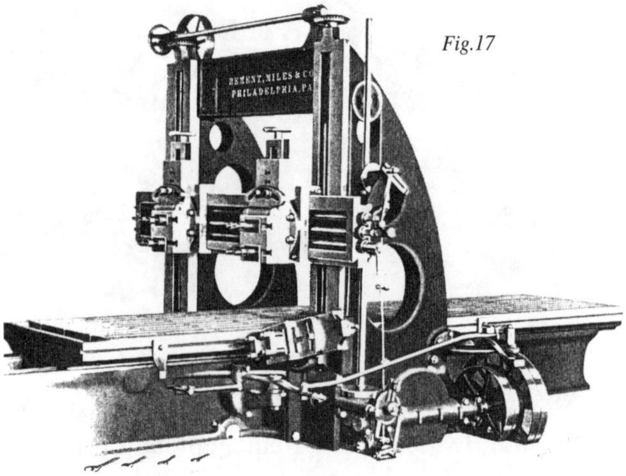

Fig.18

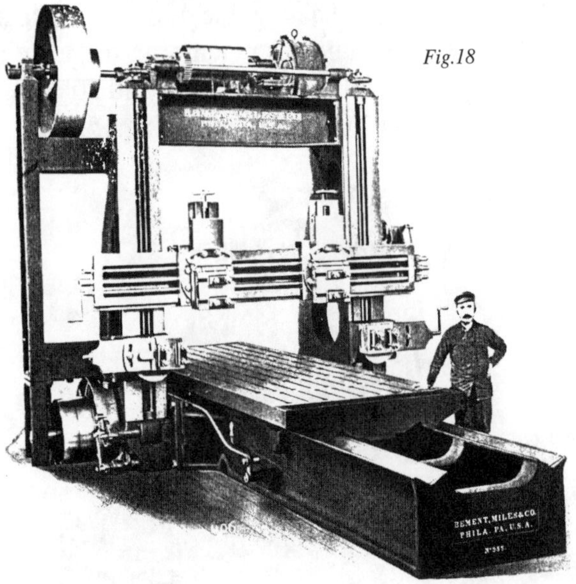

Fig.19

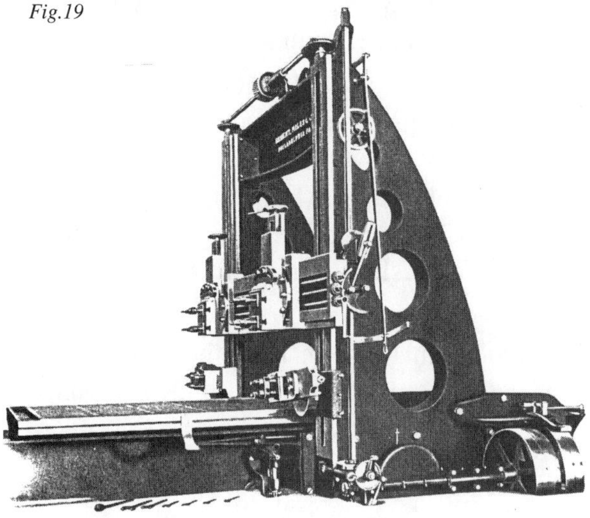

Fig.20

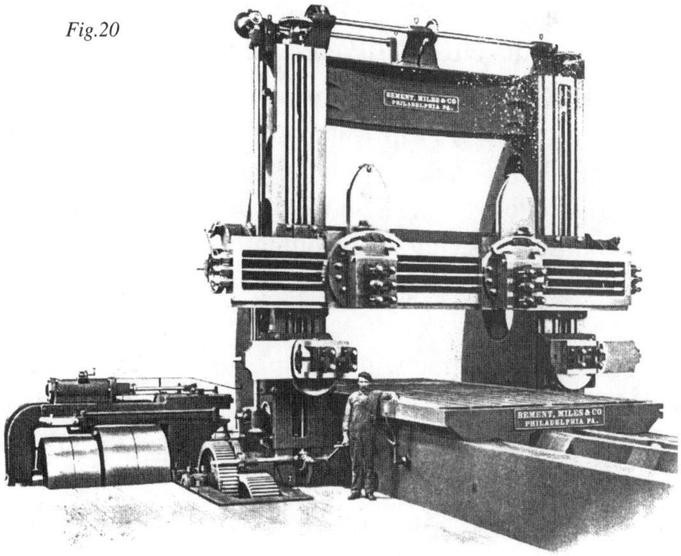

Fig.21

Size	Maximum Stroke	Vertical Adjustment of Tool	Usual Length of Bed with one Head	Saddle Traverse with one Head	Usual Length of Bed with two Heads
Inches	Inches	Inches	Feet & Inches	Inches	Feet
12	12	6	5—0	45	8
17	17	8	6—5	55	8
20	20	8	6—6	60	10
26	26	8	8—0	72	14

Fig.22

Fig.23

Fig.24

On August 15, 1899, BEMENT, MILES & CO. merged with the Niles Tool Works and Pond Machine Tool Co. to form the NILES-BEMENT-POND CO. Bement, Miles & Co. continued operation as a division.

Its 1903 catalog offered: planers in 60" (Fig.17), 72" (Fig.18), 120" (Fig.19), and 144" (Fig.20) sizes; open side planers (Fig.21) in four sizes (Fig.22); 60" rotary planers (Fig.23); vertical/horizontal planers in single column, 30' x 8' capacity (Fig.24) and wall frame in 16' x 14' capacity (Fig.25); traverse shapers in 20" (Fig.26) and 26" strokes (Fig.27); double head, 26" traverse shapers (Fig.28); 12" crank shapers (Fig.29); 42" locomotive cylinders shapers (Fig.30); slotting machines in 6" (Fig.31), 10" (Fig.32), 15" motor driven (Fig.33), 18" motor driven (Fig.34), and 22" (Fig.35) strokes; and double head, locomotive frame slotting machines (Fig.36) with strokes up to 38".

A new planer line with pneumatic clutches for reversing was introduced in 1904. In 1908 the firm, now the BEMENT WORKS of Niles-Bement-Pond, built the "largest planing machine in the world" (Fig.37). Weighing 845,000 pounds, it could plane 14'4" wide, 12'2" high, and 30' long.

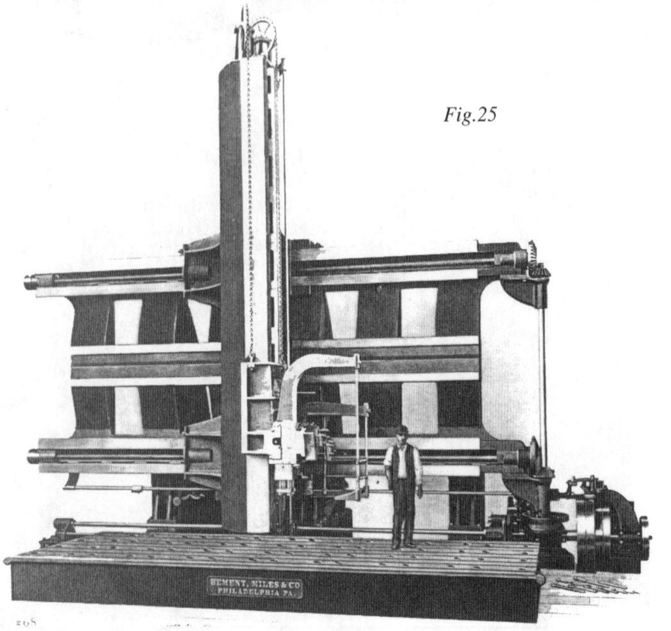

Fig.25

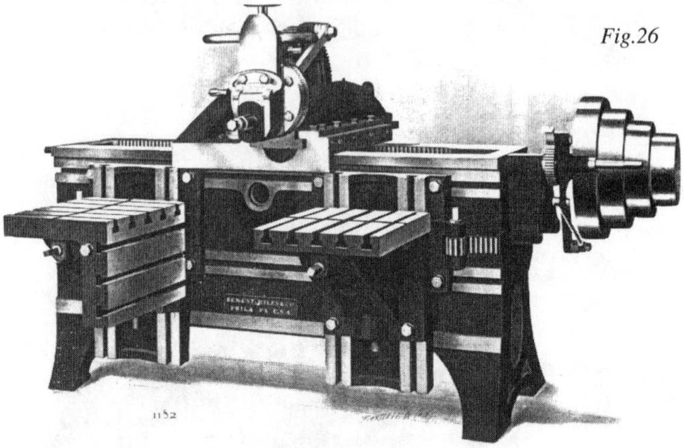

Fig.26

Fig.27

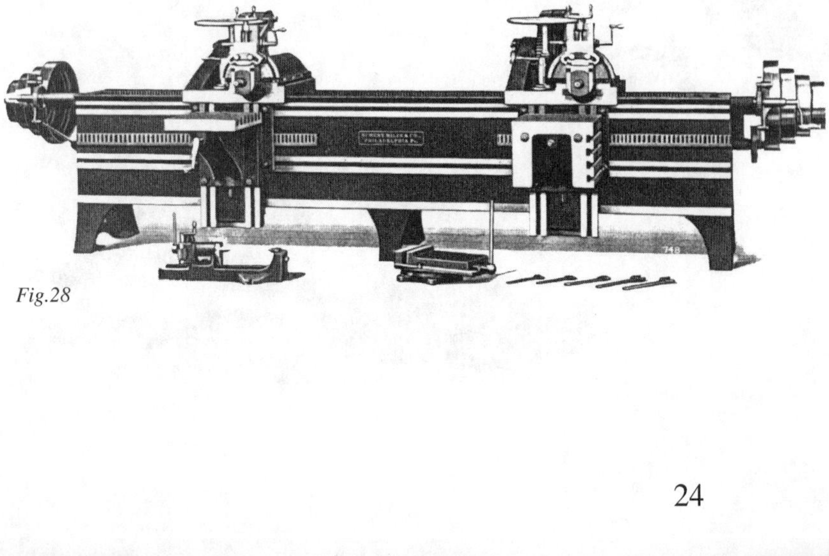

Fig.28

Fig.29

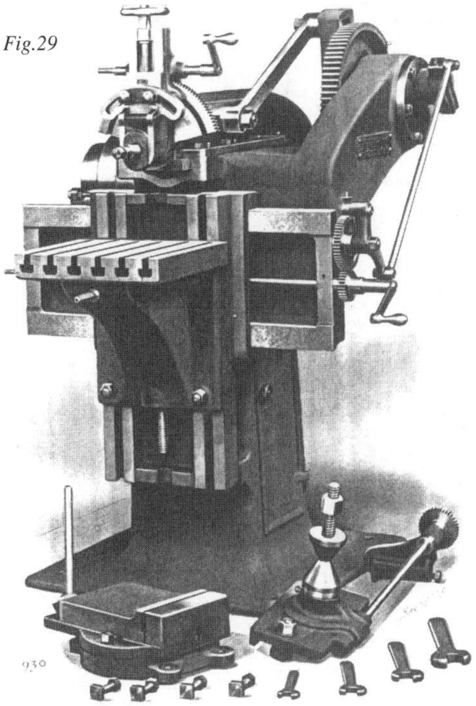

Fig.30

Fig.31

Fig.32

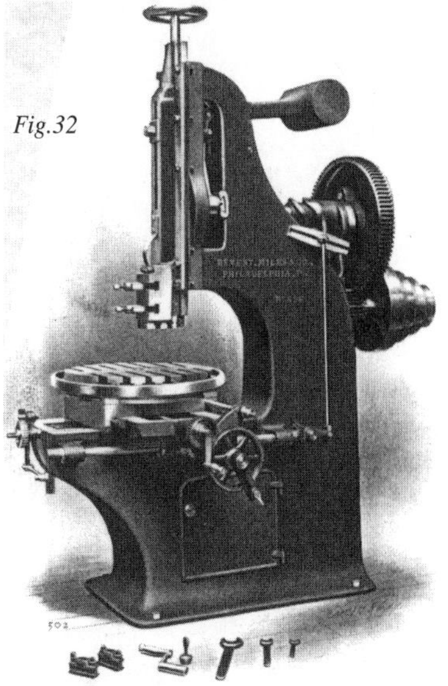

Fig.31

Fig.33

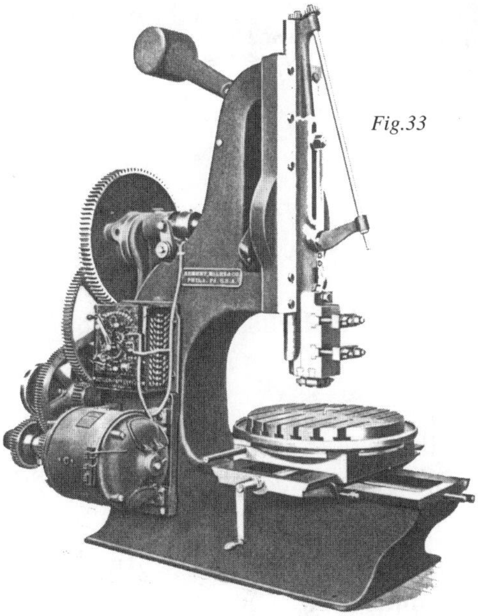

Fig.34

Fig.34

Fig.35

LARGE PLANING MACHINE, ARRANGED WITH ELECTRIC DRIVE AND PNEUMATIC CLUTCHES.

Fig.37

Fig.36

BETTS, E.& A., Wilmington, DE, later

BETTS MACHINE CO., Wilmington, DE

A partnership of Edward T. Betts (1856-1916) and his brother Alfred Betts, formed in 1861 to build machine tools. The firm continued until 1878 when it was reorganized as the BETTS MACHINE CO., which operated into the 1920s.

In 1865, the brothers advertised 24"x 24"x 6' planers "recently completed;" 32" planers and 10" shapers were available in 1866. By 1874, they were offering planers up to 50" x 50" x 25', which could widen temporarily to 72".

In 1881 Betts introduced an improved line of iron planers from 24" x 24" to a 10' x 10' size wieghing 60 tons. The new line included a 36" x 36" x 9' size, weighing 9700 pounds (Fig.1) and a 60" x 50" x 10' size (Fig.2). *(continued on next 3 pages)*

Fig.1

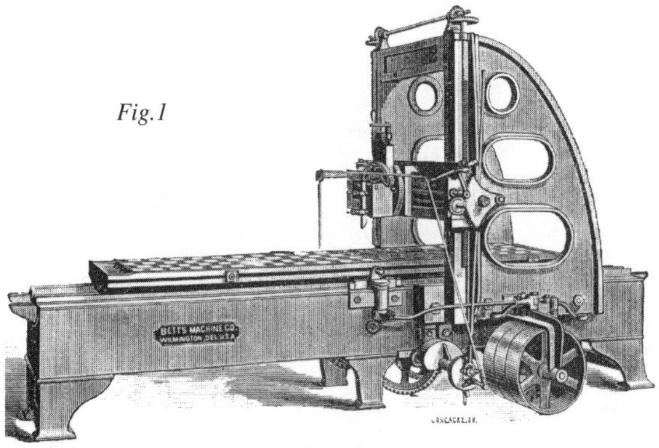

Improved Iron Planer.

Fig.2

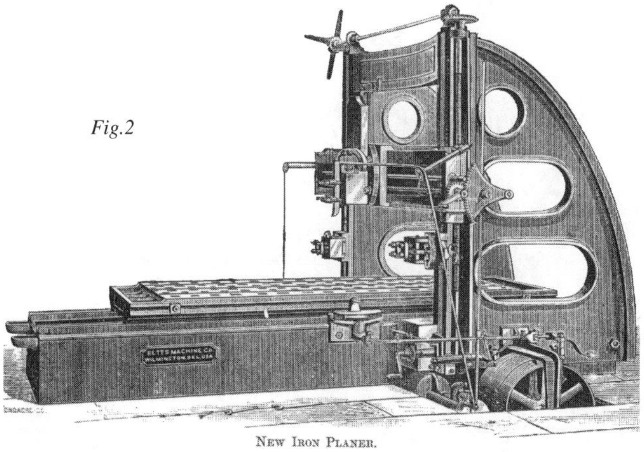

New Iron Planer.

1884 production included rotary planers in 18", 25" (Fig.3), 32" sizes and 24" with adjustable cutters (Fig.4); double table, traverse shapers in 10" x 4', 12" x 4 1/2' (Fig.5) and 16" x 6' sizes; slotting machines in strokes of 8" weighing 1300 pounds, 12" (Fig.6), 18", and 26" weighing 38,250 pounds; and a line of rack drive planers offered in 26" x 24"x 5', priced at $675; 32" x 30" x 8', priced at $1000; 40" x 36" x 10' (Fig.7), priced at $1300; 42" x 42" x 16', priced at $2250; and 48" x 48" x 16', priced at $2500. Large planers were offered in 50" x 50" weighing up to 39,500 pounds, 60" x 60" weighing up to 42,000 pounds, 72" x 72" weighing up to 77,300 pounds, and 84" x 84" weighing up to 86,800 pounds. Weight depended on table and travel length which varied from 10' to 29'.

Fig.3

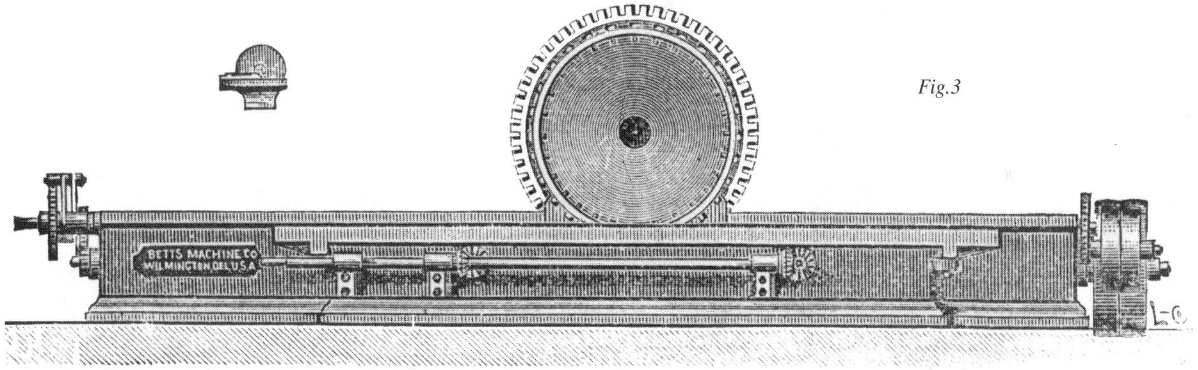

25 Inch Rotary Planer.

Fig.4

Twenty-Four Inch Rotary Planer.

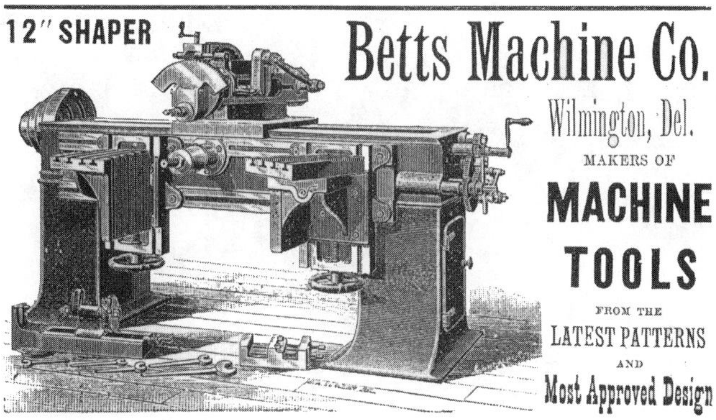

Fig.5

Fig.6

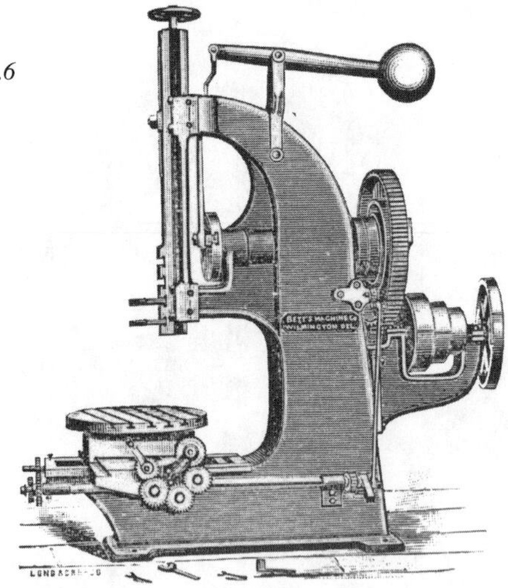

12 Inch Slotting Machine, No. 2.

Fig.7

An improved 6' x 6' planer (Fig.8) was introduced in 1888. Motor driven planers, including a 25 HP, 72" x 72" model (Fig.9) were offered by 1904.

Improved slotting machines were introduced in 1896 in 8" (Fig.10) and 15" (Fig.11) strokes. A variable speed, motor driven slotter (Fig.12) with four gear changes was introduced in 1904.

Planer, shaper and slotter production appears to have ceased about 1910 in favor of drilling machines and large boring and turning mills.

Fig.8

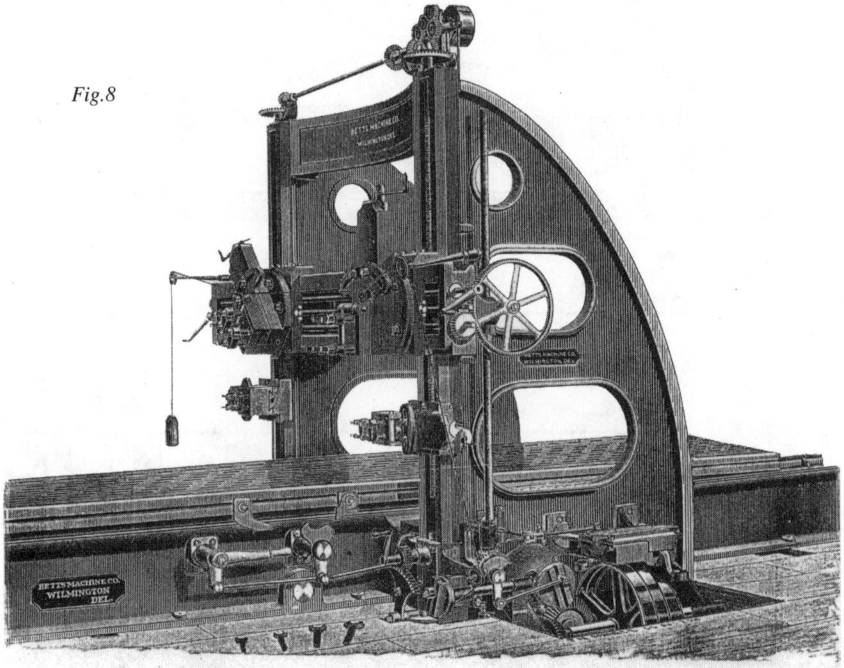

Six Foot Planing Machine.

Fig.9

Fig.10

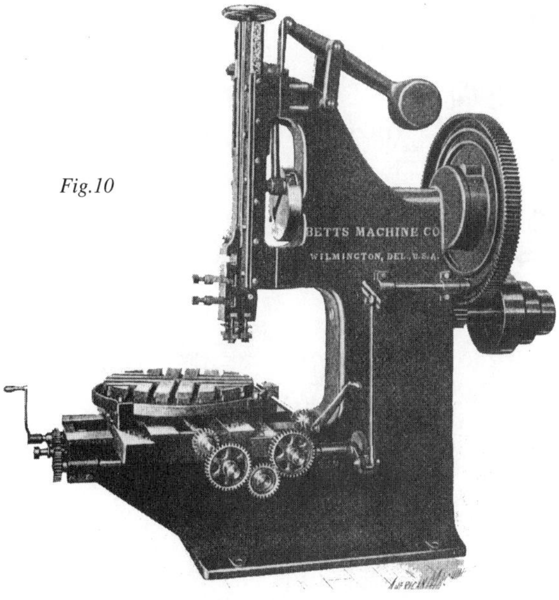

Fig.11

Fig.12

BIDDEFORD MACHINE SHOP, Biddeford, ME

A large machine shop erected about 1839 as the machinery building arm of the Saco Water Power Co. Primary products were a variety of textile machinery, but the shop also made lathes, planers and shapers c1850-1865.

Sylvanus J. Wetherell served as superintendent 1851-1854, and William H. Thompson from 1854 to 1867. Wetherell was granted a patent for a two table, traversing head shaper (below) on March 31, 1857.

(Illustration on next page)

Biddeford Machine Shop

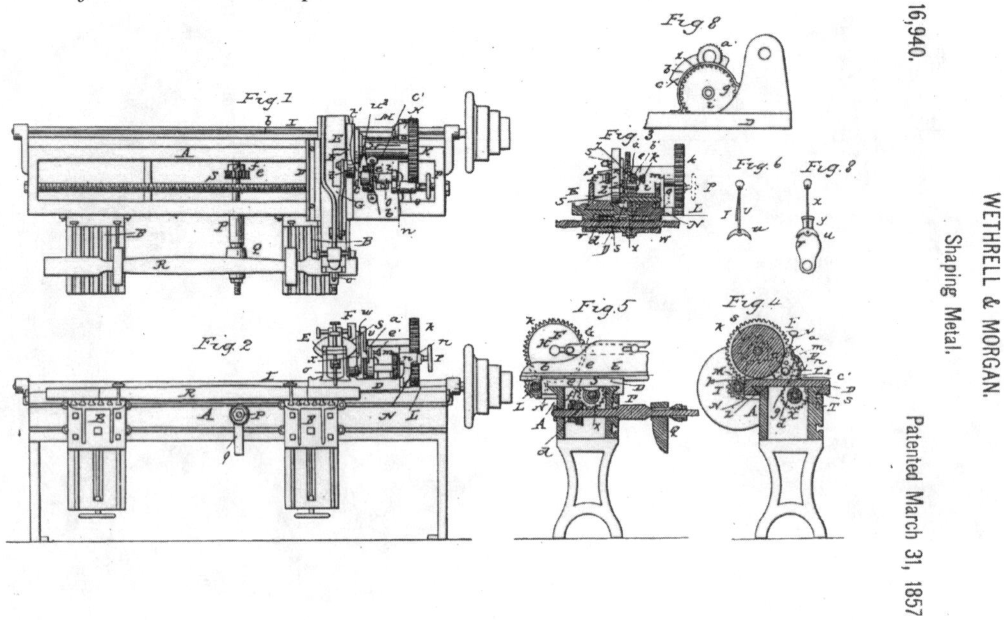

BIGNALL & KEELER MACHINE WORKS, St. Louis, MO, later

BIGNALL & KEELER MFG. CO., Edwardsville, IL

Formed in 1878 by Moses C. Bignall to make pipe threading machinery. The firm reorganized as the BIGNALL & KEELER MFG. CO. in 1892 with Bignall as president. Shortly after Bignall's death later in 1892, the company moved to Edwardsville, IL.

Production of pipe threading machinery continued but the firm also began making shapers in 1892. Called the BUSINESS shaper (Fig.1), it had a stroke of 15", side traverse of 22" and weighed 2500 pounds. The PEERLESS, a larger, 18" stroke model with 20" of side traverse, was introduced in 1894 (Fig.2).

Fig.1

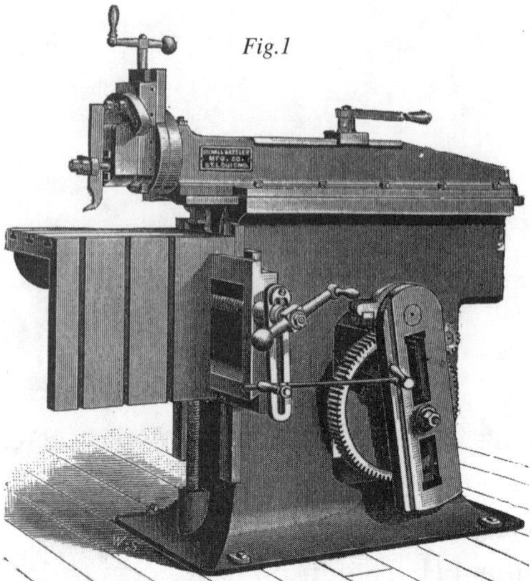

THE BUSINESS SHAPER.

Fig.2

BLAISDELL & WOOD, Worcester, MA, later

BLAISDELL & CO., P., Worcester, MA

A partnership of Parritt Blaisdell (?-1875) and Charles Wood, formed in 1865 to build engine lathes, hand lathes, planers and upright drilling machines. Wood left the firm in 1867. It then reorganized as P. BLAISDELL & CO. with John P. Jones as partner, joined in 1873 by Samuel E. Hildreth.

Blaisdell's son William A. Blaisdell took over when his father died in 1875. By 1882 the firm was the second largest machine tool builder in Worcester, employing 70 to 75 men. William A. Blaisdell operated the firm until 1905 when it was consolidated with the Whitcomb Mfg. Co. to form the Whitcomb-Blaisdell Machine Tool Co.

Crank planers were offered by 1869, with an improved 16" wide and 14" stroke model (Fig.1) introduced by 1872. Gear drive planers were also offered in 1872 (Fig.2) and were available in three sizes. Improved and slightly enlarged crank planers (Fig.3), 18" wide with 15" stroke, were available in 1893 and continued in production until the consolidation with Whitcomb.

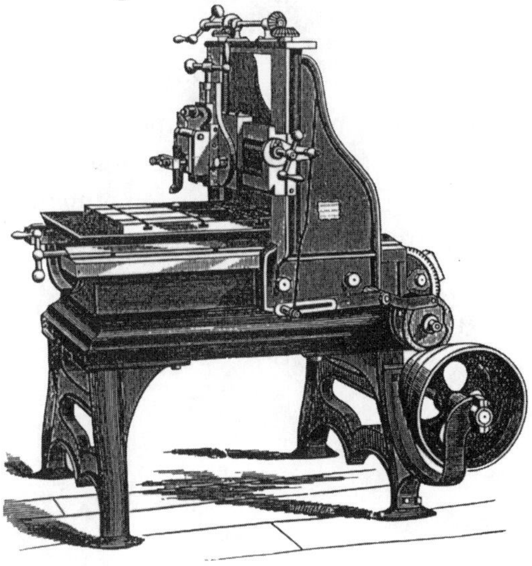

Fig.1

Planers.

LENGTH OF BD.	PLANES. FT.	WIDE. IN.	HEIGHT. IN.	WEIGHT. LBS.	PRICE.
5 ft.	3	18	18	1700	$
6 "	4	24	23	2800	
8 "	6	24	23	3500	

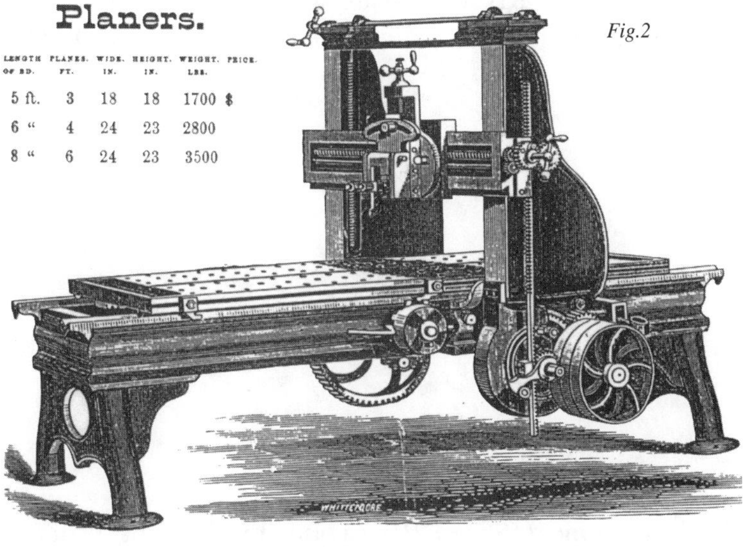

Fig.2

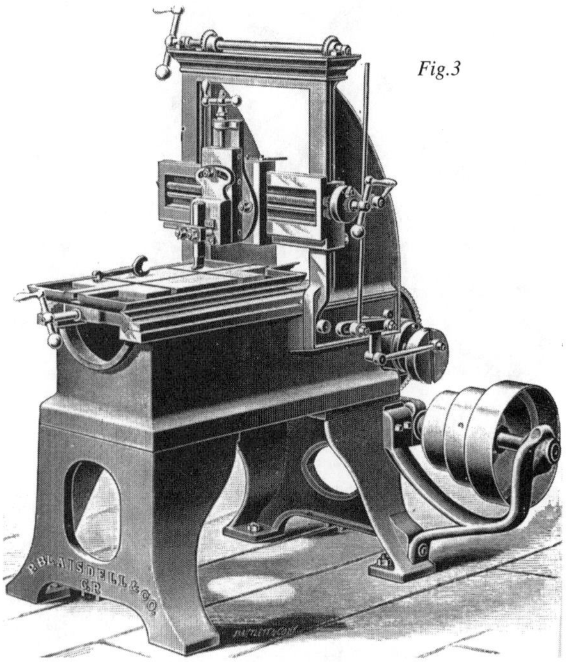

Fig.3

BLISS, E.W., Brooklyn, NY, later

BLISS CO., E.W., Brooklyn, NY

Founded in 1881 by Eliphalet W. Bliss (1836-1903) to build presses and metal forming machinery previously made by Bliss & Williams. For a few years, beginning in 1881, Bliss also built metal cutting machine tools including the 12" stroke shaper shown at right.

Bliss formed a stock company, E.W. Bliss Co., in 1886 and incorporated in 1890.

NEW METAL SHAPING MACHINE.

BOSTON MACHINE CO., Boston, MA

Builder, in 1864, of the large slotter shown at left. The machine was built for the Charlestown Navy Yard and moved, in 1910, to the Fore River Shipyard where it continued in use. The firm also made planers, patented January 19, 1869, by Charles Carr.

BOYNTON & PLUMMER, Worcester, MA

Formed in 1880 by Edwin M. Boynton and Osgood Plummer (1835- 1916) to build blacksmiths' drills and 6" stroke hand shapers (Fig.1). Boynton had previously made hand shapers under his own name and as the Worcester Hand Tool Co. Boynton left the firm in 1885; Plummer continued to operate until selling out to his superintendent, Matthew G. Fitzpatrick, in 1915.

In 1883, the firm introduced new combination hand and power planers with 8" stroke x 8 1/2" traverse (Fig.2) and 10" stroke x 8 1/2" traverse (Fig.3). An improved 10" stroke model x 15" traverse (Fig.4) was introduced in 1889, followed in 1900 by an 8" stroke x 12" traverse (Fig.5), weighing 750 pounds and priced at $200. *(continued next page)*

HAND SHAPER.

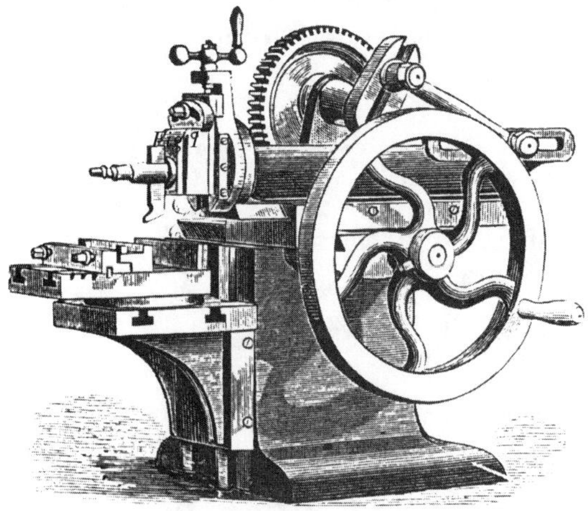

Fig.2

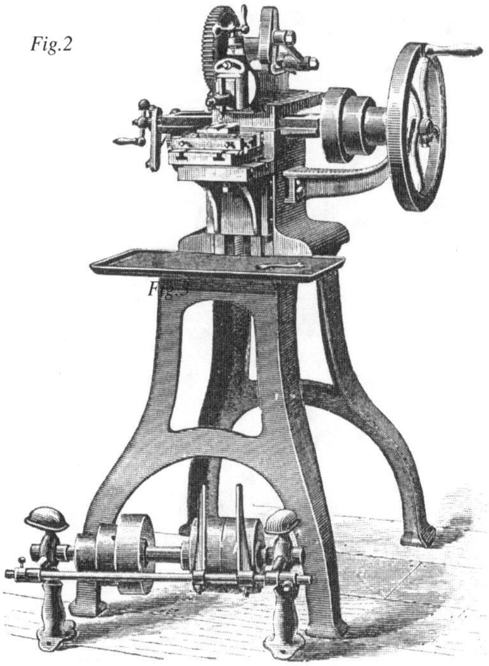

Fig3

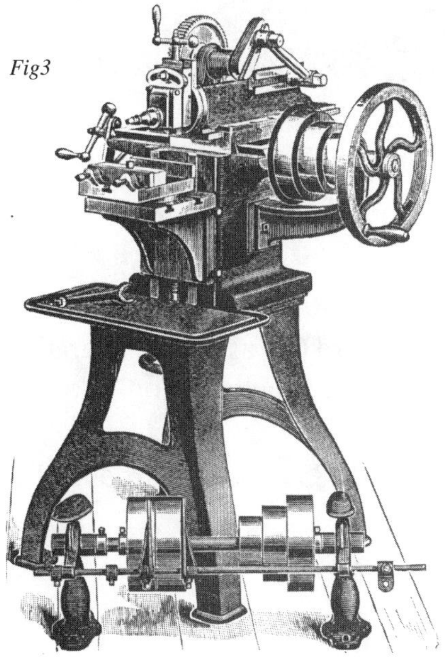

Fig.4

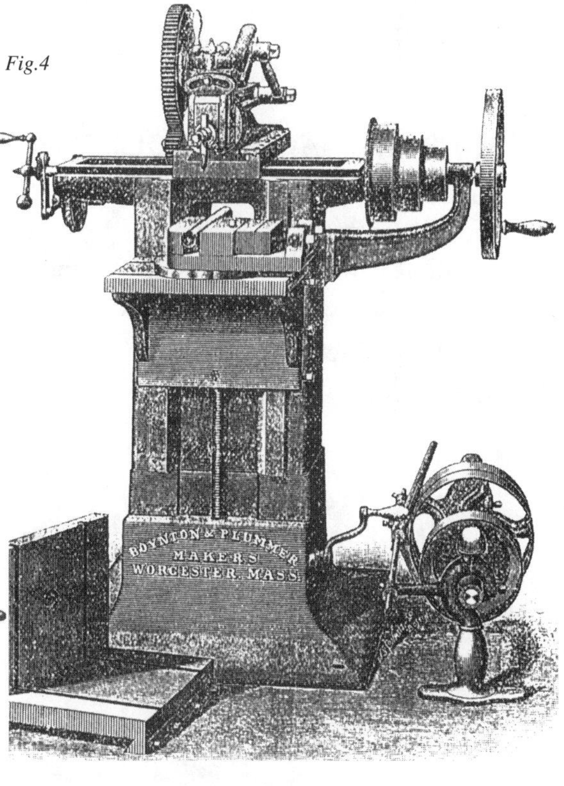

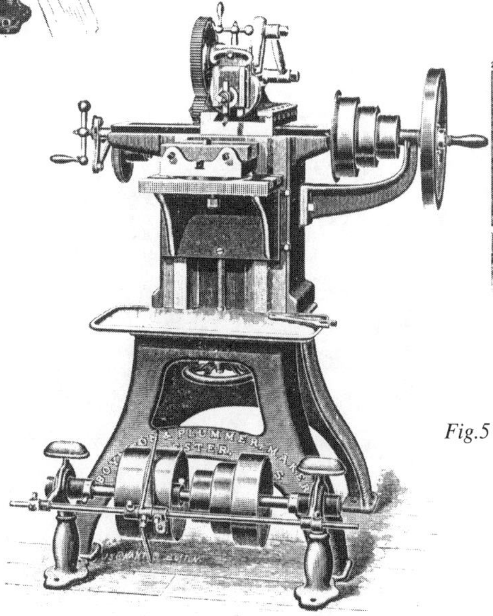

Fig.5

8 x 12-INCH TRAVERSE HEAD SHAPER

BRETTELL, G.E., Rochester, NY

Founded about 1875 by George E. Brettell, who patented an iron planer March 6, 1877, (Fig.1). By 1882 the firm was producing five planers monthly. In 1886, Brettell offered planers in six sizes "to plane any desired length" (Fig.2).

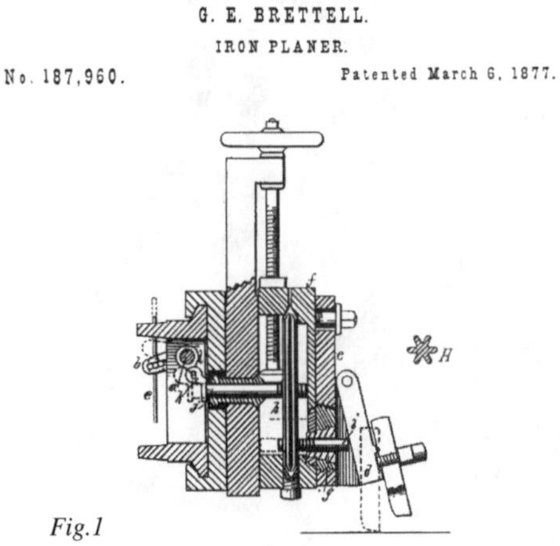

Fig.1

Fig.2

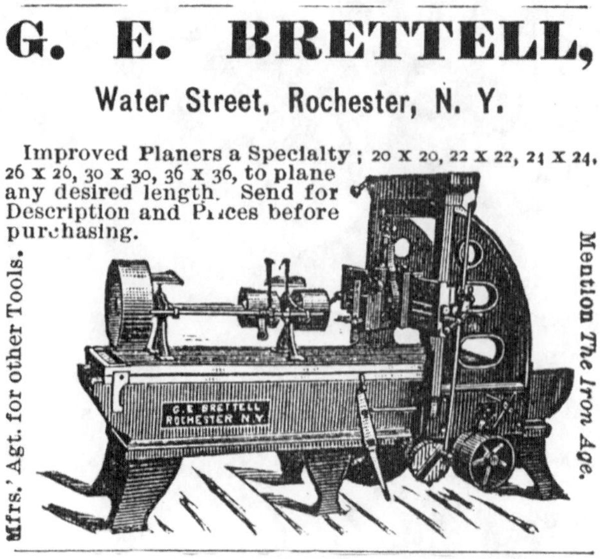

BRIDGEPORT MACHINE TOOL WORKS, Bridgeport, CT

Founded by Edward P. Bullard (1841-1906) August 20, 1880. Bullard, who had operated a series of machinery sales companies beginning in 1864, also continued to operate E.P. Bullard Co. as a sales operation. In 1894, Bullard incorporated the Bridgeport Machine Tool Works as the Bullard Machine Tool Co. which continued in business until very recent times.

Primary products were a variety of horizontal and vertical turret lathes, but in 1885 the firm introduced a 20" shaper, shown below, with a cross feed mechanism "same as our 16" planer."

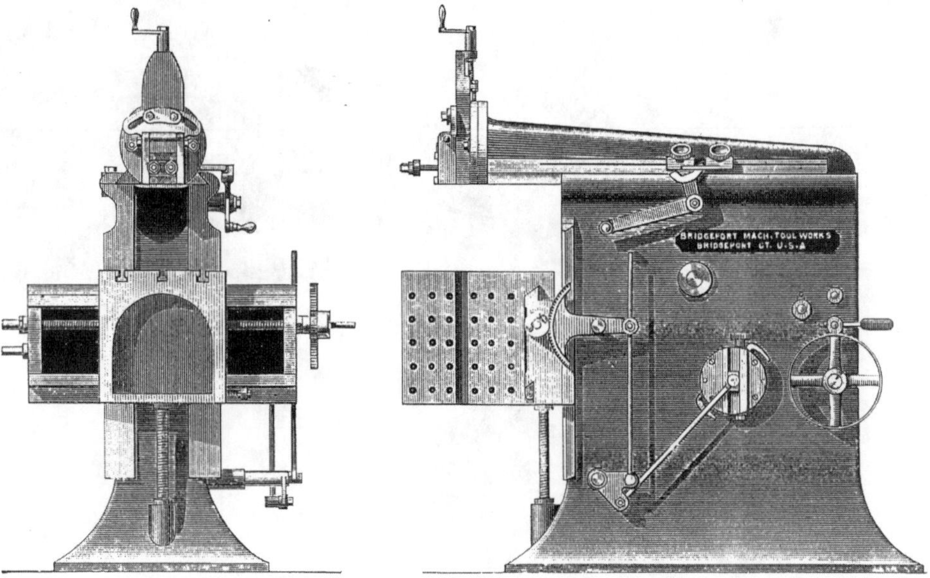

Bridgeport Twenty-Inch Shaper.

BRIGHTMAN MACHINE CO., Cleveland, OH

Maker, in 1889, of a new planer chuck made in two sizes with jaw lengths of 10" and 14" and opening 6" and 9". The chuck could be rotated 90 degrees and locked in place with dowel pins.

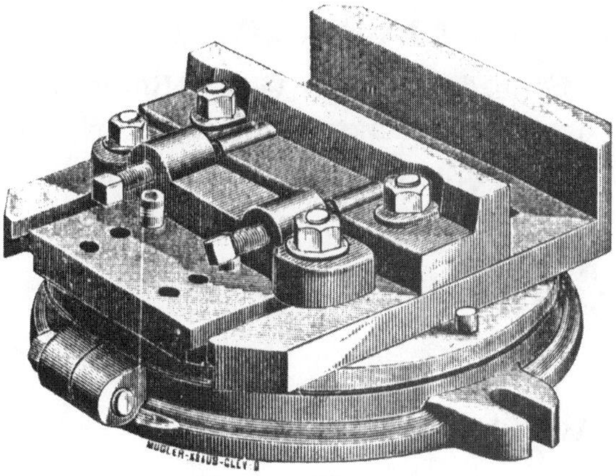

PLANER CHUCK.

BROWN, JAMES S., Pawtucket, RI

Working for Pitcher & Gay beginning in 1819, Brown developed an improvement in slide rests which, for the first time, allowed adjustment of tool height while the lathe was running. Brown replaced Gay as partner in 1824 and the firm became PITCHER & BROWN. In 1842, he bought out Pitcher and began operating under his own name, making lathes, planers, boring machines and gear cutting machines. The business continued until about 1870.

BUILDERS IRON FOUNDRY, Providence, RI

Established in 1832 as the High Street Foundry, the company became the Builders Iron Foundry in 1853. Early products were structural iron work and stove castings.

In the 1850s and 1860s, the firm built screw drive planers such as shown at left, still in operation in 1897. Note that the upright appears to be supported on a separate element rather than the main bed, probably so it could be moved in relation to the platen.

BURKE MACHINERY CO., Cleveland, OH

Founded by George H. Burke (1870-1933) about 1905. The firm specialized in small machine tools such as bench drills, tapping machines and small milling machines. In 1907, Burke introduced a 7" stroke hand shaper, shown at right, weighing 150 pounds. The machine was designed by S.N. Malterner.

BURNHAM & CO., GEO., Worcester, MA

Formed in 1882 by George Burnham (1817-1893) and Asa Goddard to build drilling machines. Burnham took over production of the JORDAN planer chuck from G.W. Jordan in 1892. Chuck production continued when the firm reorganized as the Francis Reed Co. in 1902.

PLASS' COMPOUND PLANER.

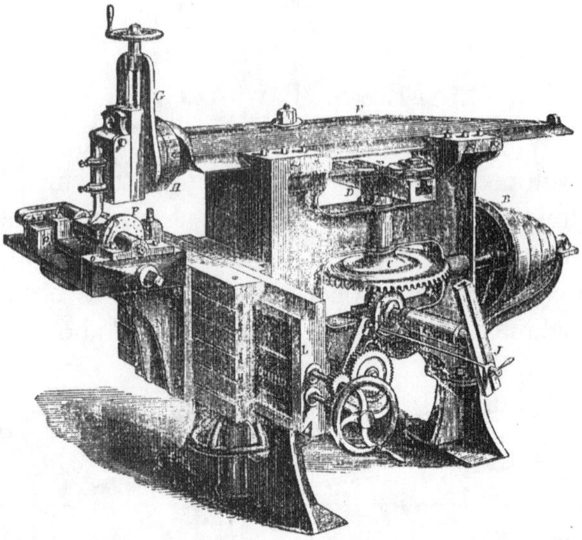

CARPENTER & PLASS,
New York, NY

Builder, in 1857, of "PLASS' compound planer," shown at right. The machine is equipped with a variable crank drive and with a unique feed mechanism. Note also the built-in indexing fixture mounted on the table.

CHAMBERLIN, D., Boston, MA

Builder of lathes and planers in 1853. The business continued until at least 1870.

CHANDLER PLANER CO., Ayer, MA

Founded by Daniel L. Chandler in 1903 as the CHANDLER CO. In 1905, Chandler sold out to George J. Burns who reorganized as the CHANDLER PLANER CO. Burns' planer design included a feature that used a third belt to reduce the rapid return rate just before the end of the stroke. The company fell on hard times in 1906 and very few machines were made after that. Its assets were auctioned in 1913.

About 1910, the planer shown below was offered by machinery dealer Chandler & Farquhar Co. It could plane 24" wide, 24" high, "any required length," and weighed 8000 pounds. Cutting feeds were 30 FPM and 50 FPM with the return at 2:1 or 4:1 ratio to cutting feed.

CHASE MACHINE WORKS, F.F., Plainfield, NJ

Builder, in 1894, of a 25" stroke, worm drive shaper (Fig.1) weighing 8500 pounds. In 1895, Chase introduced a planer vise (Fig.2) with both tilt and rotation.

Fig.1

A Worm-Driven Shaper.

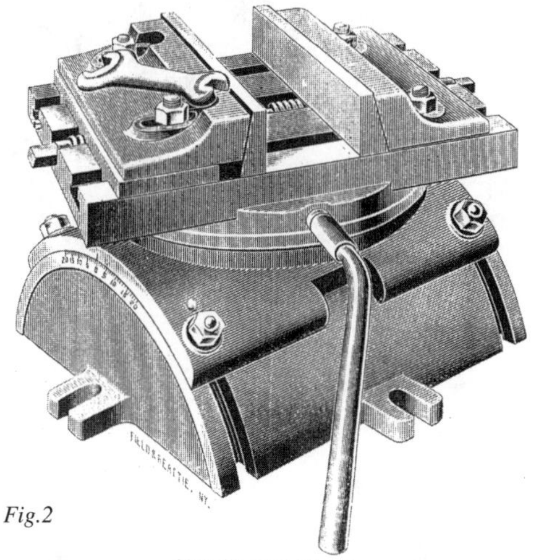

Fig.2

New Planer Chuck.

CINCINNATI PLANER CO., Cincinnati, OH

Organized January 1, 1899, by Bertram B. Quillen (1869-1945), Reuben A. Holden and William H. Burtner. Quillen, who had been associated with the American Tool Works was general manager, Burtner, previously with Davis & Eagan Machine Tool Co. was president. C.H.M. Atkins bought out Burtner in 1904 and became president.

1899 production was limited to 30", 33" and 36" (Fig.1) planers with a 4:1 quick return. Capacity was eight machines monthly. By 1901, the line was expanded to include up to 60" (Fig.2). Motor driven planers were offered beginning in 1903 including a 48" model (Fig.3) with feeds of 20, 25, 30 and 38 FPM and a constant return of 72 FPM. Heavy, motor driven, planers for use with high speed steel cutting tools (Fig.4), furnished with instantly variable feed speeds from 15 FPM to 60 FPM, were offered in sizes from 22" to 96" in 1909.

(continued on next page)

Fig.1

Planer Made By Cincinnati Planer Company.

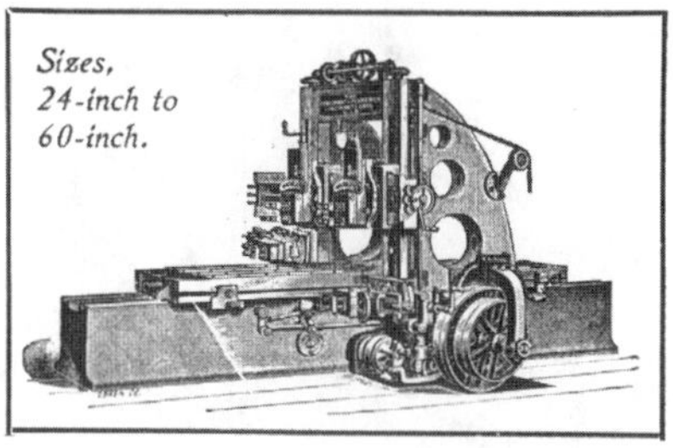

Fig.2

Fig.3

THE CINCINNATI MOTOR DRIVEN PLANER.

Fig.4

CINCINNATI SHAPER CO., Cincinnati, OH

Incorporated in 1898 by Perrin G. March (1853-1930), S.W. Skinner, William S. Rowe, Arthur Stein and Frederick A. Geier with a capital of $50,000. March served as president until his death in 1930.

In 1900 the firm offered triple geared, rack drive shapers in 26" and 30" (Fig.1) strokes equipped with a variable speed countershaft to drive the ram at feeds from 9 to 45 FPM; and 16" (Fig.2) and 20" (Fig.3) back geared crank shapers. 1901 production included motor driven crank shapers (Fig.4), and 18" double head traverse shapers (Fig.5). *(continued on next two pages)*

Fig.1

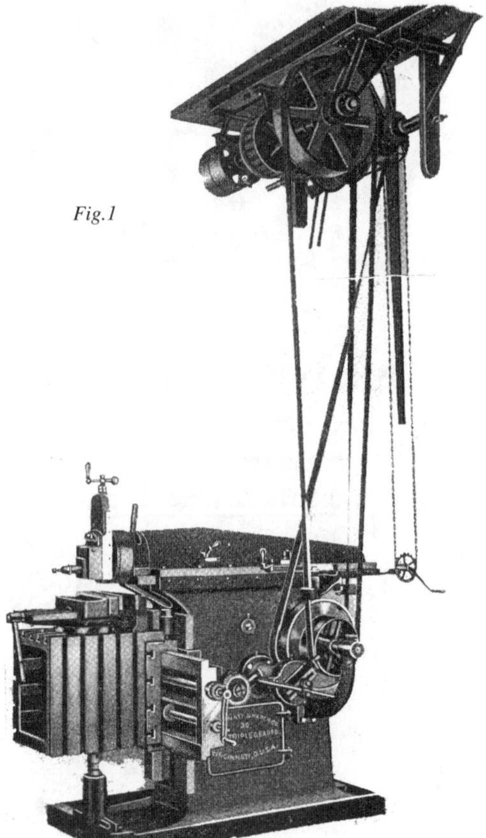

Fig.2

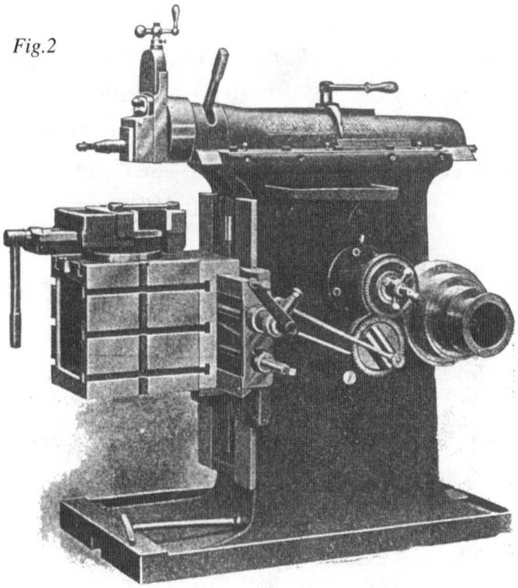

Fig.3

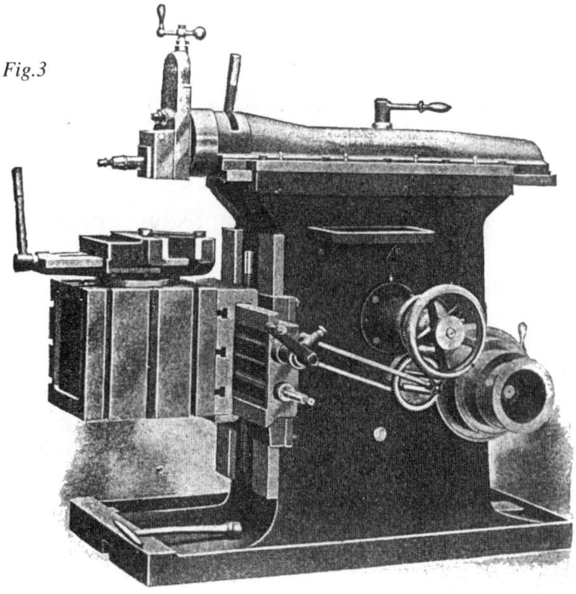

Fig.4

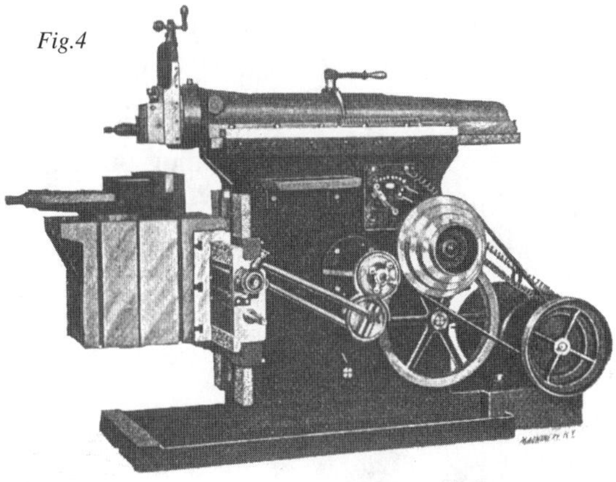

Fig.5

Fig.6

DOUBLE HEAD SWIVELING SADDLE TRAVERSE SHAPER.

Fig.7

Fig.7

New Traverse Shaper on Which Cutting Takes Place on the Return Stroke Instead of the Forward Strol

Double head, swiveling saddle traverse shapers (Fig.6), with two 5HP motor driven heads mounted on a 14' bed, were introduced in 1904, as was a similar pulling cut traverse shaper (Fig.7) designed to cut on the reverse stroke much as the Morton Machine Co. shapers. Cincinnati claimed that a heavier cut could be taken on the reverse stroke since the forces were taken against the bed, rather than tending to push the table outward.

A line of high powered shapers, designed for use with high speed steel cutting tools, was introduced in 1905 (Fig.8). An open side shaper (Fig.9) with 15" stroke and 30" traverse, weighing 3450 pounds, was introduced in 1907 and a 20"x 20"x 24" crank planer (Fig.10) in 1909.

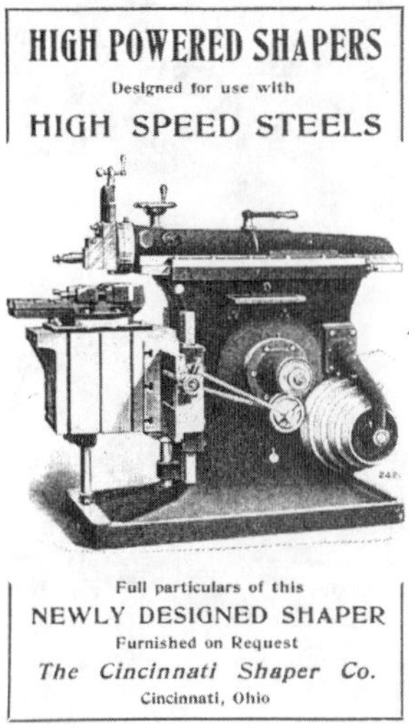

Fig.8

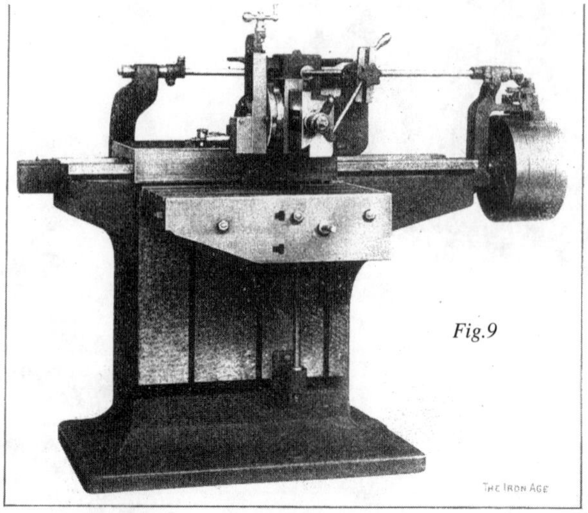

Fig.9

Fig.10

CLEVELAND PLANER WORKS, Cleveland, OH

Founded in 1903 by James G. Dornbirer (1867-1930) and George W. Ford to build open-side planers designed by Dornbirer. In 1917, Ford sold out to Dornbirer who then reorganized as the CLEVELAND PLANER CO.

Production focused on open side planers only, which in 1904 were offered in 30" (Fig.1), 36" (Fig.2), 42", 48" (Fig.3), 54", 60", and 72" widths and in any length. In 1907, the firm built a 60" size with a 52' bed (Fig.4), weighing 52,000 pounds. Motor driven planers were offered by 1910, included a 36"x 36"x 12' model (Fig.5).
(Illustrations next page)

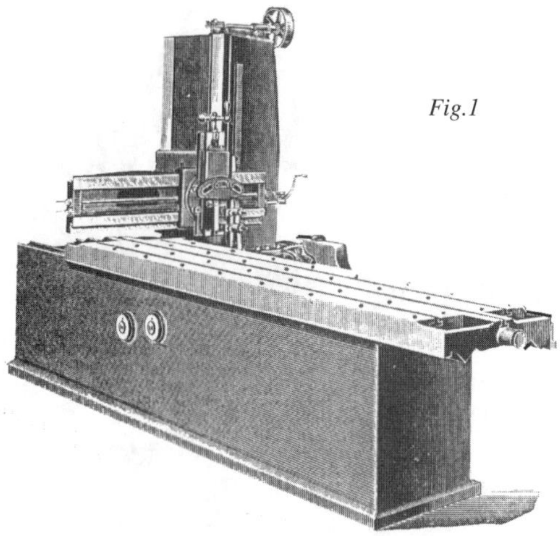

Fig.1

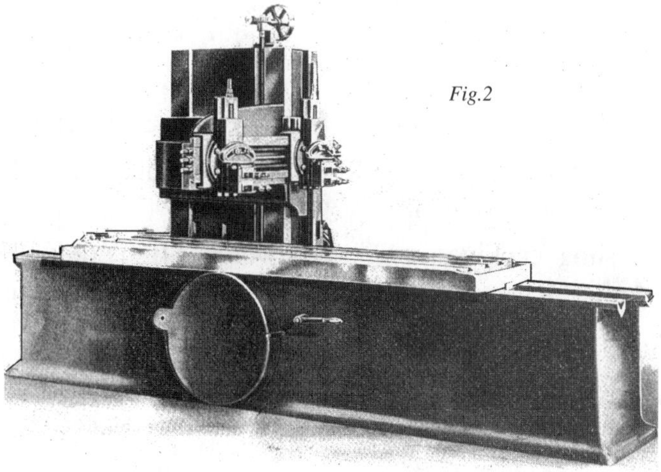

Fig.2

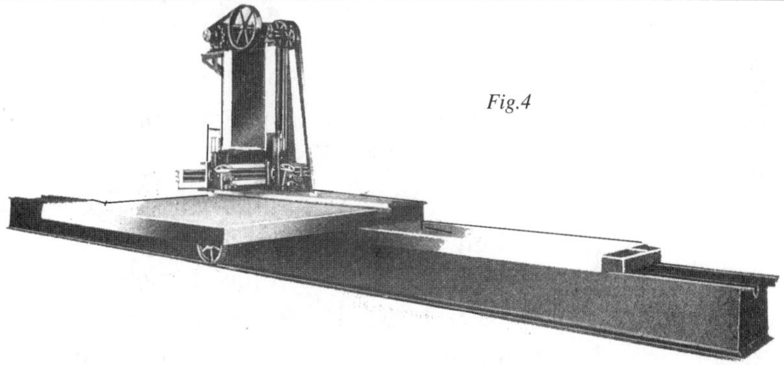

Fig.4

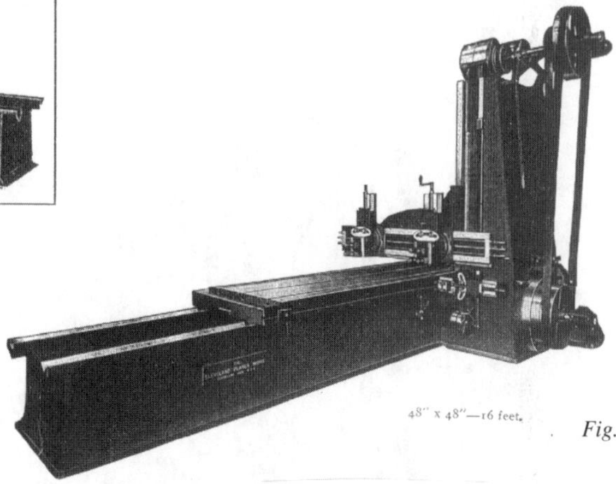

48" x 48"—16 feet.

Fig.3

Fig.5

36" x 36"—12-ft. Planer.

Motor Driven.

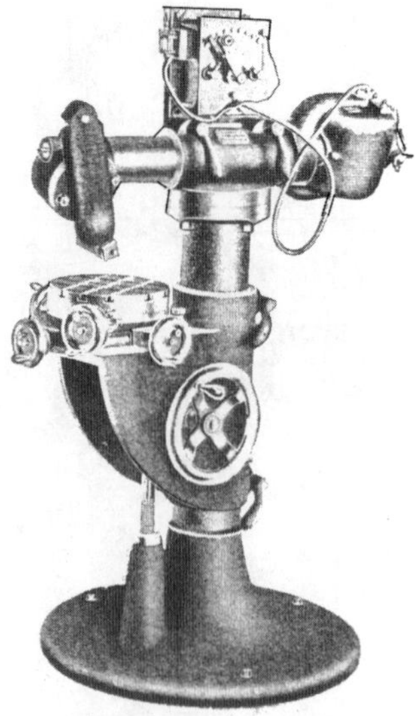

COCHRANE-BLY MACHINE WORKS, Rochester, NY

Organized in 1899 by Robert B. Cochrane, Vincent T. Bly, and Myron T. Bly with capital of only $8,000. Cochrane served as president.

Filing machines for die work were the first product, but in 1903, the company introduced the universal shaper shown right. It was equipped with a 10" diameter table, knee movement of 7", arm movement of 7", and table cross movement of 3 1/2". The head could rotate in two planes and the table in one plane. A larger version was introduced in 1912.

COES, ZORESTER B., Hamilton, OH

Coes was associated with the Brainard Milling Machine Co. in the 1880's, later moving to Hamilton, OH, where he was granted several lathe patents, all assigned to the NILES TOOL WORKS.

In 1892, Coes introduced a 26", single belt planer with a unique gear drive as shown below, and feed variable from 14 to 30 FPM. The machines were probably made at NILES TOOL WORKS under contract.

THE COES 26-INCH SINGLE BELT PLANER.

COLUMBIAN IRON FOUNDRY & MACHINE TOOL WORKS, Chicago, IL

Founded 1865 by Charles W. Parker. The firm made a "specialty of building heavy lathes and planers for the various railroads." Parker retired in 1883 and the firm appears to have lasted only a few years afterwards.

CONTINENTAL IRON WORKS, Greenpoint, LI, NY

Builder, in 1862, of a plate planer patented by T.F. Rowland. The machine was designed to plane the edges of 1" armor plates, 40" wide x 9' long for turrets and 5' square for flat surfaces. The plates would then be square and close fitting when mounted on the then new armor clad warships. Turret plate edges were planed with bevels to match the curves when mounted 11 deep on a 21' diameter turret. *(continued next page)*

Note the water barrel that supplies a trickle of water for cooling the cutting tool.

ROWLAND'S DOUBLE PLANER FOR ARMOR AND TURRET PLATES.

COOMBS & CO., S.C., Worcester, MA

A partnership of Samuel C. Coombs, Russell R. Shepard and Martin Lathe, formed in 1845. Builder of a variety of machine tools, including planers and engine lathes.

The firm was reorganized as SHEPARD, LATHE & CO. when Coombs left in 1853.

DANIELSON MACHINE & TOOL CO., Cleveland, OH

Incorporated by Gustave F. Danielson in 1899 with capital of $50,000. Products included presses, dies, special machinery and 16" shapers such as shown right. Short lived, the firm's assets were sold by the sheriff in May, 1902.

DAVIS & CO., GEORGE W., Nashua, NH, later

DAVIS, GEORGE W. & S.A., Nashua, NH

Formed in 1863 by George W. Davis (1828-1897). The firm supplied machine tools, including lathes and planers, to the Springfield Armory during the civil war. In 1879, the firm reorganized as GEORGE W. & S.A. DAVIS, which continued to build machine tools.

DAVIS & EGAN MACHINE TOOL CO., Cincinnati, OH

A partnership of Charles Davis (1853-1903) and Thomas P. Egan (1847-1922), formed September 1, 1896, as a reorganization of the LODGE & DAVIS MACHINE TOOL CO. The company was reorganized in 1898 as the AMERICAN TOOL WORKS CO. when Davis sold out to Franklin Alter. *(continued on next page)*

The firm continued production of the machine tools previously made by Lodge & Davis. Planers were offered in the nine sizes and features as shown in an April, 1898, ad (Fig.1). A redesigned, heavy duty, 48" planer with full bed (Fig.2) was introduced in early 1898.

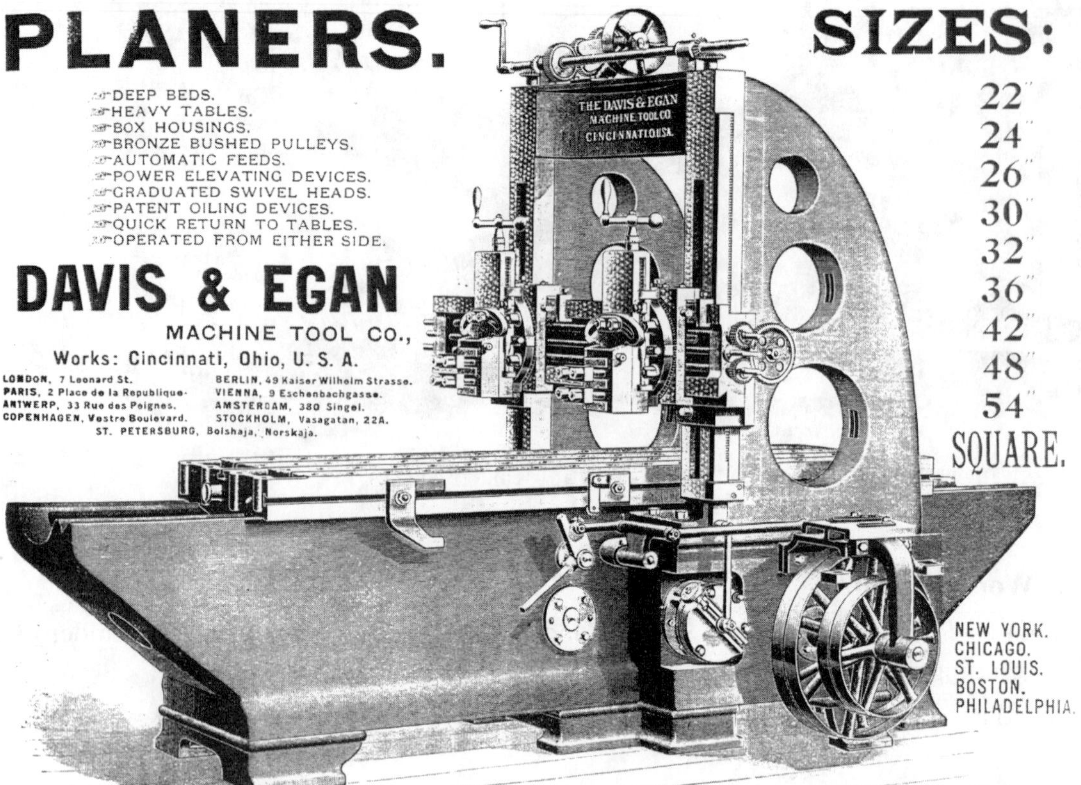

Fig.1

Fig.2

DAVIS, W.P., Rochester, NY, later
DAVIS MACHINE CO. W.P., Rochester, NY

Founded in 1887 by William P. Davis (1850-1910) to make his patented key seater. Davis operated both as a machinery dealer and a machine tool builder.

In 1894, Davis, joined by his brother Charles F. Davis (1861-1932), reorganized as the DAVIS MACHINE CO. which offered a much wider selection of machine tools. William P. Davis died in 1910; Charles F. Davis left the firm in 1914. The new owners reorganized in 1915 as the DAVIS MACHINE TOOL CO. *(continued next page)*

Lathes and keyseating machines were by far Davis' primary products. In 1889, however, Davis offered a 24"x 24"x 6' planer, shown right. The machine may have been made by another firm on contract to Davis.

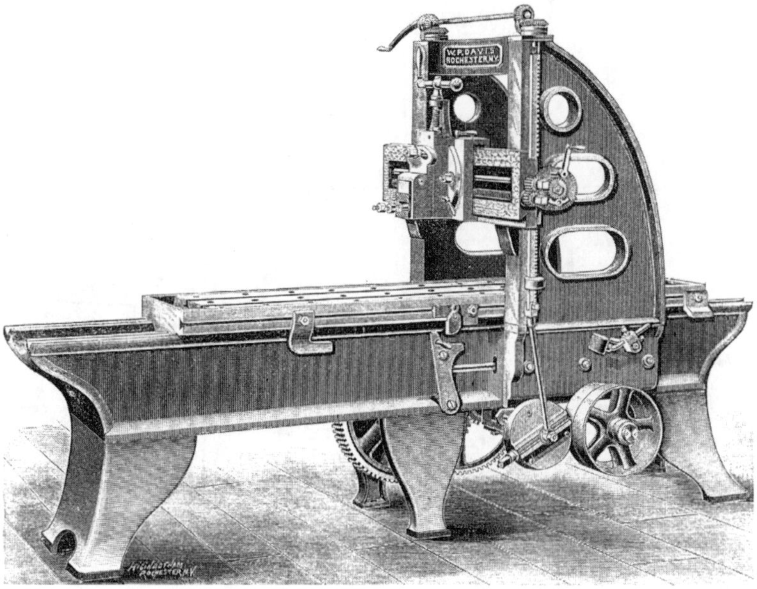

DETRICK & HARVEY, Baltimore, MD, later

DETRICK & HARVEY MACHINE CO., Baltimore, MD

Formed in 1884 as a partnership of Jacob S. Detrick and Alexander Harvey (1867-1914). Detrick was granted patents for planers on May 29, 1883, and November 5, 1889. The firm incorporated in 1890 as the DETRICK & HARVEY MACHINE CO.

1884 production was an improved version of the open side planer made by J.S. DETRICK (Fig.1), furnished with an outrigger to support overhanging workpieces. A further improved version (Figs.2-3), with heavier column and brace angled from the cross beam, was introduced in 1885. In 1887, a counterbalance was added and the planer offered in 25" (Figs.4-5), 30" and 36" sizes. 1889 production included a new 20' long, 40,000 pound, open side planer (Figs.6-7) with an extra post and bed that extended to allow a horizontal tool travel adjustable from 4' to 10'. Note the side heads and moveable outrigger. *(continued on next five pages)*

Fig.1

Improved Single Post Planer

Fig.2

Single Post or Open Side Iron Planer

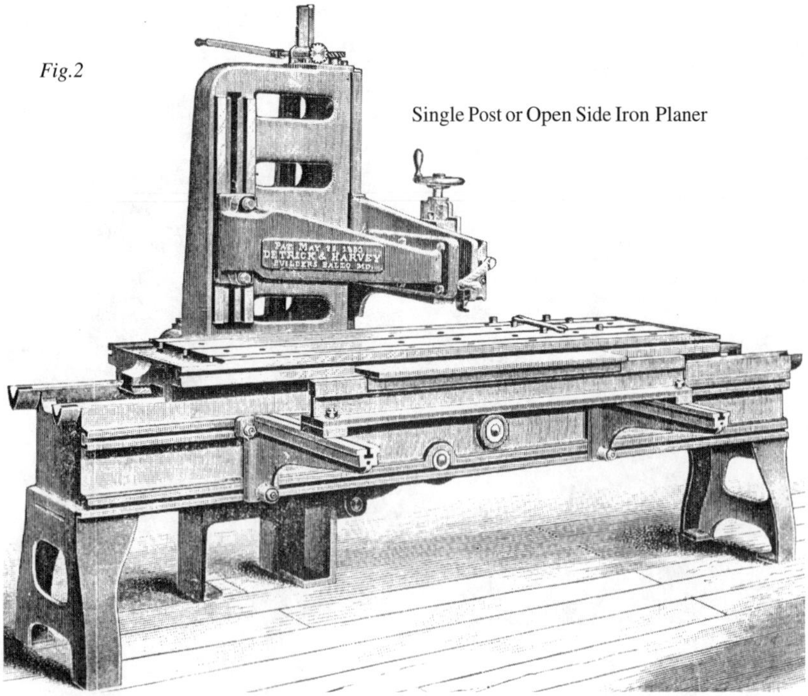

Fig.3

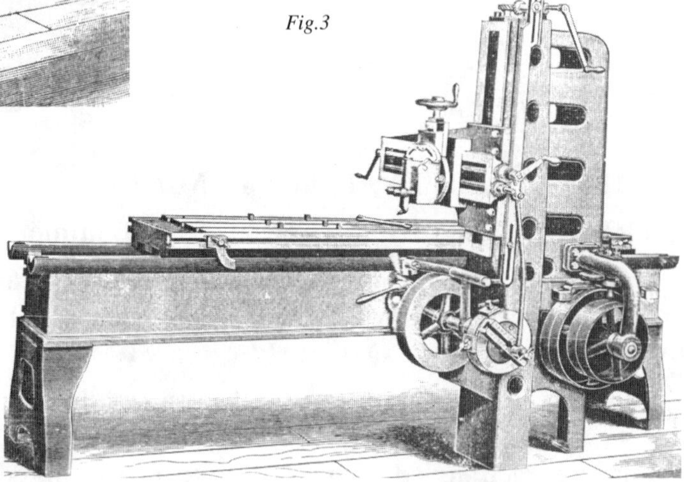

Fig.4

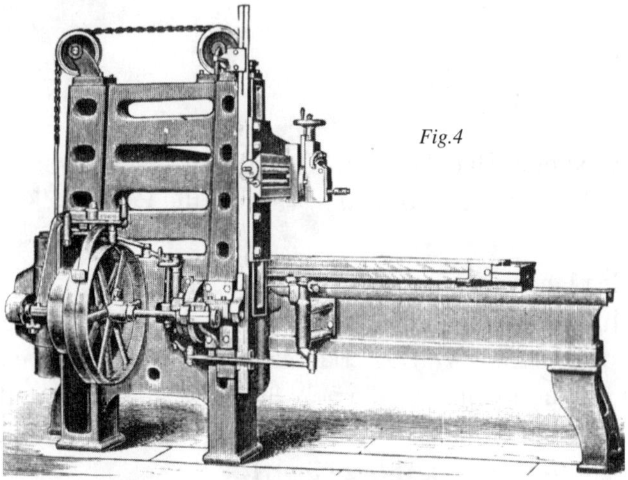

Fig.5

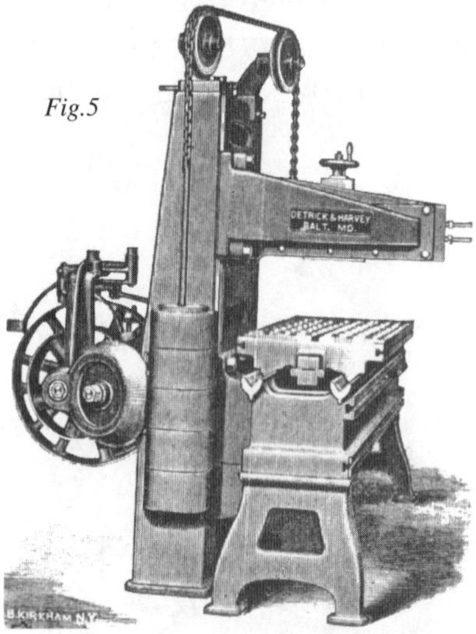

Fig.6

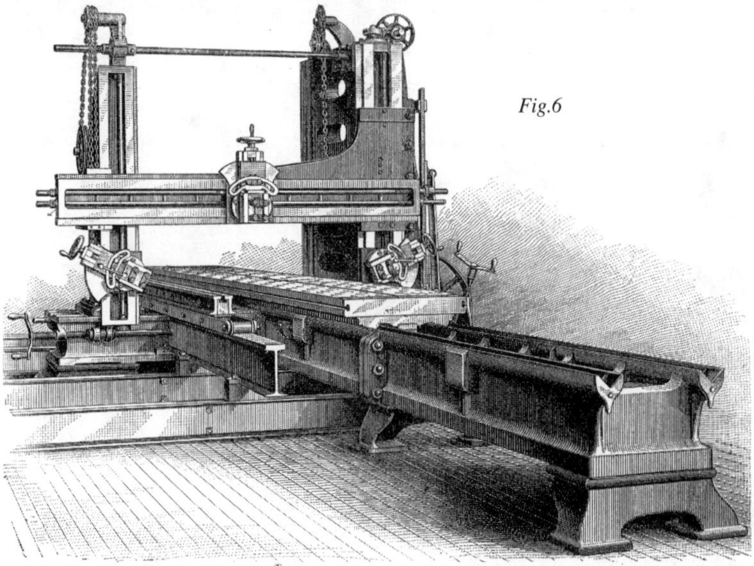

OPEN SIDE PLANER, BUILT BY DETRICK & HARVEY, OF BALTIMORE, MD.

Fig.7

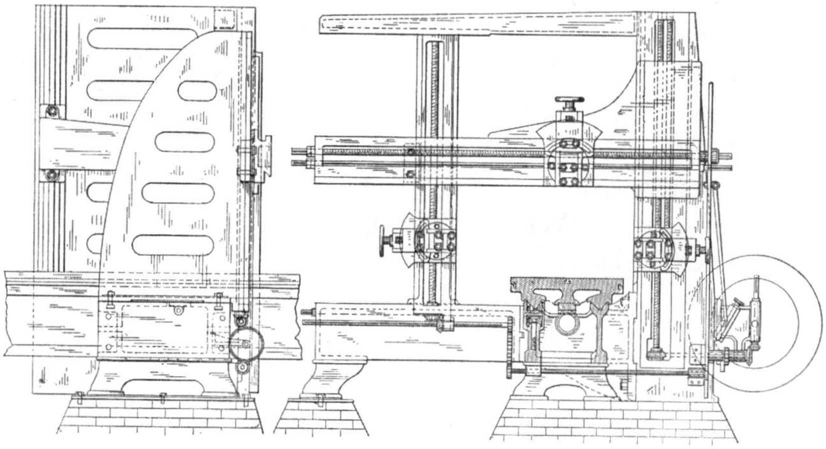

Longitudinal Elevation. *Cross-Sectional Elevation.*

OPEN SIDE PLANER, BUILT BY DETRICK & HARVEY, OF BALTIMORE, MD.

Fig.8

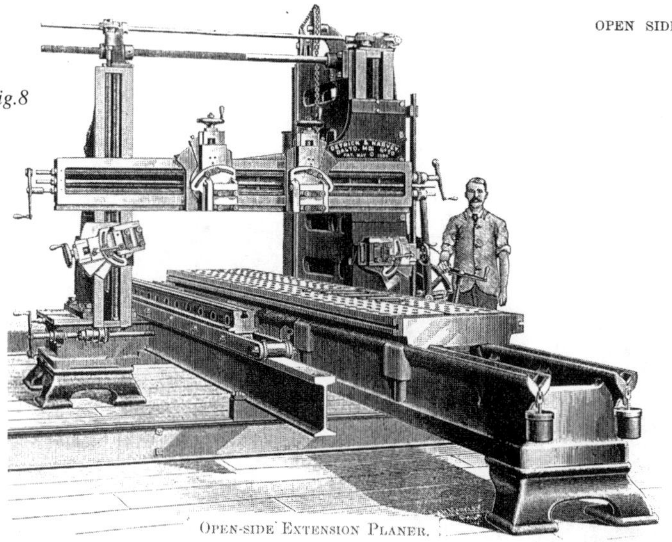

OPEN-SIDE EXTENSION PLANER.

Fig.9

OPEN SIDE FROG AND SWITCH PLANER.

In 1890, the firm introduced the extension planer with removeable upright (Fig.8) as a standard product, offered in 72" wide by 48" high by 10' long, up to 120" wide by 72" high by 20' long; and a heavy duty, open side "frog and switch" planer (Fig.9) that could plane 30"x 30" by any length. Note the large gear reduction for taking heavy cuts demanded by makers of railroad equipment. A similar machine, but with a extension upright (Fig.10) that was removeable (Fig.11), was offered in 1891. It could plane 120" wide, 96" high and 25' long, was triple geared, cut chips up to 4" wide and 1/16" thick, and weighed 140,000 pounds.

A special planer consisting of two open side planers arranged in right and left hand and bolted together (Figs.12-13) was introduced in 1893. It could be used as a double planer or taken apart and used as two open side planers. A plate scarfing machine (Fig.14) designed for shipbuilders and capable of scarfing plates up to 6' wide was offered in 1898. Weighing 35,000 pounds, the machine was one of the few made by Detrick & Harvey without the open side feature.

The firm made open side grinding machines in 1905 and continued production of open side planers until selling out to the Bethlehem Steel Co. in 1915.

Fig.10

THE DETRICK & HARVEY OPEN-SIDE EXTENSION PLANER.

Fig.11

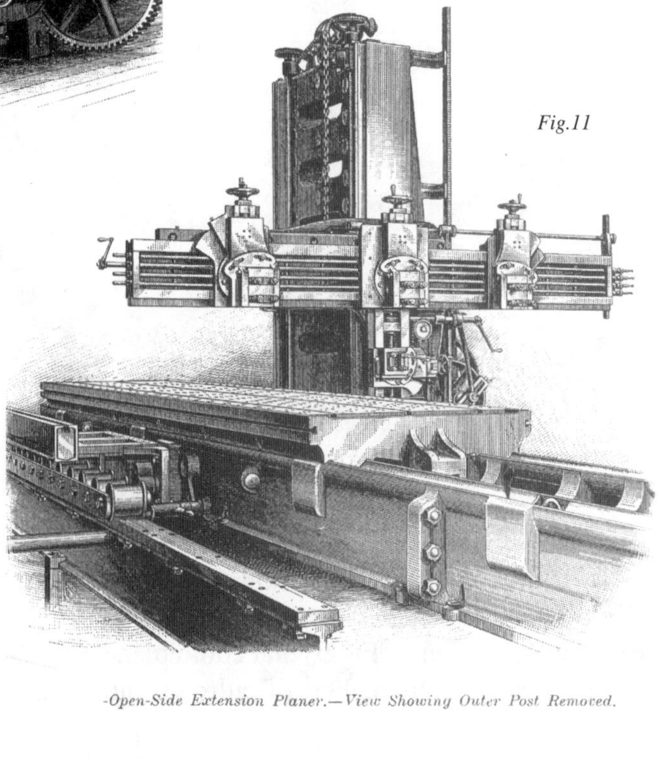

Open-Side Extension Planer.—View Showing Outer Post Removed.

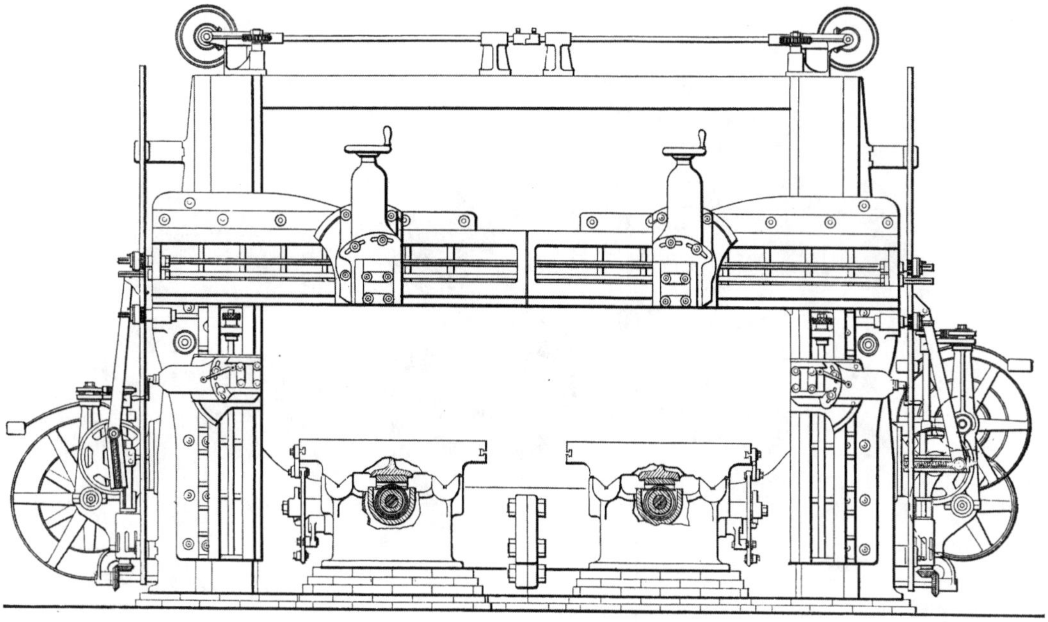

Cross Sectional Elevation.

Fig.12

DOUBLE PLANER.

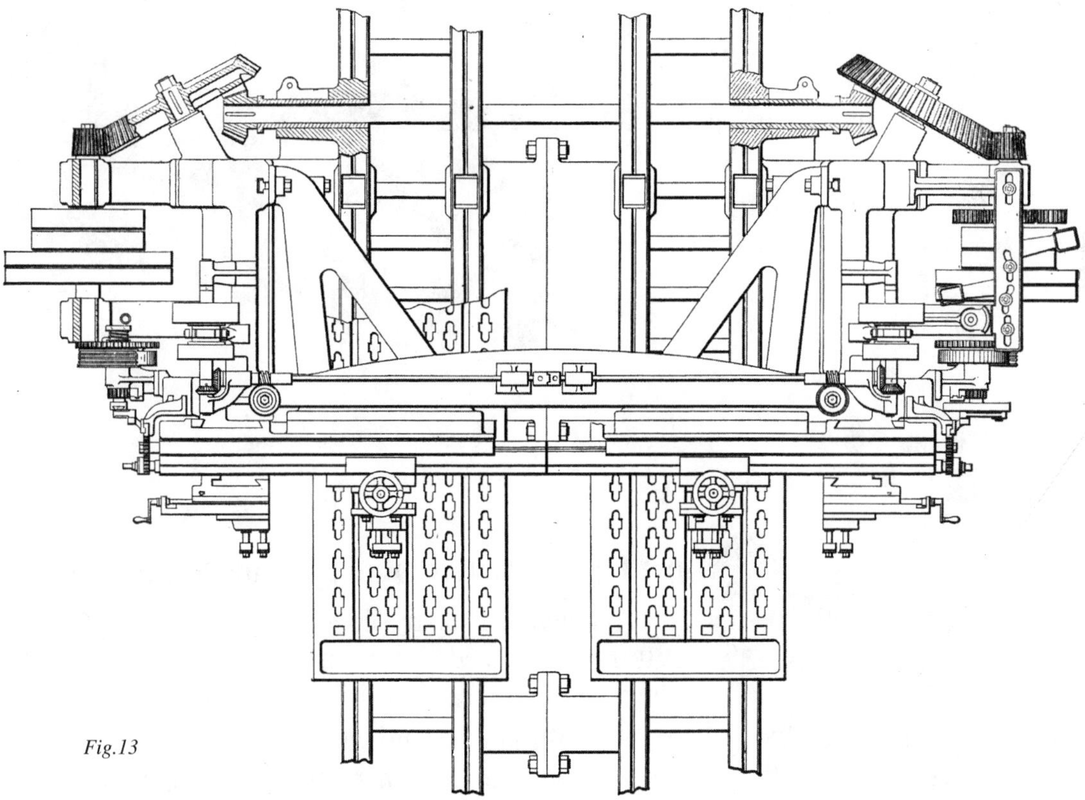

Fig.13

Sectional Plan.

Detrick & Harvey

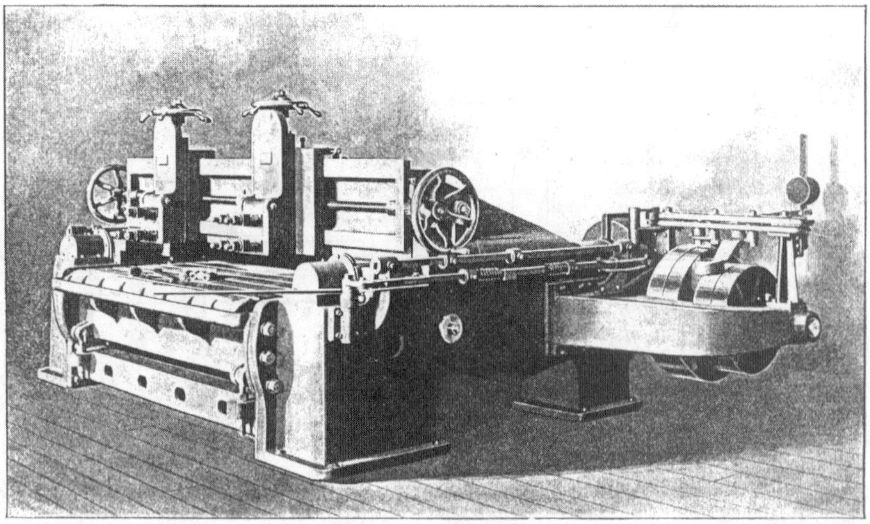

Fig.14

PLATE SCARFING MACHINE.

DETRICK'S NEW SINGLE POST IRON PLANER.

DETRICK, J.S., Baltimore, MD

Founded about 1881 by Jacob S. Detrick to build a single post iron planer of his invention, patented May 29, 1883. The machine, shown at right, was probably the first open side planer, as it came to be known, commercially produced. Note the light outboard support (item C) which could be removed to give a completely open side.

In 1884, Detrick formed a partnership with Alexander Harvey and reorganized as DETRICK & HARVEY.

The range of work an ordinary size **Dill Slotter** will cover is a matter of amazement to a person unacquainted with the special features of this machine.

DILL MACHINE CO., T.C., Philadelphia, PA

Founded in 1888 by Thomas C. Dill (1865-1922) to build the Dill traveling head slotting machine, patented October 1, 1889. The firm incorporated in 1895 with capital of only $10,000.

The Dill slotter, shown left, was equipped with a traveling head, which greatly increased the range of workpiece size compared to the conventional, fixed head type.

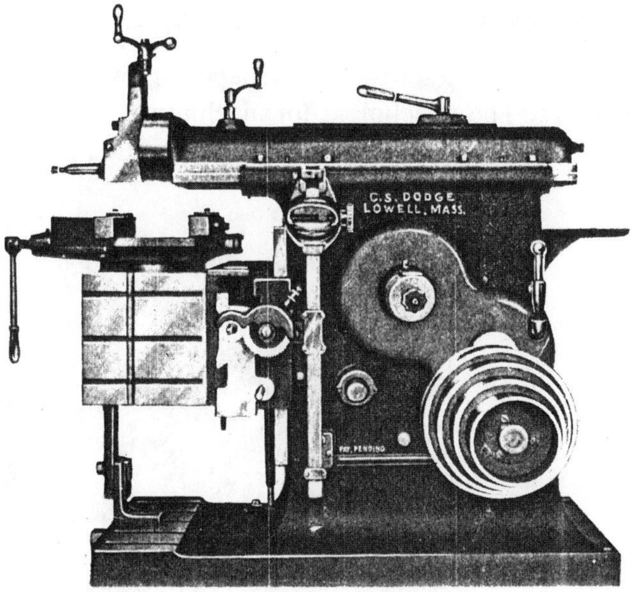

DODGE, C.S., Lowell, MA

Builder, in 1910, of the 24" heavy duty crank shaper shown right. Note the extension base with outboard support for the box table.

DRAPER MACHINE TOOL CO., Worcester, MA

Formed in 1892 when William F. Draper (1842-1910), owner of a large loom-making firm, bought the assets of the defunct Lathe & Morse Tool Co. Production of crank planers, hand lathes and engine lathes continued, based on Lathe & Morse designs.

The firm was absorbed into the Whitcomb-Blaisdell Machine Tool Co. in 1905.

Keyway Cutting Machine.

DUNHAM MACHINE WORKS, Danbury, CT

Maker, in 1891, of a keyway cutting attachment for planers, shown right. Cutting bars and angle plates were made in several sizes for use on a variety of workpiece sizes.

DURKEE & DOE, Chicago, IL

A partnership of George B. Durkee and Albin K. Doe. In 1882, the firm announced they were "bringing out an improved iron shaper, and a new pulley, drilling and tapping machine."

DURKEE & KEEFER, Chicago, IL

Builder of a screw driven shaper believed to have been made about 1870 and still in use when photographed in 1912. The attachment for machining circular work was added long after the machine was built. Note the complex mechanism for reversing ram direction by shifting belts.

Old Screw-operated Shaper

Details of Ram-reversing Mechanism

DUVINGE, LEWIS, New York, NY

Builder, in 1868, of shapers and engine lathes.

EBERHARDT BROTHERS MACHINE CO., Newark, NJ

Formed in 1904 by Henry E. Eberhardt (1851-1934) and his sons Elmer G. Eberhardt (1881-1908), Frank E. Eberhardt, Henry J. Eberhardt and U. Seth Eberhardt when they sold their interest in Gould & Eberhardt. The firm reorganized as the Newark Gear Cutting Machine Co. in 1908.

Production was primarily gear cutting machines but, beginning in 1906, the firm also built shapers, at right, with the same drive mechanism as its gear cutting machines.

EDDY, W.H., Worcester, MA, later

EDDY CO. WILLIAM H., Worcester, MA

Founded in 1873 by William H. Eddy (1831-1903) to build twist drill grinders, lathes and planers. Eddy sold out in 1900 to parties who reorganized as the WILLIAM H. EDDY CO. Production in the 1890s was marketed through Hill, Clarke & Co., which offered the machines under the Hill, Clarke name.

Shaper of Peculiar Design.

ENTERPRISE MACHINE CO., Geneva, OH

Builder, about 1890, of shapers with variable stroke and Whitworth quick-return. An example is shown right.

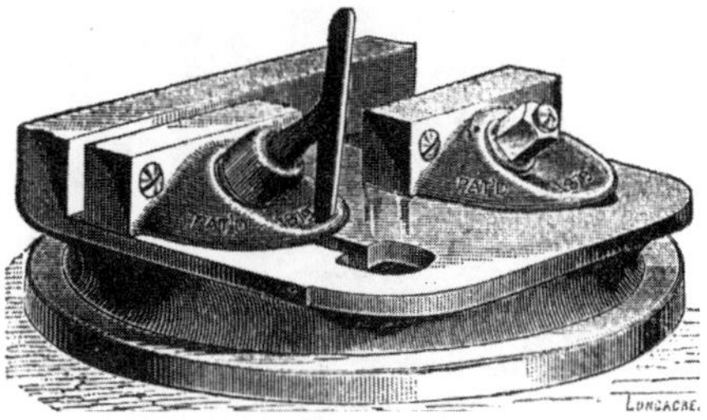

ERMENTROUT, W.H., Reading, PA

Builder, in 1893, of planer chucks as shown left. They were made in seven sizes and with square, circular, and graduated bases.

FAIRBANKS, BANCROFT & CO., Providence, RI

A partnership including Edward Bancroft formed in 1837 and reorganized as Bancroft, Nightingale & Co. in February, 1846. Products included planers to machine up to 48" wide, 48" high and 21' long. Bancroft, when a partner in Bancroft & Poole, is credited with making the first iron planer in the U.S.

FALES & JENKS, Providence, RI

A partnership of David G. Fales and Alvin Jenks formed in 1830 to make textile machinery and pumps. The firm also made machine tools, including the planer shown at right. Photographed in operation at Fales & Jenks in 1913, the planer was thought to have been built before 1840.

Fales & Jenks also made milling machines for government armorys during the civil war.

FAY & SCOTT, Dexter, ME

A partnership of Norman H. Fay (1852-1919) and Walter Scott, formed in 1881 to build machine tools and woodworking machinery. They were best known for their patternmakers' lathes. Fay bought out Scott in 1896 and became president when the firm incorporated in 1901.

In 1882, the firm introduced a traveling head shaper with 12" stroke and 40" of lateral movement. The machine weighed 3100 lbs. and was equipped with the Whitworth quick-return motion.

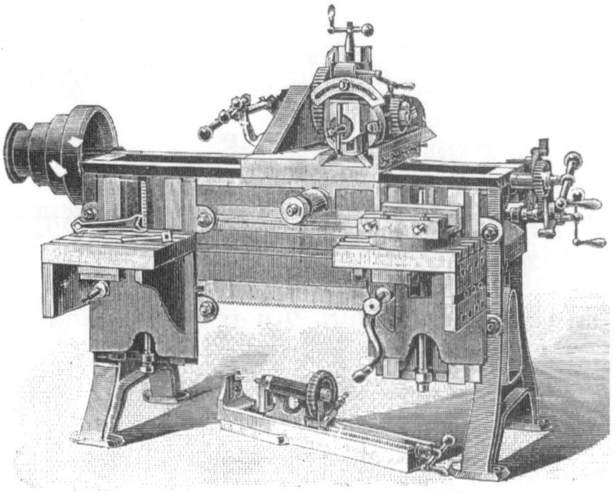

Twelve-inch Shaping Machine.

ROSETTE LATHES.

Excentric, Double Excentric, Oval, Stud and Button Chucks, Rosettes of all sizes, made and cut to order.

CRANK PLANERS,

With the quick return attachment.
Planer Centres and Jaws, Spinning-Lathes, etc.

H. N. FENNER & CO.,

(Manufacturers of Special Machinery,)

178, 180, and 182 Eddy Street,
PROVIDENCE, R. I.

July 1y]

FENNER & CO., H.N., Providence, RI

Builder, in 1872, of crank planers with quick return attachment, planer centers, Rosette lathes, and special machinery.

FERRIS & MILES, Philadelphia, PA

A partnership of Oscar C. Ferris and Frederick B. Miles, formed in 1871. The partners sold out to James Dougherty in 1880, who reorganized the firm as the MACHINE TOOL WORKS.

Products included crank shapers (Fig.1) and iron planers (Fig.2). Miles was granted a patent on September 2, 1873, for a counterbalanced cross head for planing machines (Fig.3).

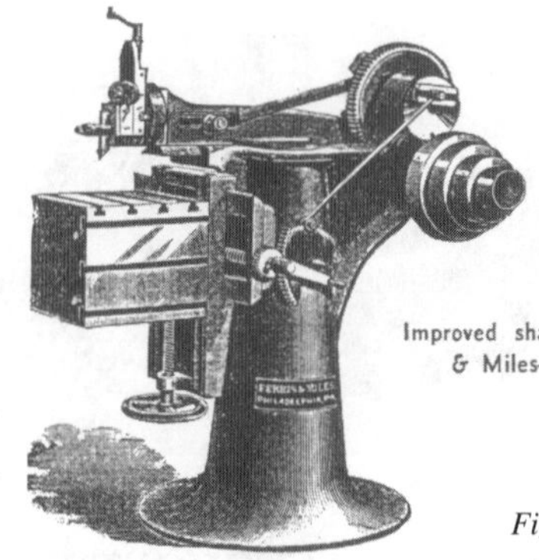

Improved shaper, Ferris & Miles—1877

Fig.1

Fig.2

F. B. MILES.
Planing-Machines.
No. 142,493. Patented September 2, 1873.

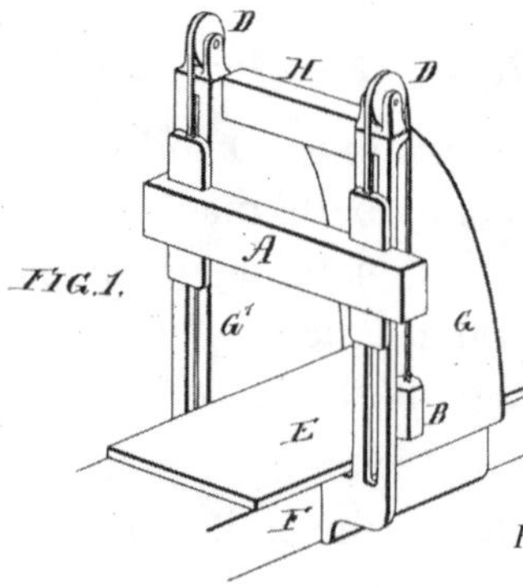

Fig.3

FITCHBURG MACHINE CO., Fitchburg, MA, later
FITCHBURG MACHINE WORKS, Fitchburg, MA

Formed January 1, 1867, as a stock company reorganization of S.C. Wright & Co. Sylvester C. Wright (1816-1880) was superintendent, his son-in-law, James L. Chapman (?-1914) was secretary. In June, 1877, the company was reorganized as the FITCHBURG MACHINE WORKS. Chapman retired in 1902 and was replaced by Frank B. Manville.

New lines of planers and shapers were introduced in 1881, including a 25"x 25"x 6' planer (Fig.1) and 20" stroke shaper (Fig.2). Improved planers, including 36"x 36"x 12' (Fig.3) and 72"x 72" (Fig.4) sizes, were introduced in 1887.

George D. Chapman, son of James L. Chapman, was appointed chief draftsman and designer in 1894, serving until 1899. The company's 1895 catalog offered planers from 18"x 18" (Figs.5-6) to 72"x 72" (Fig.7), and the No.1 shaper (Fig.8) in four sizes. An 18"x 54" traverse shaper (Fig.9) was offered by 1900.

Marcus A. Coolidge (1865-1947) bought the company in 1905 and, in 1924, merged it with the Seneca Falls Mfg. Co. to form the Seneca Falls Machine Co. *(continued next page)*

Fig.1

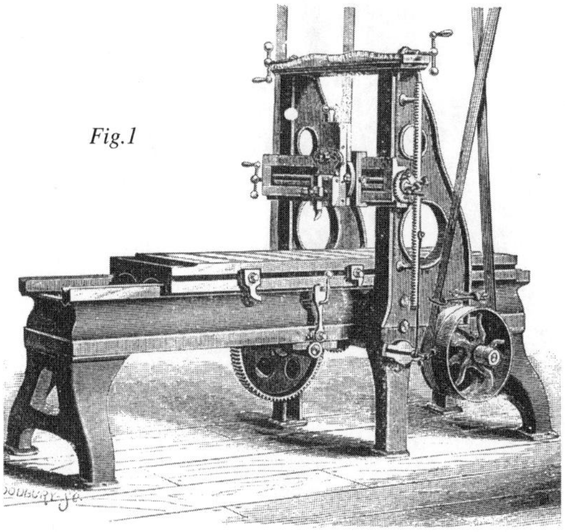

New Iron Planer.

Fig.3

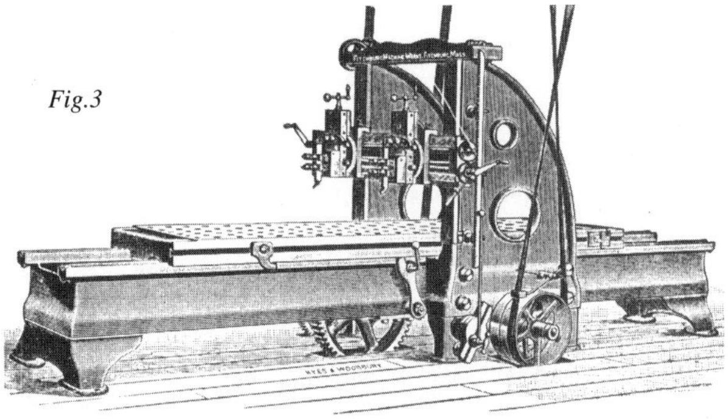

Improved Iron Planer.

Fig.2

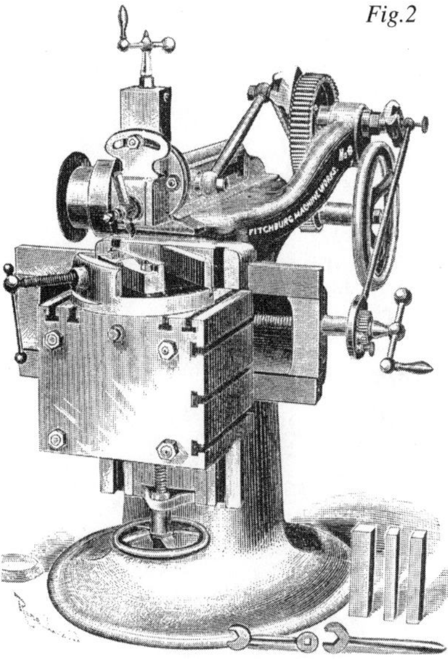

New Shaper.

Fig.4

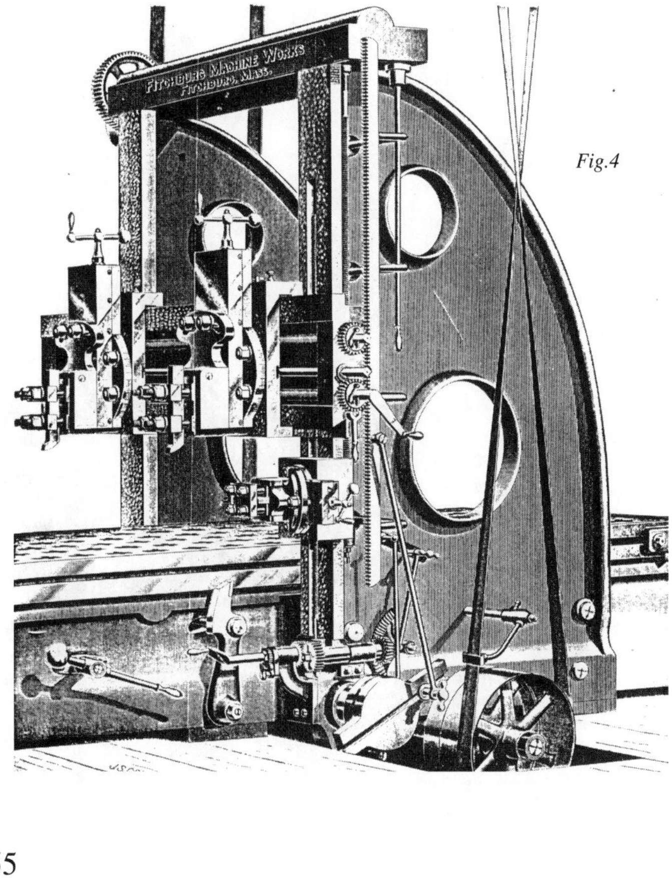

Fig.5

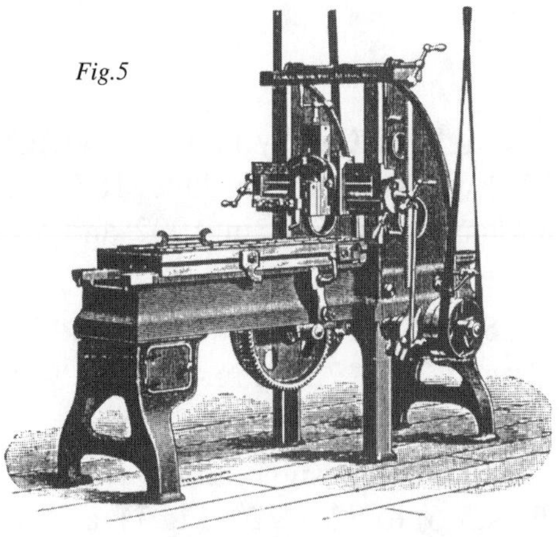

IRON PLANER TO PLANE 18 IN. X 18 IN. X 4 FEET.

Fig.6

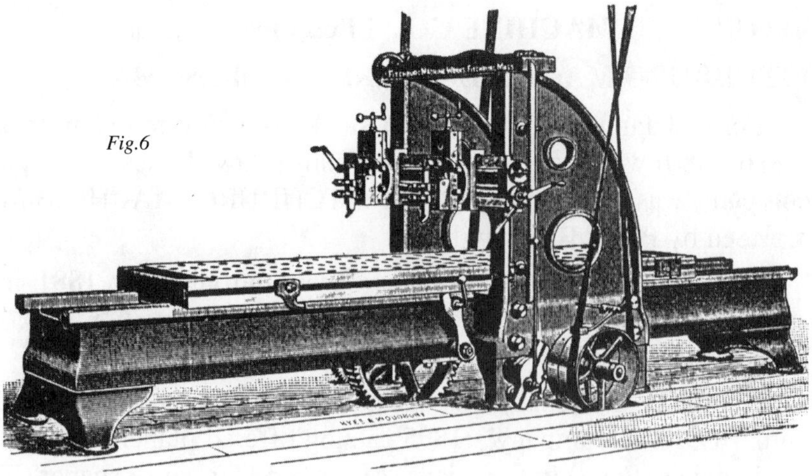

Iron Planer to Plane 36 in. x 36 in. x 12 ft. 2 Heads on Cross Beam.

To plane in Length.	To plane in width.	To plane in Height.
3 feet.	18 in.	18 in.
4 "	18 "	18 "
3 "	20 "	20 "
4 "	20 "	20 "
5 "	22 "	22 "
6 "	22 "	22 "
6 "	24 "	24 "
8 "	24 "	24 "
6 "	26 "	26 "
8 "	26 "	26 "
8 "	28 "	28 "
10 "	28 "	28 "
8 "	30 "	30 "
10 "	30 "	30 "
10 "	32 "	32 "
12 "	32 "	32 "
12 "	36 "	36 "
14 "	36 "	36 "
14 "	42 "	42 "
16 "	42 "	42 "
14 "	48 "	48 "
16 "	48 "	48 "
16 "	54 "	54 "
18 "	54 "	54 "
16 "	60 "	60 "
18 "	60 "	60 "
18 "	72 "	72 "
20 "	72 "	72 "

Fig.7

Fig.8

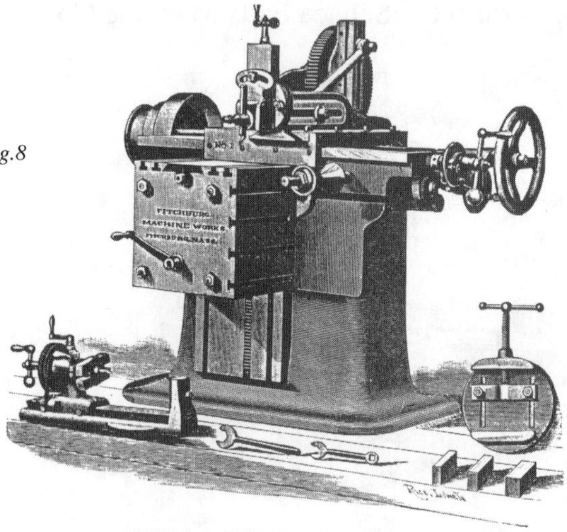

NO. 1 SHAPING MACHINE.

It gives a stroke from zero to 14 inches, with a quick return motion, thereby gaining full one-third over ordinary crank motion. It will plane 28 inches long, has an adjustable table 14 x 16 inches, forming an angle iron 14 x 16 inches, circular mandrel with independent feed. The circular mandrel can be almost instantly attached to or detached from the machine. Made from improved patterns, very heavy, and will do at least one-third more work than a common planer, and is more convenient to use. All sizes are furnished with Chuck, Wrenches and Countershaft. No. 1 and larger sizes furnished with Centres and Circular Mandrel with Independent Feed.

No. 0, Stroke 10 in.	Planes 20 in.	Weight 2,000 lbs.	Price, $........
" 1, " 14 "	" 28 "	" 2,750 "	" ....
" 2, " 16 "	" 42 "	" 4,700 "	" ....
" 3, " 19 "	" 66 "	" ...... "	" ....

Centres for No. 0, $........extra.

Fig.9

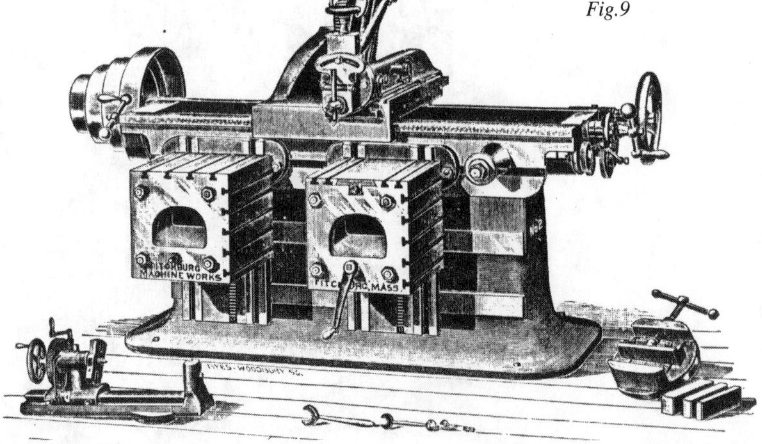

Fitchburg Shaper No. 2, 18-inch by 54-inch

FLAGG, S.H., Worcester, MA, later
FLAGG & CO., SAMUEL, Worcester, MA

Flagg is believed to have been the first machine tool builder in Worcester, MA. He began operation in 1839 and, in 1847, formed SAMUEL FLAGG & CO. as a partnership with Lucius W. Pond, Ephraim H. Bellows, and Henry Holland. Flagg sold out to Pond after the shop burned in 1854. Pond continued business under the Flagg name until reorganizing as L.W. Pond in 1856. Flagg, with others, formed the Worcester Machinist Tool Co. in 1856.

The firm made a variety of machine tools, including, by 1845, "planing machines for iron, capable of planing from 2 to 36 feet long; weighing from 500 pounds to 30 tons."

FLANDERS MACHINE WORKS, L.B., Philadelphia, PA

Founded by L.B. Flanders (?-1881). Builder, beginning about 1860, of a variety of portable machine tools for machining large workpieces such as locomotive and marine engine parts. Daniel W. Pedrick and Henry C. Ayer took over the firm when Flanders died in 1881 and continued operation under the Flanders name until 1886 when they reorganized as Pedrick & Ayer.

In early 1886, the firm introduced a planer chuck, shown right, with an attachment for planing concave or convex parts. The arm G is adjusted to cause the workpiece to rotate as the planer tools pass over.

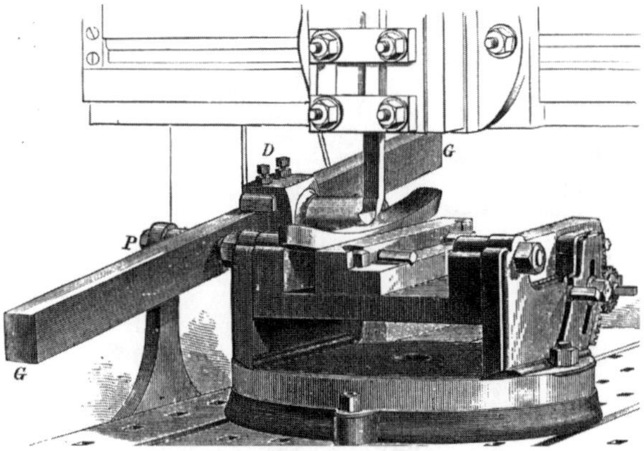

It's a Flather!

Our Planers are just as noticeable for design and good workmanship as our lathes, 25 years' experience allows us to make these tools "conspicuously better" in the eyes of mechanics. Booklet free.

Flather & Company,
Nashua, N. H.

AGENTS:
Hill, Clarke & Co., Boston and Chicago.
Garvin Machine Co., New York.
Chas. Churchill & Co., London.
Adolphe Janssens, Paris.
V. Lowener, Copenhagen.

FLATHER & CO., Nashua, NH

A partnership of Edward W. Flather (1839-1902) and his brothers, William J. Flather (1841-1912), Mark Flather, Jr. (1851-1926) and Joseph Flather (1837-1907), formed in 1867 to build engine lathes, hand lathes, foot lathes and tapping machines.

The firm was incorporated in 1900 with Joseph Flather as president. Mark Flather had left in 1884 to found the MARK FLATHER PLANER CO. William J. Flather left in 1900 and joined the E.J. Flather Mfg. Co. which was operated by his son.

Planers and shapers were advertised (Fig.) from 1897 to 1900. It is uncertain, however, whether the machines were made by Flather & Co. or if the company was agent for Mark Flather Planer Co. products.

The company operated into the mid-1920s.

FLATHER PLANER CO., MARK, Nashua, NH, later

FLATHER PLANER & SHAPER CO., Nashua, NH

Formed in 1884 by Mark Flather (1851-1926) when he left the family business, Flather & Co. Flather served as treasurer until he left in 1912, when the company reorganized as the FLATHER PLANER & SHAPER CO.

Early production was limited to a line of planers in 22", 24", 26" and 30" sizes (Fig.1). By 1893 a new pattern planer (Fig.2) was offered in the same sizes.

A combination planer was introduced in 1903. Available in 42" size, it could be arranged as a standard planer (Fig.3) or converted to an open side planer (Fig.4).

By 1904, Flather offered "light pattern" planers (Fig.5) in lighter construction 27", 36" (Fig.6) and 48" sizes; and standard planers in 22" (Fig.7), 24", 27" 30" (Fig.8), 36", 38" and 42" sizes (Fig.9). Electric motor drive (Fig.10) could be added to all sizes. A new, rapid action, 30" planer (Figs.11-12) was introduced in 1909.

Shaper production began about 1894 when Flather introduced an 18" model (Fig.13) weighing 2000 pounds. By 1896, the 18" shaper was improved (Fig.14) and by 1900 it was offered in 14", 18" and 24" strokes (Figs.15-16). A new 16" shaper (Fig.17) was introduced in 1907. *(continued next three pages)*

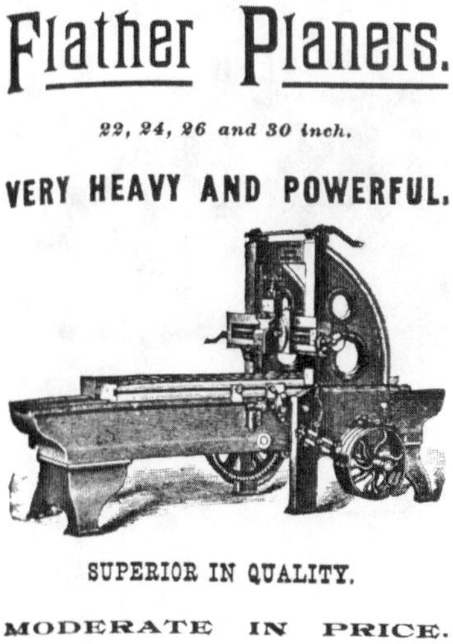

Fig.1

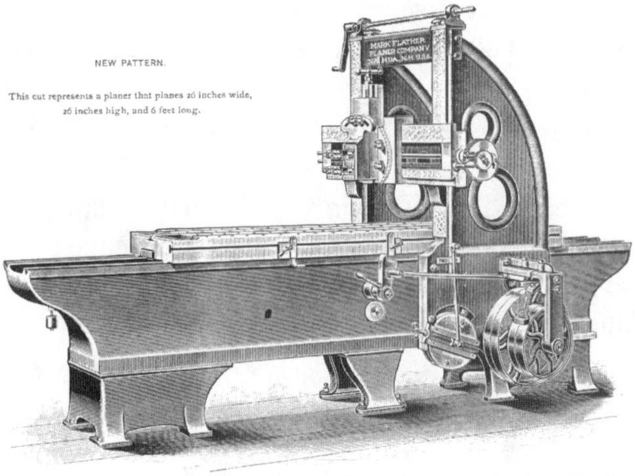

Fig.2

	22 Inch.	24 Inch.	27 Inch.	30 Inch.
Standard lengths . . .	5-foot.	6-foot	6-foot.	8-foot.
Weight standard lengths	4,400 lbs.	5,100 lbs.	7,000 lbs.	8,500 lbs.
Size and face counter pulley	12 x 4 in.	12 x 4 in.	12 x 4 in.	14 x 4 in.

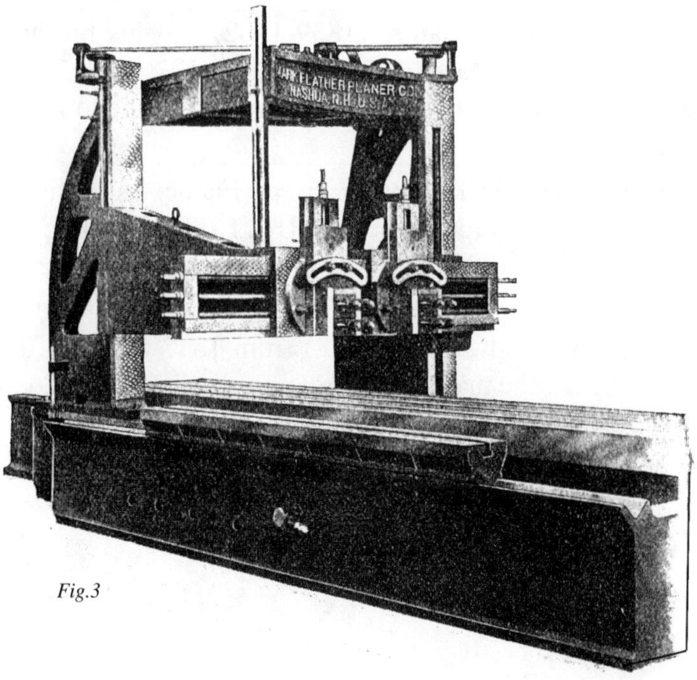

Fig.3

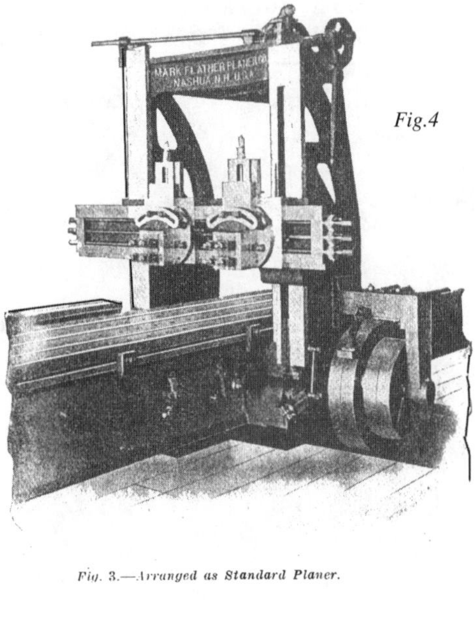

Fig.4

Fig. 3.—Arranged as Standard Planer.

DIMENSIONS OF LIGHT PATTERN PLANERS

SIZE	27-in.	36-in.	48-in.
Planes wide	27¾"	36¾"	48¾"
Planes high	27¾"	36¾"	48¾"
Planes long between pockets	6' 2"	8' 2"	12' 2½"
Range of automatic, vertical and angular feed	7½"	9½"	14½"
Revolutions of countershaft per minute	300	325	350
Tight and loose pulleys	12" x 4"	14" x 4"	18" x 6"
Net weight	6,000 lbs.	10,200 lbs.	23,100 lbs.
Gross weight (boxed for export)	6,600 "	11,500 "	25,500 "
Weight per additional foot	400 "	625 "	1,300 "

Fig.5

Flather 36-inch Light Pattern Planer

Fig.6

"Flather" 22 x 22-Inch x 6-Foot Planer.

Fig.7

"Flather" 30 x 30-Inch x 8-Foot Planer.

Fig.8

SIZES AND DIMENSIONS
OF REGULAR PLANERS

SIZE	22-in.	24-in.	27-in.	30-in.	36-in.	38-in.	*42-in.
Will plane wide	22¾"	24¾"	27¾"	30¾"	36¾"	38¾"	42¾"
Will plane high	22¾"	24¾"	27¾"	30¾"	36¾"	38¾"	42¾"
Plane long between pockets	5' 2"	6' 2"	6' 2"	8' 2"	10' 2"	10' 2½"	10' 2½"
Range of automatic, vertical and angular feed	7"	7½"	9½"	9½"	12½"	14"	14½"
Tight and loose pulleys on C. S.	12"x3¼"	12"x4"	12"x4"	14"x4"	16"x4"	18"x5½"	18"x6"
Revolutions of C.S., per min.	300	300	325	325	325	350	350
Net weight, lbs.	4,700	5,400	8,200	9,000	15,000	18,500	21,000
Weight, boxed for export, lbs.	5.300	6,200	9,200	10,000	16,400	20,500	23,500
Weight per additional foot, lbs.	350	375	500	550	1,000	1,150	1,250

Fig.9

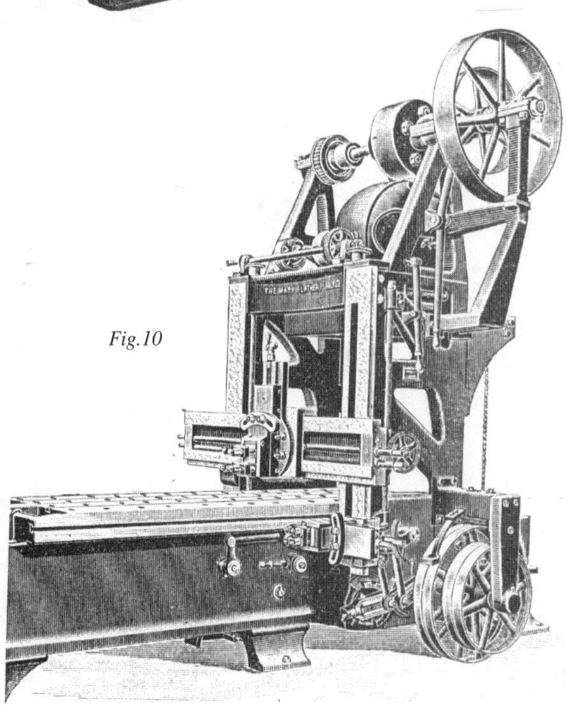

Fig.10

Fig.11

Fig.12

—Detail Side View, Showing the Drive and Control.

Fig.13

EIGHTEEN INCH SHAPER.

Fig.14

NEW 18-INCH SHAPER.

Flather 24-inch Shaper

Fig.15

SIZES AND DIMENSIONS

SIZE	14-inch	18-inch	24-inch
Planes long	14"	18"	24"
Planes wide	18"	22½"	26"
Planes high	14½"	14"	16½"
Down-feed	6"	6½"	7"
Vise, between jaws	9"	10"	13¼"
Ram-bearing surface, long	22"	27½"	36"
Changes of speed	4	8	16
Countershaft pulleys	10" x 3½"	12" x 3½"	14" x 4"
Revolutions per minute	200	120 & 240	100 & 200
Weight	1,600 lbs.	2,500 lbs.	4,200 lbs.

Fig.16

Fig.17

New 16-inch Shaper

FOX MACHINE CO., Grand Rapids, MI

Founded in 1880 by William R. Fox (1853-1934) to make woodworking machinery. In 1892, the firm incorporated with Fox as president and capital of $150,000.

Machine tool production began in 1891 when Fox introduced his patented, 28" stroke, "open side" shaper (Figs.1-2) weighing 3500 pounds. The design gave much better support to the ram by extending the slide support over the work table and turning it on end to minimize interference. Even so, interference must have been a major problem. An improved, 30" stroke model (Fig.3) was introduced in 1895.

In 1893, Fox introduced a conventional crank shaper (Fig.4) with stroke adjustable from 1/2" to 15" and weighing 1800 pounds. A heavy, 18" planer vise (Fig.5) was introduced in 1898.

Shaper production appears to have ceased soon after 1900 when the company began to concentrate on milling machines and bicycle machinery. *(continued next page)*

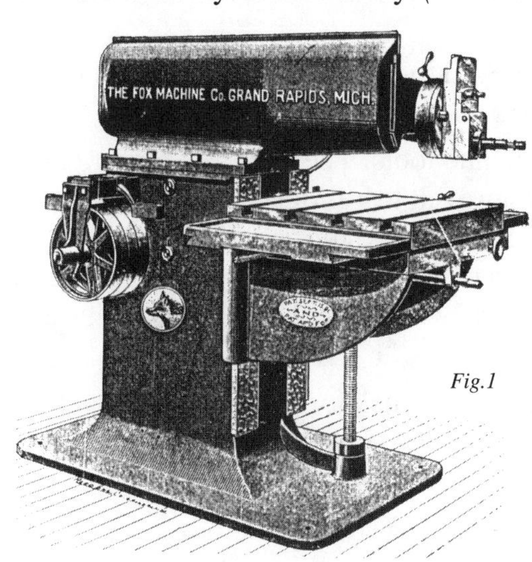

Fig.1

Fig.2

Fig.3

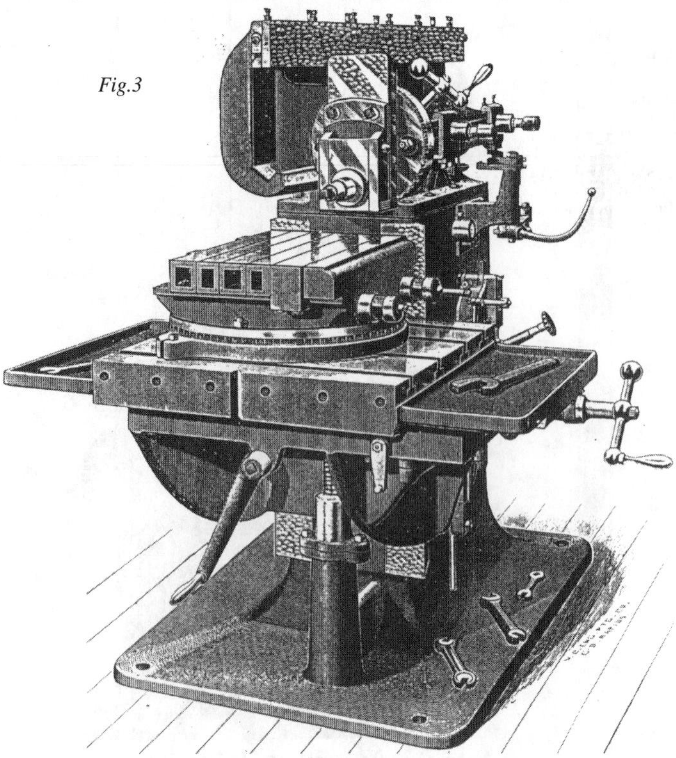

Fig.4

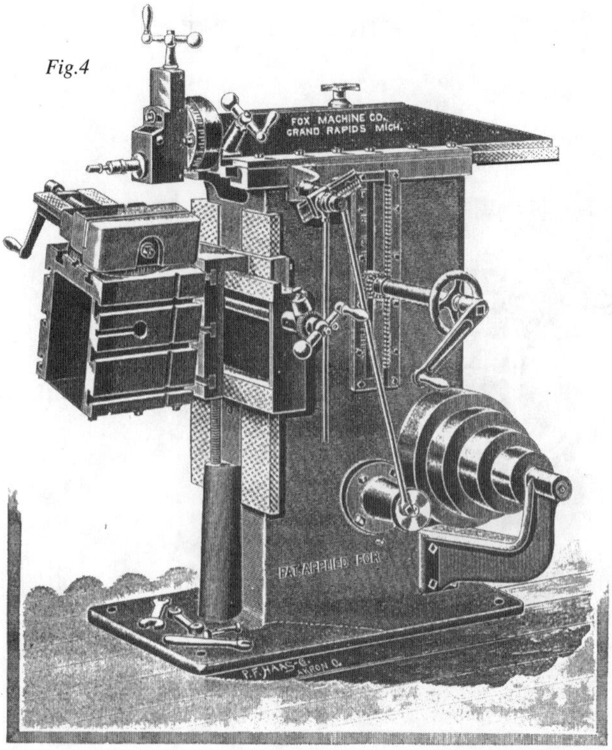

A New Crank Shaper.

Fig.5

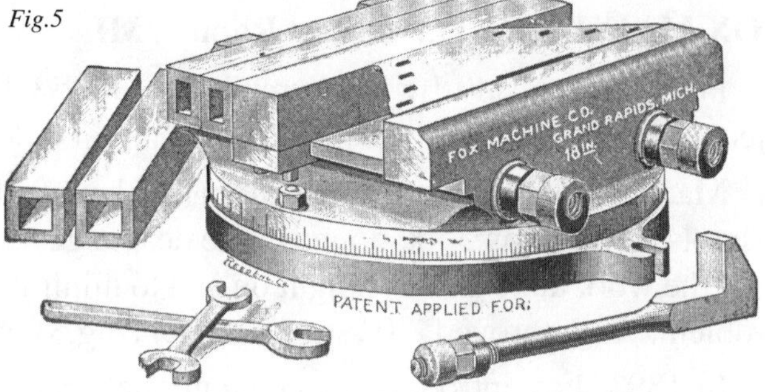

FREELAND TOOL WORKS, New York, NY

Founded about 1845 by Aaron M. Freeland (?-1871), the firm is believed to be the first machine tool builder in New York City, offering a variety of machine tools, including planers and engine lathes.

Freeland was reported to have copied his designs from English machine tools. The 24"x 24" planer (Fig.1) shown below, built in 1852 and photographed still in use in 1906, shows English influence, especially in the ways. A larger planer (Fig.2) built in 1854 was also still in use in 1906. It had begun life as a 42" x 42" x 16' size but had been modified at some point to handle workpieces up to 50". Both planers were equipped with rack drive and a two belt design with differential shifting patented by Freeland August 27, 1867, and licensed to both Hewes & Phillips and Bement & Doughterty.

In 1871, Freeland's widow advertised the business, patterns, drawings, and stock for sale. The eventual buyer is unknown, but the firm continued in business until 1906. About 1878, a heavy, 8' x 6' planer (Fig.3) was offered with an improved drive and V ways. Machine tool production appears to have ceased about 1880.

(continued next page)

Fig.1

Fig.2

Fig.3

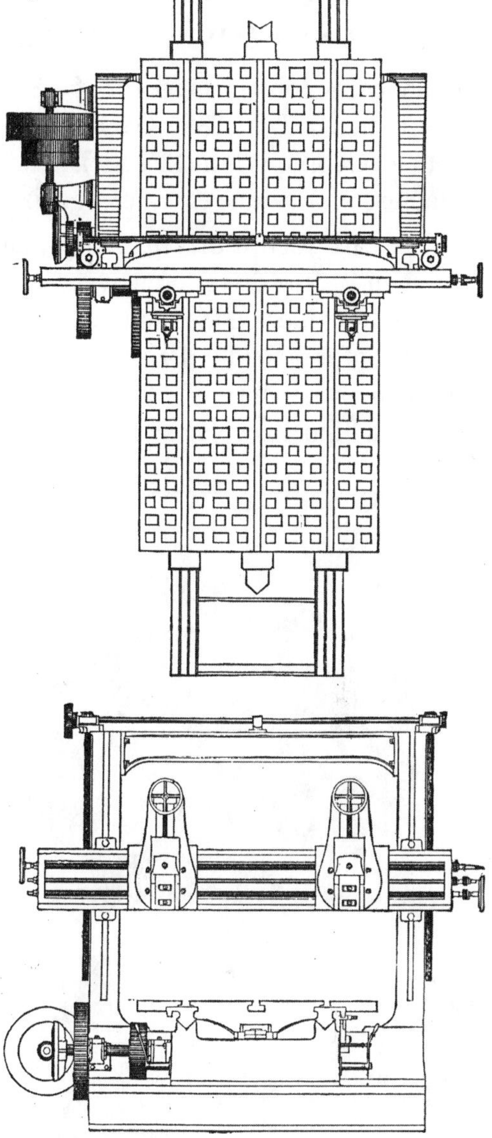

FULLER & WILSON, Worcester, MA, later

FULLER & CO., J.A., Worcester, MA

A partnership of James A. Fuller (1824-1912) and James E. Wilson, formed in 1881 to build 18" engine lathes and planers. In 1882 the firm reorganized as J.A. FULLER & CO., which operated until about 1899.

GAGE, JOHN H., Nashua, NH, later
GAGE, WARNER & WHITNEY, Nashua, NH

Founded by John H. Gage (1815-1862) who began making lathes, planers and other machine tools under his own name in 1837. In 1851 Gage formed a partnership, GAGE, WARNER & WHITNEY, with David A.G. Warner and George Whitney. The firm, which is believed to be the first American firm devoted exclusively to the manufacture of machine tools, reorganized as WARNER, WHITNEY & CO. when Gage died in 1872.

A very early, screw driven planer, marked JOHN H. GAGE (Fig.1), was photographed, still in use, in 1921. The front end of the drive screw was fitted with a small gear which meshed with a large gear to operate the cross feed. Note the braces added to the very weak appearing legs. Another screw driven planer (Fig.2), built about 1860 and photographed in 1920, still in operation, shows much heavier legs, a different feed mechanism, and the reversing mechanism (Fig.3) also used on the earlier planer. Note the change in gear ratio when changing from forward to a higher reverse speed.

Fig.1

Fig.2

Fig.3

GARVIN & CO., E.E., New York, NY, later
GARVIN MACHINE CO., New York, NY

A partnership of Eugene E. Garvin (1858-1916) and his brother George K. Garvin (1859-1919) formed in 1879 as a reorganization of Smith & Garvin. In 1889 the firm organized as a stock company, the GARVIN MACHINE CO., with George K. Garvin as president and Eugene E. Garvin, vice president. Capital was increased from $100,000 to $500,000 in 1899. Operations ceased in 1925 when the firm was liquidated.

(continued next page)

The Garvin firm specialized in milling machines and screw machines, but a die slotter was introduced in 1892. The slotter (Fig.1) had a stroke of 2 1/2", two cross motions, a 12" rotary table and was intended for small die work. An improved version (Fig.2) was introduced in 1904.

Fig.1

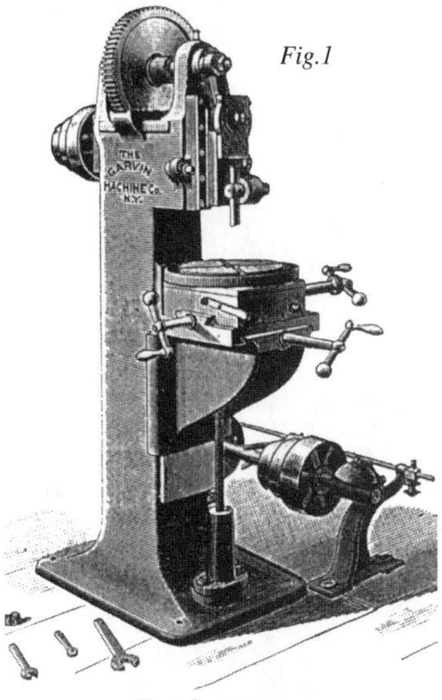

DIE SLOTTER.

Fig.2

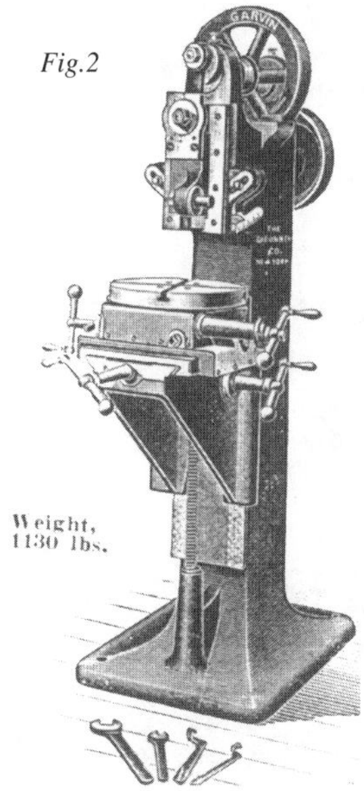

GAY, IRA & ZIBA, North Chelmsford, MA, later
GAY, SILVER & CO., North Chelmsford, MA

A partnership of brothers Ira Gay (?-1835) and Ziba Gay (?- 1857), formed in 1830 to build textile machinery, lathes and other machine tools.

The firm reorganized as GAY, SILVER & CO. when Ira Gay died in 1835 and was replaced by Harvey Silver. Frederick W. Howe learned the machinist trade here before joining Robbins & Lawrence about 1853. The firm was again reorganized, as SILVER, GAY & CO., in 1857 when Ziba Gay died and was replaced by his son Ziba Gay, Jr. (1823-1902).

Products included a granite bed, chain drive, 42" planer built in 1836 and believed to be one of the first built in the U.S. Photographed in 1908 (Fig.1), still in use at the old Silver, Gay & Co. shop, the machine had long since been given a more rigid set of uprights, but the original uprights were still in place (Fig.2). The ways, one V and one flat, were of cast iron, bolted to the stone bed and had been chipped and filed to fit. A smaller, 27" planer, built in 1844 (Fig.3), was also in use in 1908. It had been permanently fitted with an elaborate fixture for fluting textile rolls four at a time. *(continued next page)*

Fig.1

Fig.2

Fig.3

GILKERSON MACHINE WORKS, Homer, NY

Builder, in 1885, of the swivel jaw planer vise shown below. The vise was offered in nine sizes, from 4" to 24" width of jaw.

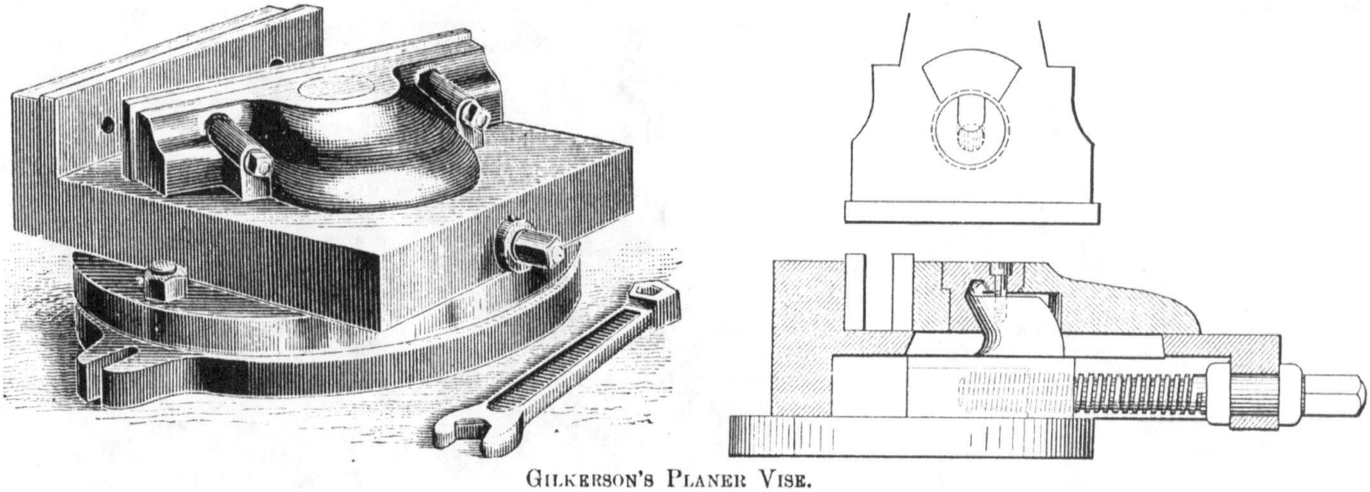

GILKERSON'S PLANER VISE.

GLEASON, WILLIAM, Rochester, NY, later
GLEASON TOOL CO., Rochester, NY

Formed in 1875 by William Gleason (1836-1922) when he took over the Kidd Iron Works. Gleason's primary products were gear cutting machines, but for a time he also offered engine lathes, planers (patented July 10, 1883) and drilling machines.

The firm was reorganized as the Gleason Tool Co. in 1890 and incorporated as the Gleason Works in 1903. In 1900, Gleason sold his lathe and planer lines to the PITTSBURG MACHINE TOOL CO.

Planers offered in 1893 included 32" x 6' (Fig.1), 36" x 8' (Fig.2), 42" x 8', 48" x 10', 54" x 10', 60" x 12' (Fig.3), 72" x 12', 84" x 12' and 96" x 12'. Gleason also offered an extension planer (Fig.4) with a telescopic cross-rail and one upright adjustable to allow added planing width. It was made in 38" extending ot 56", 42" extending to 60", and 48" extending to 72". *(continued next page)*

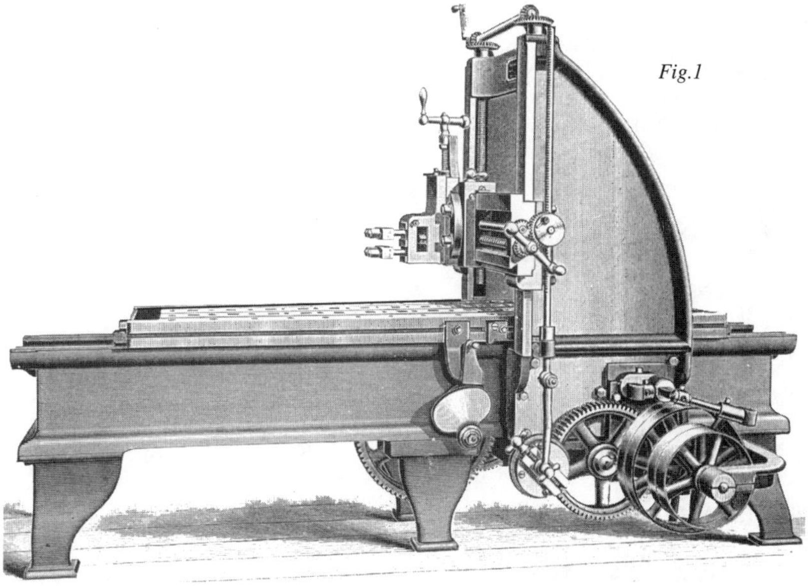

Fig.1

36 Inch Gleason Planer.

Fig.2

Fig.3

Gleason 48 Inch Extension Planer.

PLANES 72 INCHES WIDE WITH UPRIGHT MOVED OUT.

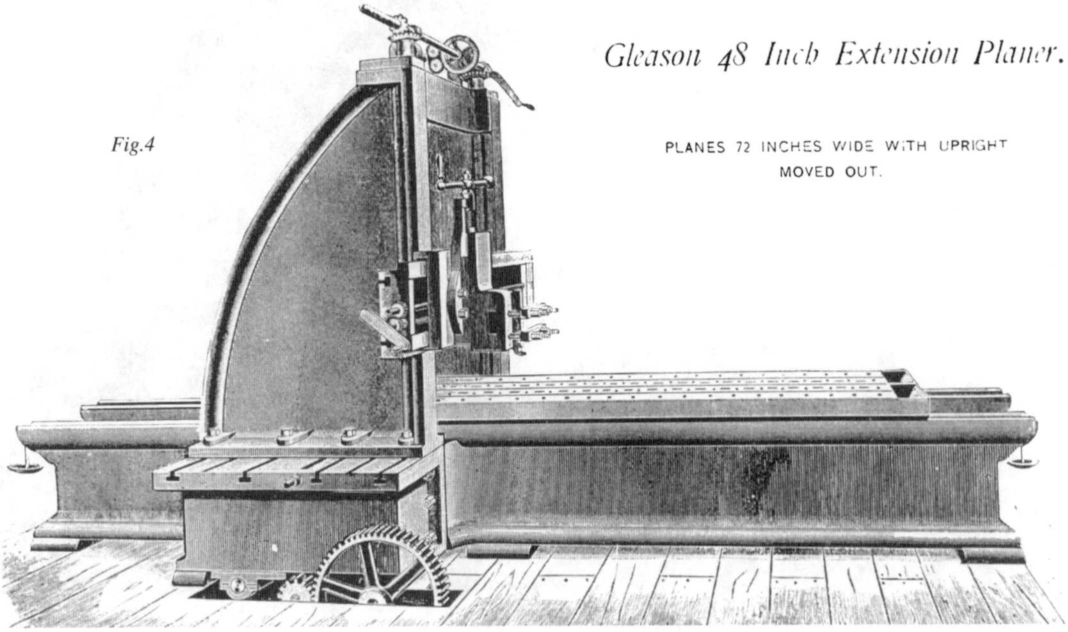

Fig.4

GOULD, E., Newark, NJ, later

GOULD & CO., E., Newark, NJ, later

GOULD MACHINE CO., Newark, NJ, later

GOULD, E. & R.J., Newark, NJ, later

GOULD, E., Newark, NJ

Formed in 1833 by Ezra Gould (1808-1901) as a machine shop, the firm became E. Gould & Co. 1857 when his brother Stephen D. Gould became a partner. In 1862, the firm reorganized as the Gould Machine Co., operated by Ezra Gould and his sons Roscoe J. Gould and Frank Gould. The firm again reorganized, in 1870, as E.& R.J. Gould, which operated until 1873 when it once again became E. Gould. In 1877 the firm became E. GOULD & EBERHARDT.

During this period, Ezra Gould was granted patents for a mortising machine (woodworking) September 25, 1855, and a screw-threading machine, July 14, 1868.

Gould is known to have made metal lathes for gun makers during the Civil War. Ads in 1866 offered "Iron and Wood-working Machinery, Steam Fire Engines;" in 1867 "Iron and Wood-working Machinery, Steam Engines, Boilers, Saw Mills, etc.;" in 1871 "Machinists' Tools at greatly reduced prices;" in 1872 "New Patterns, Machinists' Tools-all sizes-at low prices;" in 1876 "Lathes, Planers, Shapers, Drills, Gear & Bolt Cutters, etc." and "E. Gould's Shaper, Best in Market."

Gould has been credited with building the first shaper in America in 1854 (Fig.1), but this appears to be based on a dubious claim made by GOULD & EBERHARDT when they donated the machine to a museum. Another surviving early Gould shaper (Fig.2), clearly marked E. Gould & Co., is claimed to have been made in 1857, but could have been made as late as 1862. Both machines show a strong English influence and may have been copies of imported machines.

Fig.1

Fig.2

GOULD & EBERHARDT, E., Newark, NJ, later
GOULD & EBERHARDT, Newark, NJ

A partnership of Ezra Gould (1808-1901), Ulrich Eberhardt (1841-1901), and Henry E. Eberhardt (1851-1934), formed when Gould, who had previously operated as E. GOULD, took the Eberhardts as partners in 1877. The firm reorganized as GOULD & EBERHARDT when Gould retired in 1890 and incorporated in 1900. Henry E. Eberhardt, with his four sons, left the company in 1904 to found Eberhardt Brothers. Ulrich Eberhart's sons, Frederick L. Eberhardt (1868-1946) and Ulrich Eberhardt, Jr. (1872-1957) took over the firm when their father died in 1901; Frederick served as president until his death in 1946.

Production in 1879 included lathes, shapers, planers, drills, bolt cutters, gear cutters, and presses including bank note printing presses. By 1882, the firm had 140 hands building machine tools, including 60 shapers "under way."

In 1882, planers were built in 14 sizes (Fig.1), including 24" x 24" (Fig.2) and 32" x 32" (Fig.3). Planers were no longer advertised after 1886, when shapers and gear cutting machines became the primary products.

An improved shaper (Fig.4) made in 8", 10", 15" 17" and 20" strokes was introduced in 1880, followed in 1881 by a shaper patented May 17, 1881, by E. Gould and H.E. Eberhardt. The patent covered a return stroke adjustable while the machine was in motion, a major advance in shaper design. The new shaper was offered in 10" stroke (Fig.5) weighing 1300 pounds and 15" stroke (Fig.6) weighing 1800 pounds. *(continued on next four pages)*

PRICES.

Planes Wide.	Planes High.	Planes Long.	Weight, About.	Prices.
18 inches.	18 inches.	3 feet.	2,050 lbs.	$460 00
18 "	18 "	4 "	2,250 "	490 00
24 "	24 "	5 "	4,325 "	650 00
28 "	28 "	6 "	5,800 "	820 00
28 "	28 "	8 "	6,400 "	920 00
28 "	28 "	10 "	7,000 "	1,080 00
32 "	32 "	6 "	9,500 "	1,200 00
32 "	32 "	8 "	11,000 "	1,350 00
32 "	32 "	10 "	12,500 "	1,500 00
36 "	36 "	6 "	10,000 "	1,400 00
36 "	36 "	8 "	12,000 "	1,600 00
36 "	36 "	10 "	14,000 "	1,800 00
42 "	42 "	8 "	13,500 "	1,800 00
42 "	42 "	10 "	16,000 "	2,050 00

Fig.1

Fig.2

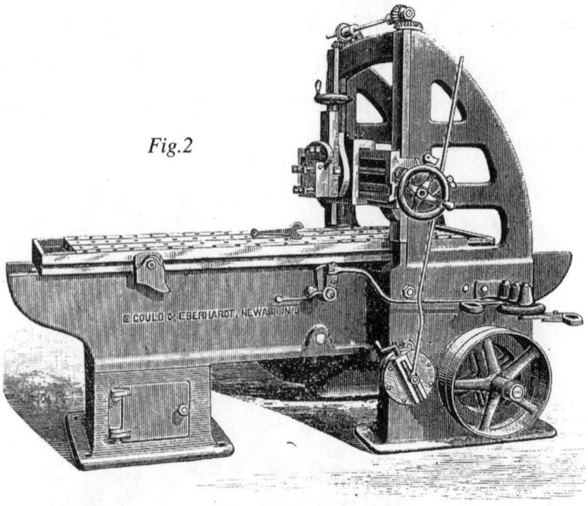

Twenty-Four-Inch Planer.

Fig.3

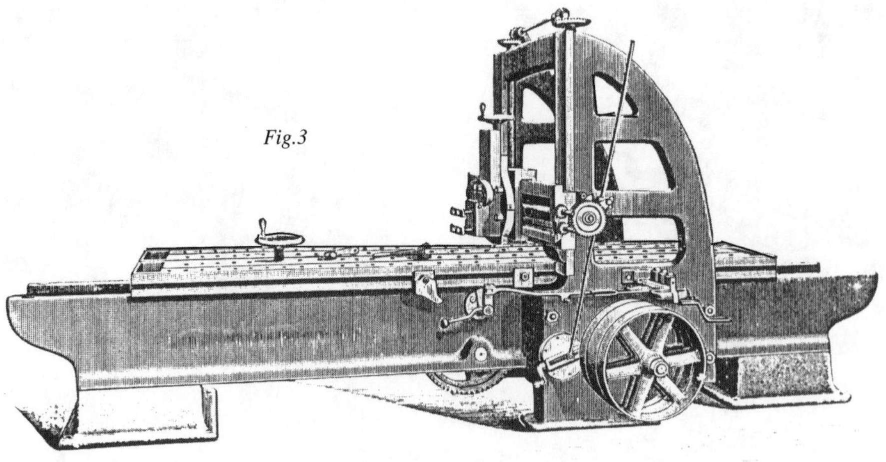

Represents 32 inch Planer.

Fig.4

Fig.6

Improved Shaping Machine

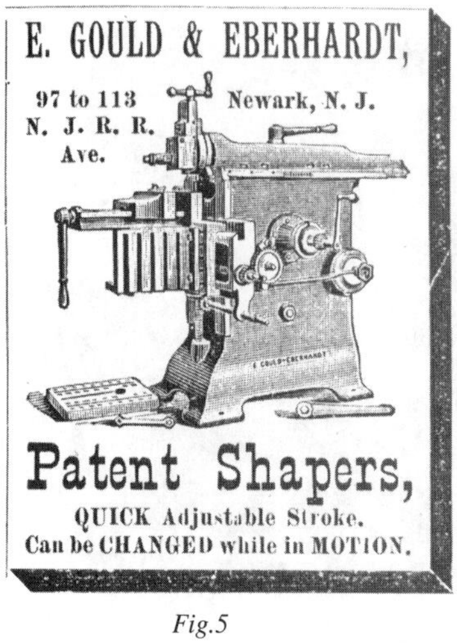

Fig.5

—PRICES.

Stroke.	Planes Width.	Height.	Diameter and Face of each Pulley on Counter.	Weight, about	Prices.
10 inch.	14 inch.	6 inch.	10 x 2	900 lbs.	$260 00
15 "	17 "	10 "	12 x 3	1,400 "	350 00
20 "	22 "	12 "	12 x 3	2,000 "	450 00
25 "	28 "	12 "	14 x 3	2,500 "	550 00
30 "	28 "	13 "	14 x 3	3,600 "	650 00

Rack Cutting Attachment for 15 in. stroke, $125; for 20 and 25 in. stroke, $160.

Fig.7

Fig.8

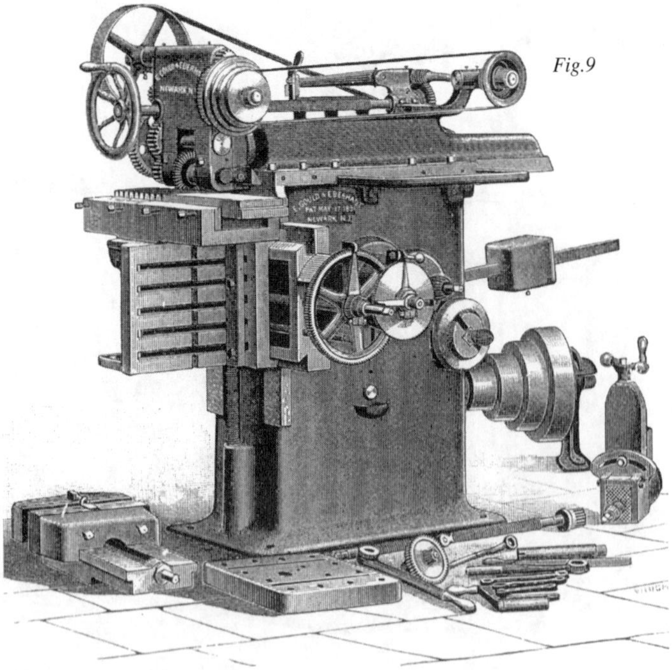

Fig.9

Rack Cutter Attachment on a Shaper.

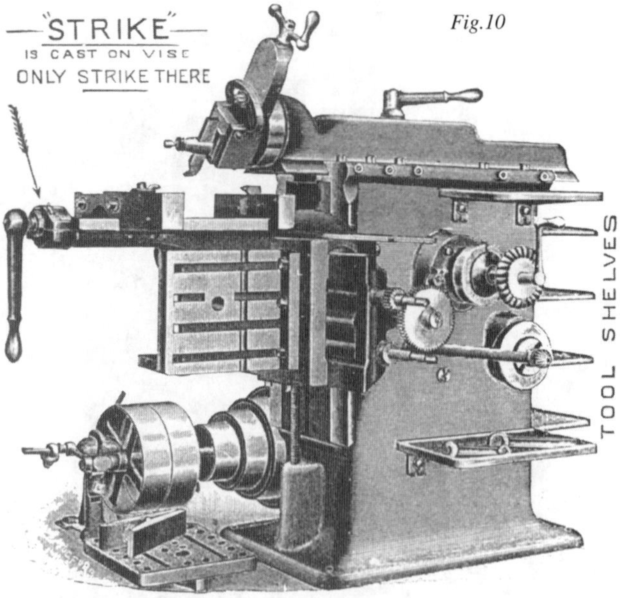

Fig.10

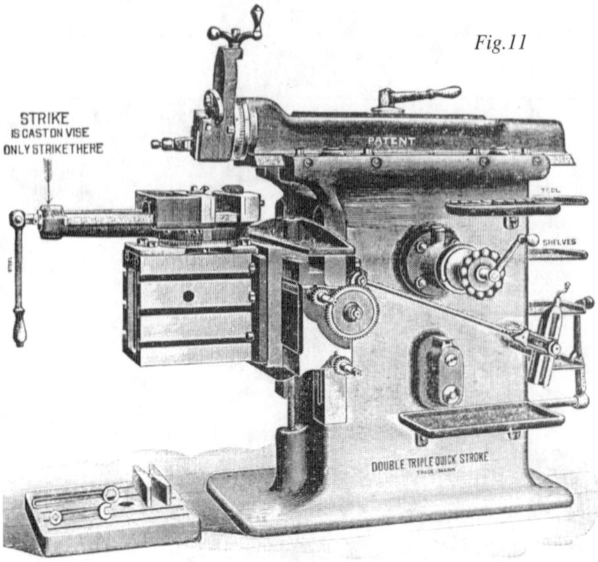

Fig.11

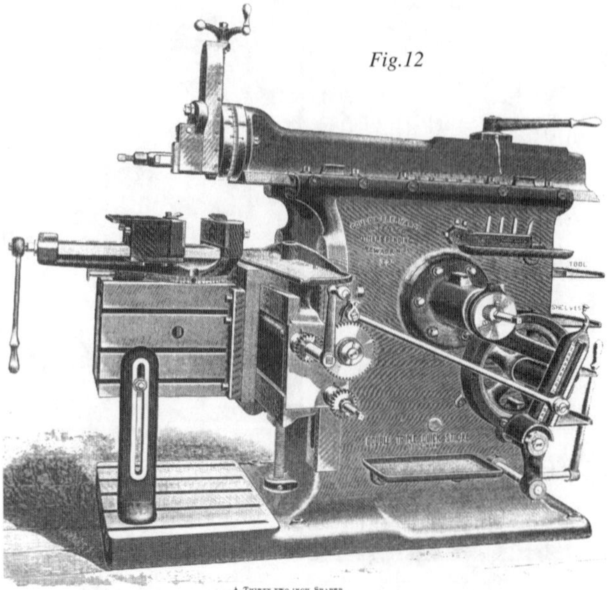

Fig.12

A Thirty two inch Shaper.

SINGLE GEARED SHAPER WITH OUTSIDE SUPPORT.

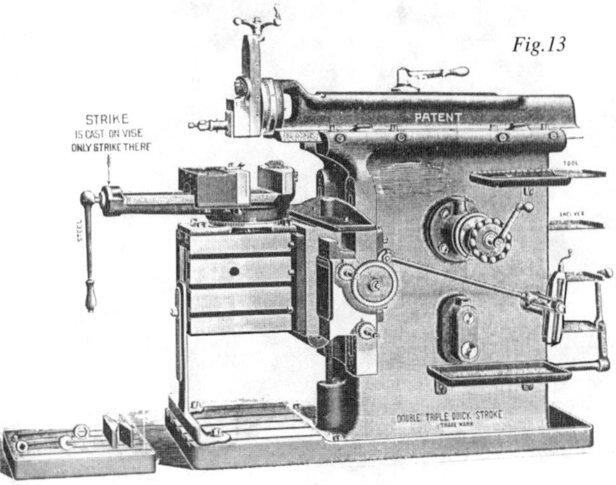

Fig.13

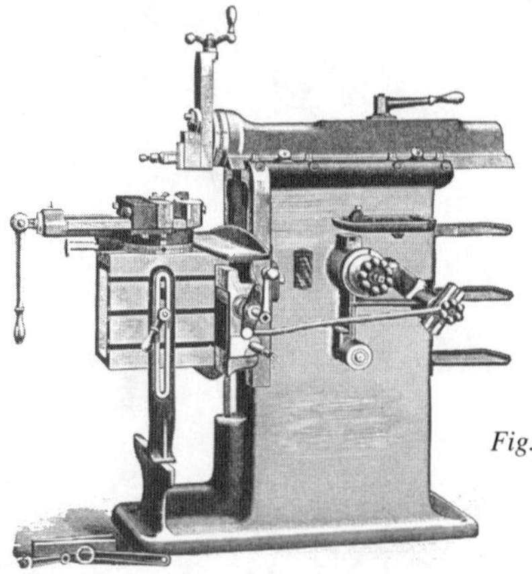

Fig.14

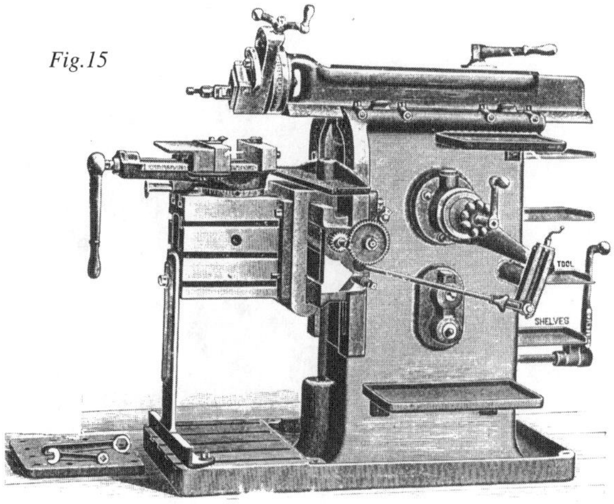

Fig.15

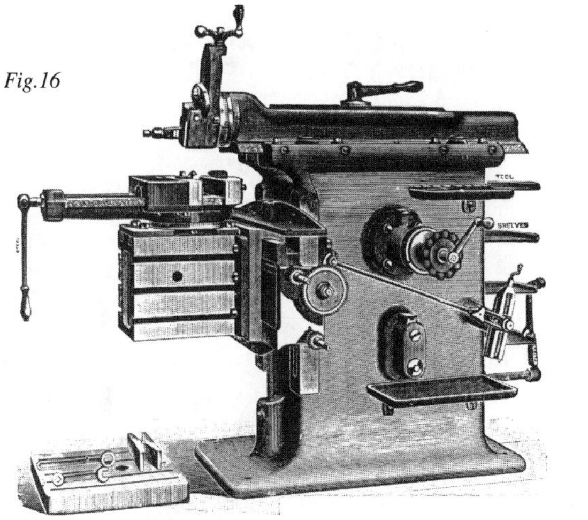

Fig.16

EXTENSION BASE SHAPER WITH CIRCULAR TABLE.

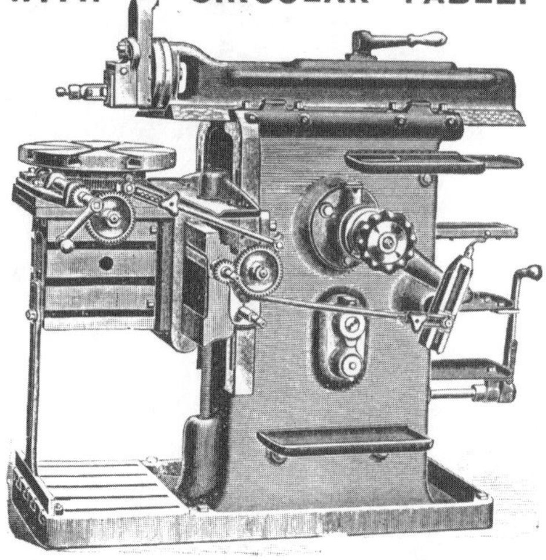

Fig.17

INDEX CENTERS

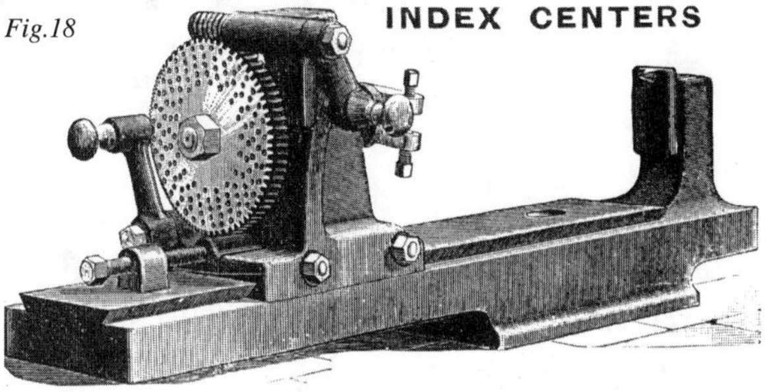

Fig.18

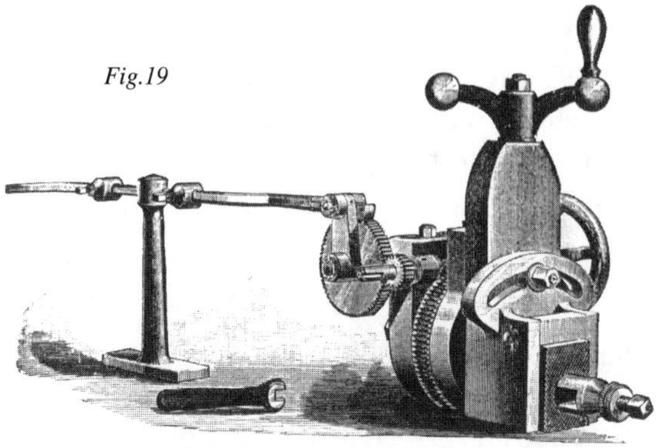

Fig.19

TO KEY-WAY OR SLOT A HOLE WITH SHAPERS.

With this attachment key-ways, slots, and oil grooves can be rapidly cut in change wheels, collars, and work of a similiar nature.

Fig.20

NEW SHAPER SPIRAL CUTTING ATTACHMENT.

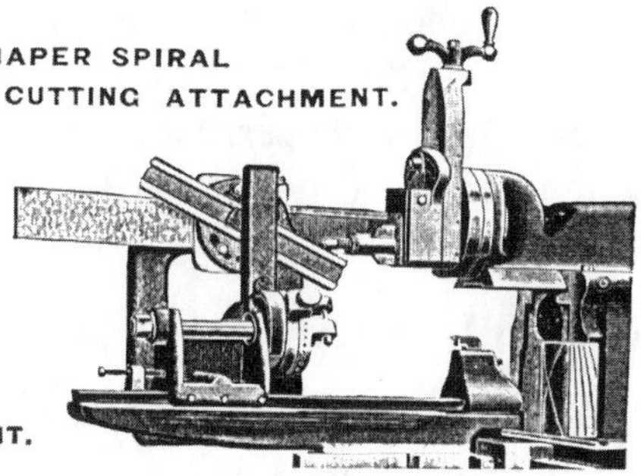

Fig.24

Fig.21

NEW SHAPER CIRCULAR MOTION.

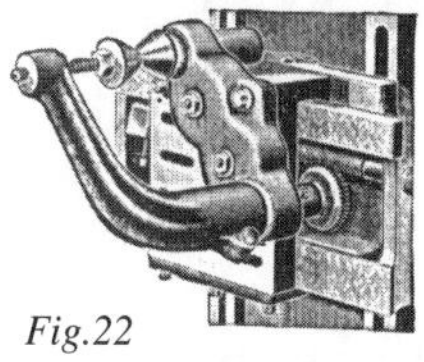

Fig.22

SHAPER CONVEX ATTACHMENT.

Fig.23

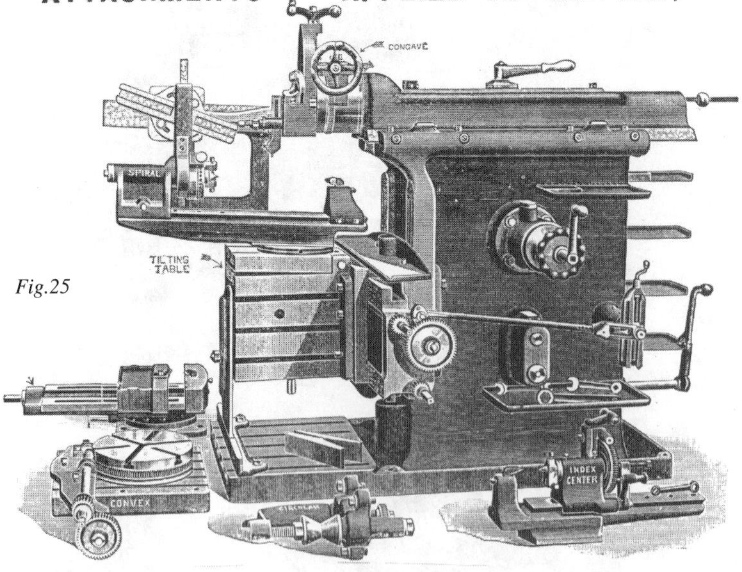

Fig.25

Fig.26

Fig.27

THE NEW GOULD & EBERHARDT SHAPER.

By 1884, the shaper line was further improved and offered in five sizes (Fig.7), 10", 15" (Fig.8), 20", 25" and 30". A rack cutter attachment (Fig.9) for 15", 20", 25" and 30" shapers was offered in 1887. Shapers with tool shelves and an improved vise, patented October 21, 1890, were offered in 1891 (Fig.10).

In 1892 the company introduced a completely new line of shapers which, it claimed, "gives 50 to 100 per cent more strokes per minute than any other make of shaper now built," Dubbed the Double Triple Quick shaper, the normal stroke rate could be doubled by throwing a lever at the rear of the machine. It was offered in 16", 20" and 24" strokes. By 1899 the standard model was offered in 12", 14", 16" (Fig.11), 18", 20", 24", 28", and 32" (Fig.12) strokes. A newly patented extension base model (Fig.13) was offered in 16", 20", 24", 26", 28", and 32" strokes.

Shapers offered in 1901 included a new 14", single geared model with outside support (Fig.14), 16" and 20" extension base shapers (Fig.15), 20" and 24" regular shapers (Fig.16), extension base shapers with circular tables (Fig.17). Also offered were a variety of attachments such as index centers (Fig.18), concave attachment (Fig.19), key-way and slotting attachment (Fig.20), tilting table (Fig.21), circular motion attachment (Fig.22), convex attachment (Fig.23), and spiral cutting attachment (Fig.24). Fig.25 shows the attachments in relation to a 24" extension base shaper. Motor driven shapers (Fig.26) were available by 1901 and a new design shaper (Fig.27) with improved drive, in 1903.

GRAY, Jr. & CO., G.A., Cincinnati, OH, later
GRAY CO., G.A., Cincinnati, OH

Founded in 1881 by George A. Gray Jr. (1839-1905), who had previously been associated with the Niles Tool Works and the Universal Radial Drill Co. His first product was a 17" engine lathe offered in 1881.

Gray began building planers in 1883, under his patent of April 15, 1884, and reorganized as the G.A. GRAY CO. in 1886. Gray served as president until four months before his death in 1905. Planers became Gray's primary product by 1888; subsequent designs were covered by Gray's patents of April 9, 1889, and January 14, 1890.

(continued next three pages)

Planer production began with the introduction of a 26" x 26" model (Fig.1) in 1883 and expanded in 1888 when a railroad frog planer (Fig.2) was introduced. Made very heavy to meet production requirements, the frog planer could plane 36" x 36"x 14' and weighed 40,000 pounds. By 1889 the planer line had expanded to 24", 26', 32", 36", 42" and 56" sizes.

Ernest Richter took over machine design when he was appointed chief engineer in 1888, serving until his retirement in 1919. In 1890, Gray introduced a new line of spiral geared planers (Fig.3) utilizing a form of the Sellers drive, the Sellers patent having long since expired. It was offered in a range of sizes, including 30"x 30" (Fig.4).

Special planers were also built, including a lithographic stone planer (Fig.5) to plane 36" wide, 5' long, and 12" thick, offered in 1891; and extension planers (Fig.6) offered in 1896. The extension feature allowed 30" pattern planers to be widened to 40" or 50", 38" pattern to 48" or 60", 48" pattern to 60" or 72", and 60" pattern to 72" or 84". Note the outrigger support for wide workpieces.

1899 production included 42" (Fig.7), 36" (Fig.8), 24" (Fig.9), 22" (Fig.10) sizes with spur gear drive, and 30" (Fig.11) and 48" in spiral gear drive. By 1901, improved models were offered in both spur gear (Fig.12) and spiral gear (Fig.13) types. 1903 production expanded to include spur gear models (Fig.14) from 22" to 72", spiral gear models from 30" to 72" (Fig.15), widened planers (Fig.16) in both spur and spiral gear types, and 36" frog and switch planers (Fig.17). An 84" x 60" widened planer with motor drive (Fig.18) was offered in 1904.

Planer production continued until the mid-1980s when the company was liquidated. *(continued next four pages)*

Fig.1

Gray's New Planer.

Fig.2

Fig.3

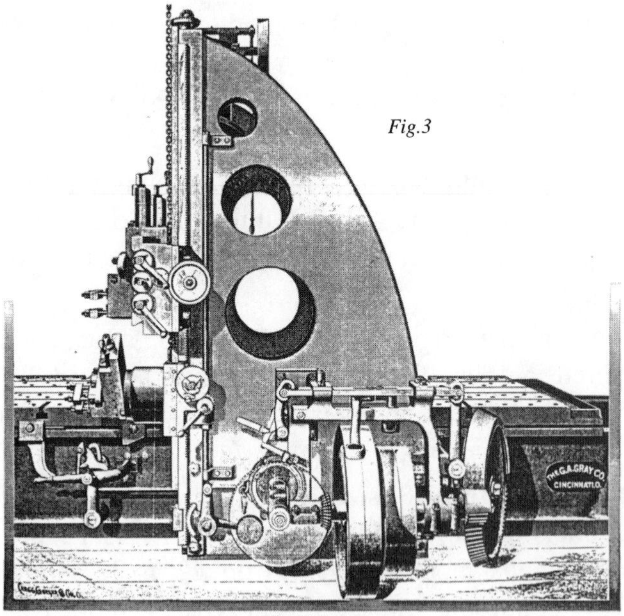

New Iron Planer.

Fig.4

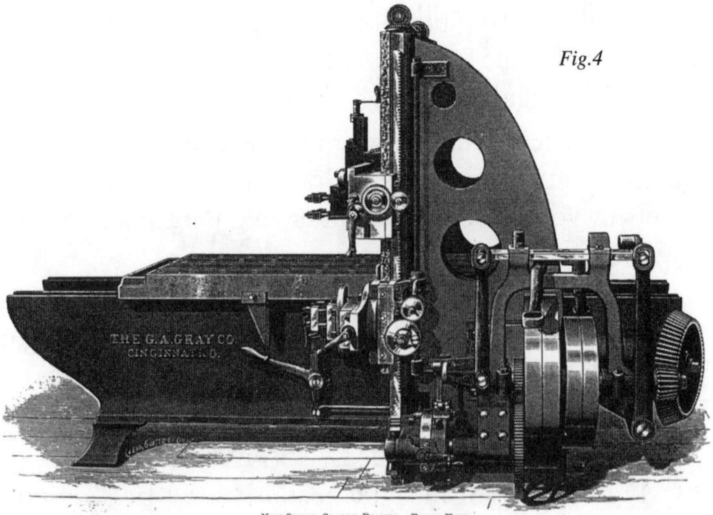

New Spiral Geared Planer.—Front View.

Fig.5

The Gray Lithographic Stone Planer.

Fig.6

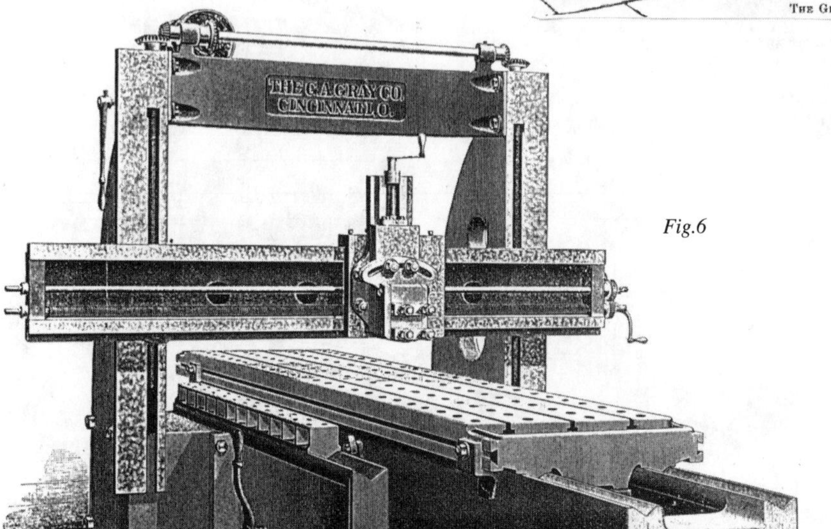

Fig.7F

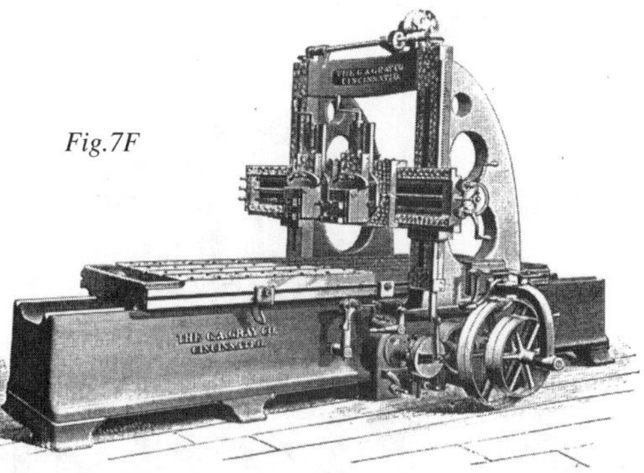

Fig. 103.

42″ x 10′ PLANER.

Planes in Width and Height.	Planes in Length.	Weight about, Lbs.	Planes in Width and Height.	Planes in Length.	Weight about, Lbs.	Planes in Width and Height.	Planes in Length.	Weight about, Lbs.
42 in.	8 ft.	20,000	48 in.	10 ft.	25,600	56 in.	10 ft.	29,500
42 "	10 "	22,000	48 "	12 "	28,000	56 "	12 "	32,000
42 "	12 "	24,000	48 "	14 "	30,400	56 "	14 "	34,500
42 "	14 "	26,000	48 "	16 "	32,800	56 "	16 "	37,000
42 "	16 "	28,000	48 "	18 "	35,200	56 "	18 "	39,500
42 "	18 "	30,000	48 "	20 "	37,600	56 "	20 "	42,000
42 "	20 "	32,000	48 "	22 "	40,000	56 "	22 "	44,500
42 "	22 "	34,000	48 "	24 "	42,400	56 "	24 "	47,000
42 "	24 "	36,000	48 "	26 "	44,800	56 "	26 "	49,500

Fig.8

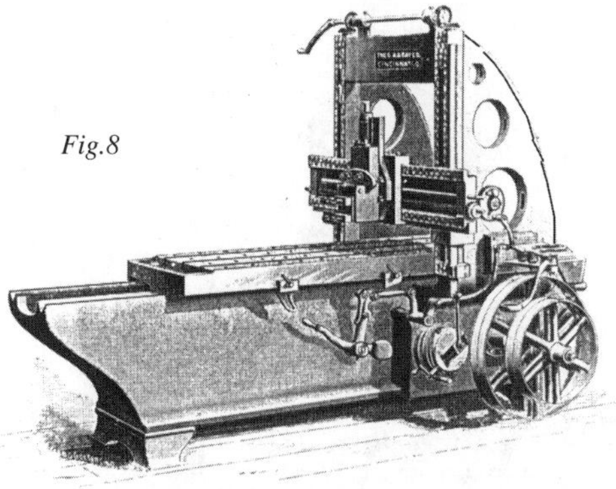

Fig. 104.

36″ x 8′ PLANER.

Planes in Width and Height.	Planes in Length.	Weight about Lbs.	Planes in Width and Height.	Planes in Length.	Weight about Lbs.	Planes in Width and Height.	Planes in Length.	Weight about, Lbs.
30 in.	6 ft.	8,100	32 in.	6 ft.	9,000	36 in.	8 ft.	12,000
30 "	7 "	8,800	32 "	7 "	9 750	36 "	10 "	13 600
30 "	8 "	9,500	32 "	8 "	10,500	36 "	12 "	15,200
30 "	10 "	10,900	32 "	10 "	12,000	36 "	14 "	16,800
30 "	12 "	12,300	32 "	12 "	13,500	36 "	16 "	18,400
30 "	14 "	13,700	32 "	14 "	15,000	36 "	18 "	20,000
			32 "	16 "	16,500			

Fig.9

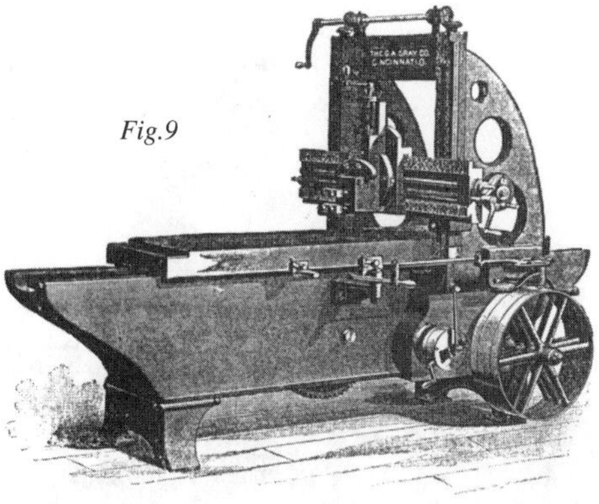

Fig. 105.

28″ x 6′ PLANER.

Planes in Width and Height.	Planes in Length.	Weight about, Lbs.	Planes in Width and Height.	Planes in Length.	Weight about, Lbs.	Planes in Width and Height.	Planes in Length.	Weight about, Lbs.
24 in.	5 feet.	5,225	26 in.	5 feet.	6,000	28 in.	6 feet.	7,300
24 "	6 "	5,700	26 "	6 "	6,500	28 "	7 "	7,900
24 "	7 "	6,175	26 "	7 "	7,000	28 "	8 "	8,500
24 "	8 "	6,650	26 "	8 "	7,500	28 "	10 "	9,700
24 "	10 "	7,600	26 "	10 "	8,500	28 "	12 "	10,900

Fig.10

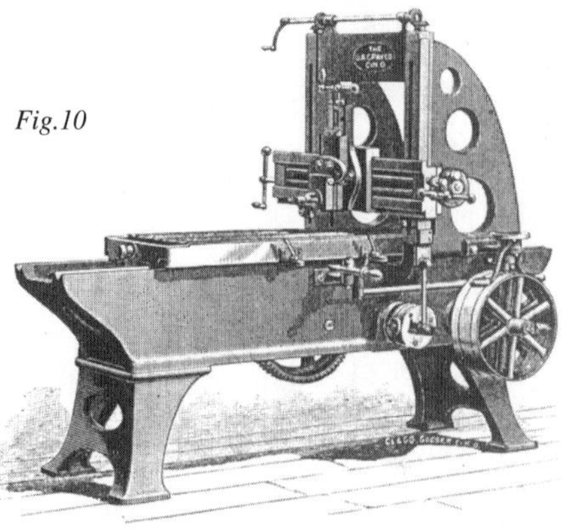

Fig. 106.

22″ x 4′ PLANER.

Planes in Width.	Planes in Height.	Planes in Length.	Weight about.
22 inches.	22 inches.	4 feet.	3,500 lbs.
22 "	22 "	5 "	3,900 "
22 "	22 "	6 "	4,300 "
22 "	22 "	7 "	4,700 "

Fig.11 on next page

Fig.12

Our new pattern 36″ x 36″ Spur-geared Planer, herewith illustrated, embodies that policy. It weighs about 4,000 lbs. more than the old, and has all our latest improvements, but the price has not been advanced.

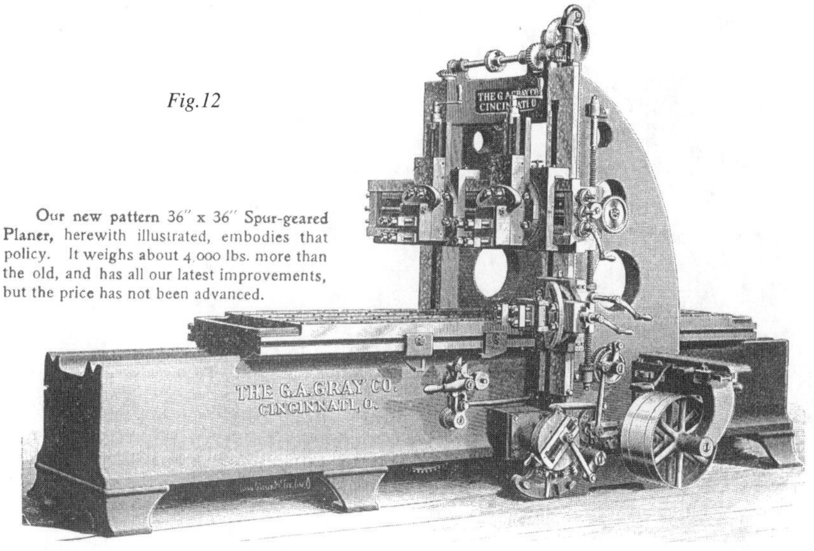

30″ x 8′ SPIRAL-GEARED PLANER. ("Sellers Motion.")

Fig.11

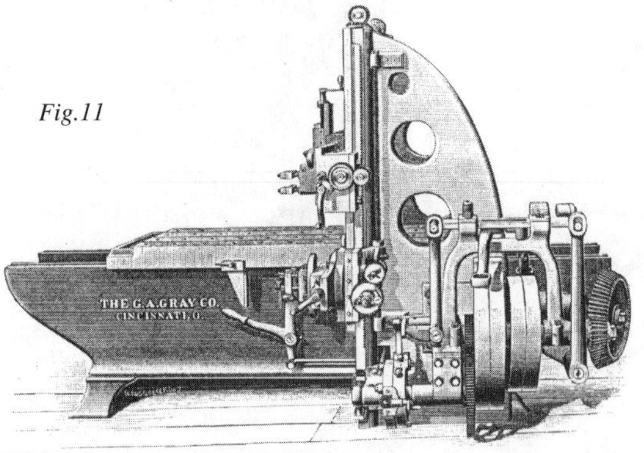

Planes in Width	Planes in Height.	Planes in Length.	Weight about.	Planes in Width.	Planes in Height.	Planes in Length.	Weight about.
30 in.	30 in.	6 feet.	11,300 lbs.	38 in.	38 in.	8 feet.	17,000 lbs.
30 "	30 "	7 "	12,000 "	38 "	38 "	10 "	19,000 "
30 "	30 "	8 "	12,700 "	38 "	38 "	12 "	21,000 "
30 "	30 "	10 "	14,100 "	38 "	38 "	14 "	23,000 "
30 "	30 "	12 "	15,500 "	38 "	38 "	16 "	25,000 "
30 "	30 "	14 "	16,900 "	38 "	38 "	18 "	27,000 "
30 "	30 "	16 "	18,300 "	38 "	38 "	20 "	29,000 "
48 in.	48 in.	10 feet.	27,400 lbs.	60 in.	60 in.	12 feet.	40,000 lbs.
48 "	48 "	12 "	30,000 "	60 "	60 "	14 "	43,200 "
48 "	48 "	14 "	32,600 "	60 "	60 "	16 "	46,400 "
48 "	48 "	16 "	35,200 "	60 "	60 "	18 "	49,600 "
48 "	48 "	18 "	37,800 "	60 "	60 "	20 "	52,800 "
48 "	48 "	20 "	40,400 "	60 "	60 "	22 "	56,000 "
48 "	48 "	22 "	43,000 "	60 "	60 "	24 "	59,200 "
48 "	48 "	24 "	45,600 "	60 "	60 "	26 "	62,400 "
48 "	48 "	26 "	48,200 "	60 "	60 "	28 "	65,600 "

Gray 36-inch Spur Geared Planers

Fig.14

Gray Spiral Geared Planers

Fig.15

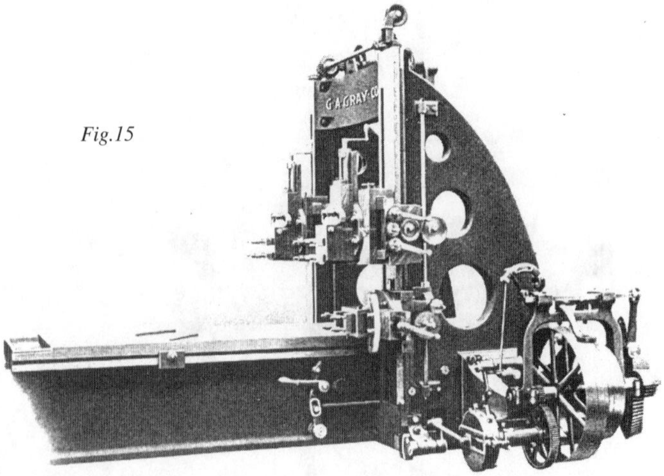

Fig.13

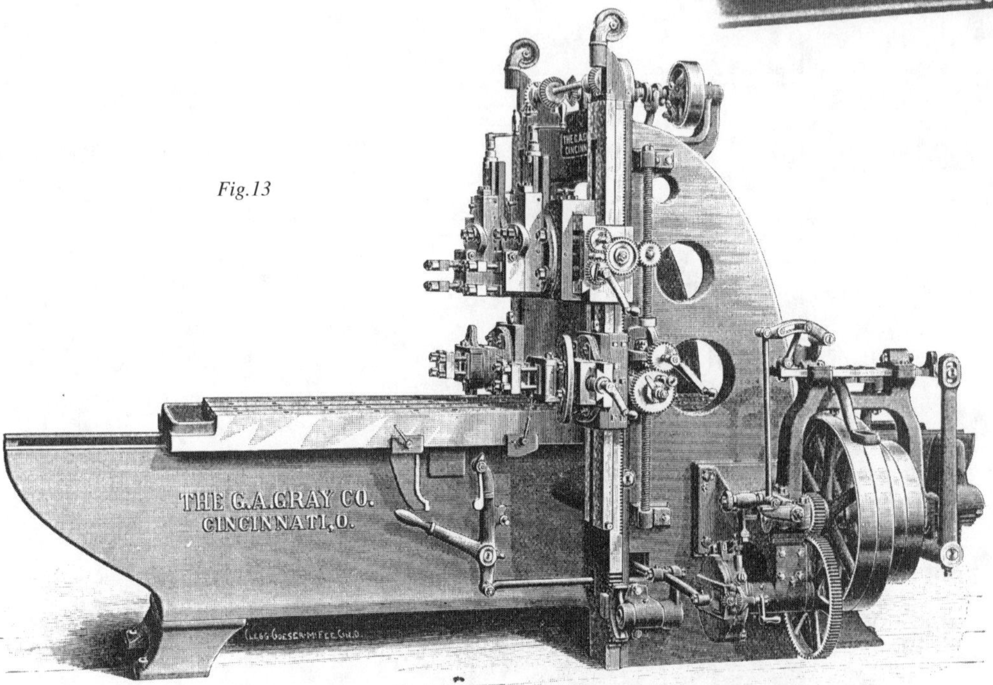

30-in. x 30-in. x 8-ft. Spiral-geared Planer, ("Sellers Motion.")

Gray Widened Planers

Fig.16

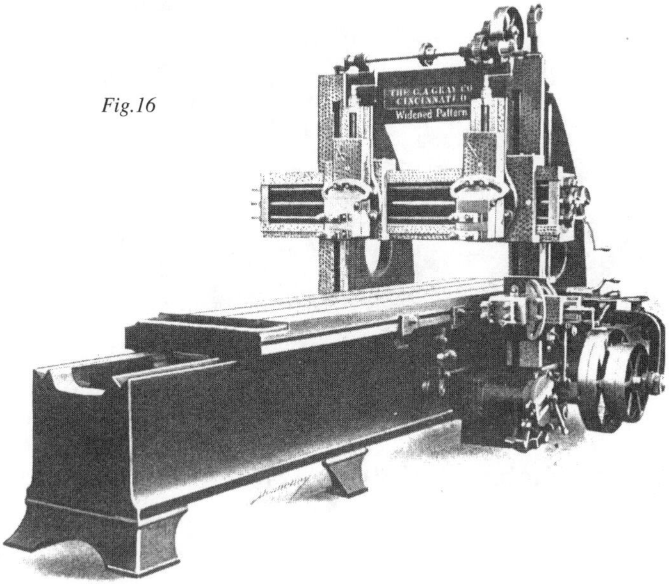

Gray 36-inch Frog and Switch Planer

Fig.17

Fig.18

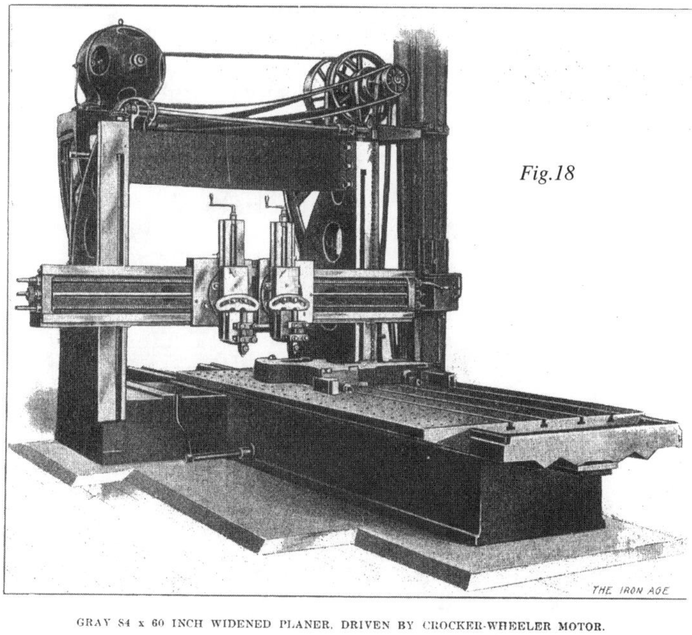

GRAY 84 x 60 INCH WIDENED PLANER. DRIVEN BY CROCKER-WHEELER MOTOR.

HADLEY FALLS MACHINE CO., Holyoke, MA

A large machine shop built in 1850 as the textile machinery making arm of the Hadley Falls Co. Some machine tools, including lathes and planers, were made c1855. The parent company went bankrupt in 1857 leaving the machine shop idle until bought by P. Whitin & Sons in 1860.

HAMILTON MACHINE TOOL CO., Hamilton, OH

Formed about 1890 to build a line of upright drills. Lathes were added about 1898 and, in 1909, planers and shapers were also offered.

The firm incorporated in 1903 with capital of $300,000 and reorganized as the HAMILTON TOOL CO. in 1927. Charles F. Hilker was president from 1903 to about 1927.

HANGOCZKY, JACOB, Newark, NJ

Builder, beginning in 1890, of a hand shaper (Fig.1), patented October 22, 1889, (Fig.2). The shaper had a 10" stroke and weighed 70 pounds.

Fig.1

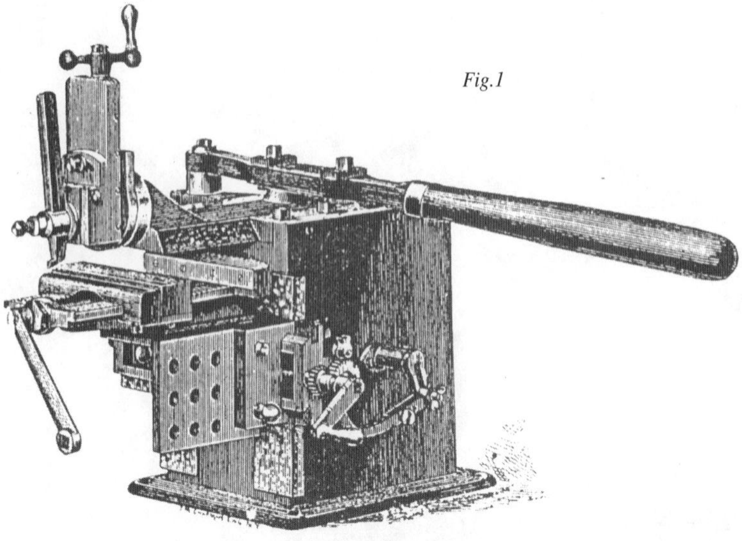

HANGOTZKY'S HAND SHAPER.

J. HANGOCZKY.
HAND PLANING MACHINE.
No. 413,444. Patented Oct. 22, 1889.

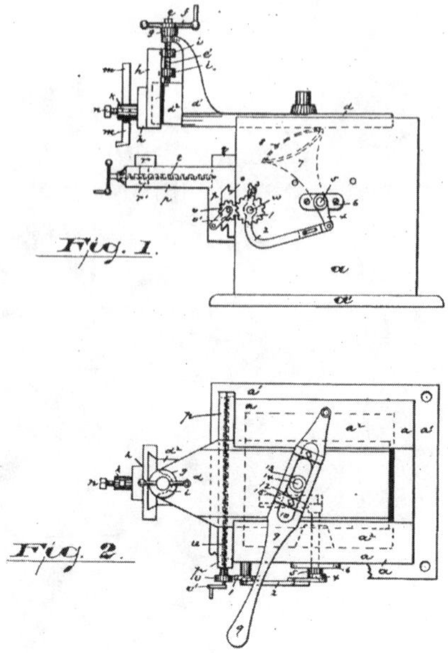

Fig.2

HARRINGTON & SON, EDWARD, Philadelphia, PA, later
HARRINGTON, SON & CO., EDWIN, Philadelphia, PA

A partnership of Edward Harrington and his son Edwin L. Harrington (1854-1899), formed about 1875 as a reorganizaton of Harrington & Haskins. In 1882, the firm reorganized as EDWIN HARRINGTON, SON & CO. and, about 1891, as Edwin Harrington, Son & Co., Inc. which operated into the 1920s.

The primary product was a line of extension bed lathes but the firm also made boring mills; radial, upright, suspension, multiple, level, and blacksmiths' drills; and, from 1880 to 1884, a line of planers (Fig.) in six sizes and planer centers (Fig.2) in two sizes. *(continued on next page)*

Fig.1

Fig.2

IMPROVED PLANER CENTERS.

Designed for heavy work, provided with an improved index of four dircular plates or disks, each 7-16 inch thick and 12 inches diameter, accurately cut with 48, 110, 126 and 140 notches, respectively, (giving a wide range of divisions, and these plates are readily taken off and others substituted, with different numbers for special work). These plates being cut through like a gear, gives a much stronger pin than a drilled index. This index is revolved by means of a worm, and gear, which are readily disconnected, (by loosening one bolt), when not required. Tongues are inserted in bottom of head, and tail stocks, and are readily taken out and fitted to the slot in any planer (by planing or filing off one side) without destroying the alignment.

The spindles, worm and screw are of steel.

13-inch, $35.00.
20-inch, 60.00.

HARRIS & CO., D.L., Springfield, MA

A partnership of D.L. Harris, R.F. Hawkins, and W.H. Burrall. Builder, in 1865, of lathes, planers and a variety of other machinery.

HAWES & CO., WM. M., Fall River, MA

Builder, beginning in 1864, of "lathes, planers, upright drills, etc. of best workmanship."

HAZEN, address unknown

Builder, in 1876, of the smallest known power planer made in the U.S. Shown right, it was priced at $150, and planed 10" wide and 24" long. Probably concerned that it would be considered an amateur machine, Hazen was careful to state: "it is no plaything."

The above, taken from the 1876 Hill, Clarke & Co. catalog, is the only information available.

HECKENDORN & WILHELM, Reading, PA, later
HECKENDORN, H.C., Reading, PA

A partnership of Henry C. Heckendorn and William H. Wilhelm, formed about 1880 to build light duty engine lathes. The partnership dissolved in 1887 but Heckendorn continued under his own name and announced that "he has brought out a line of machine tools, consisting of engine and speed lathes, milling machines, planers, planer chucks, pulley hangers, and shafting."

HENDERSON MACHINE TOOL CO., Philadelphia, PA

Formed in 1891 with George Henderson, president, and E.L. Hall, secretary and treasurer. The first products were metalforming presses but, in 1892, the firm offered shapers, as shown in the ad at left, and milling machines.

HENDEY MACHINE CO., Wolcottville, later Torrington, CT

Formed in 1870 as a partnership of Henry J. Hendey (1844-1906) and his brother Arthur Hendey (1846-1926), the firm incorporated August 22, 1874. Arthur Hendey left in 1875, claiming poor health. Henry J. Hendey continued to operate the firm until his death in 1906.

Planer production began in 1870 with an 8" x 6" x 24" bench top hand planer (Fig.1). An improved model (Fig.2) was brought out in 1873. Larger, 16" x 16" x 42" friction planers (Fig.3), based on E.J. Manville's patent of January 20, 1874, were introduced in 1877. Improved 24" x 24" x 6' geared friction planers (Fig.4) were introduced in 1881 and a new four-foot planer (Fig.5) in 1882. *(continued next eight pages)*

Fig.1

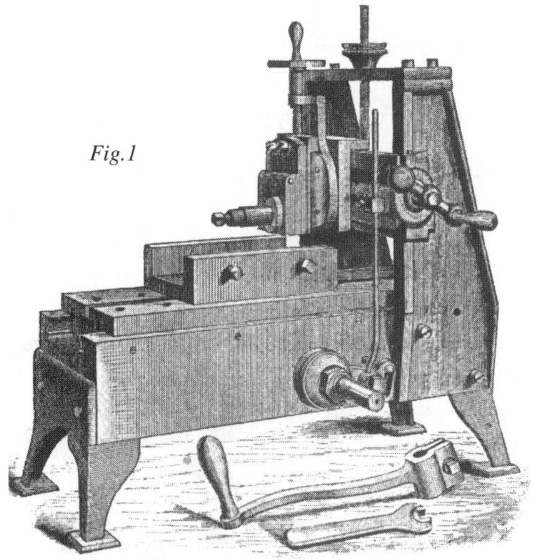

HAND PLANER—1870

Fig.2

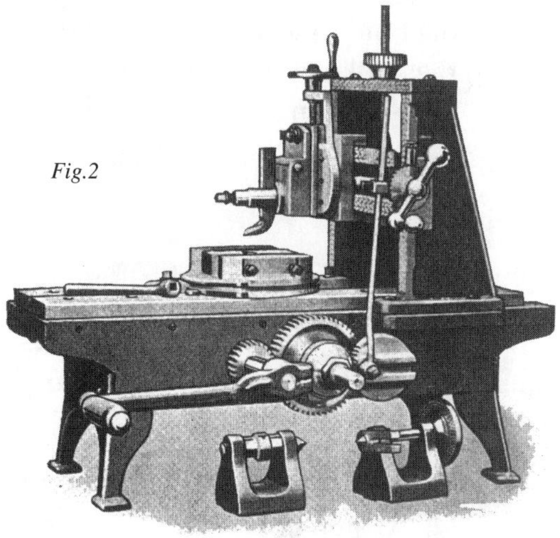

HAND PLANER—1873

Fig.3

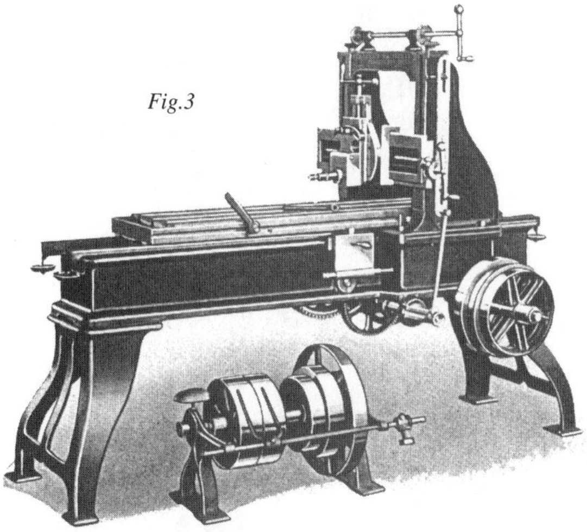

16" FRICTION PLANER—1877

Fig.4

IMPROVED IRON PLANER.

Fig.5

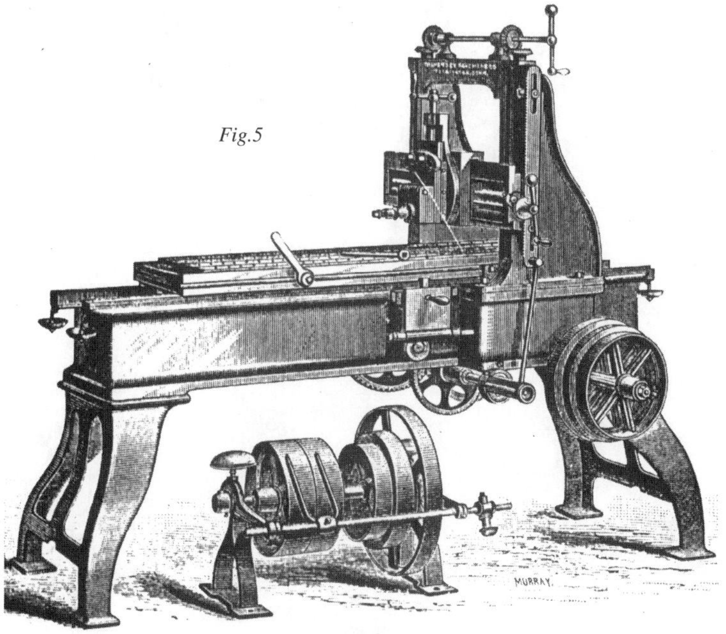

NEW FOUR-FOOT PLANER

Shaper production began in 1874 with the introduction of the Manville patent (January 20, 1874), 24" friction shaper (Fig.6) the stroke of which could be adjusted while the machine was operating. A 15" model (Fig.7) was introduced in 1875 with an improved version (Fig.8) in 1876 and a further improved model (Fig.9) in 1882.

By 1882, Hendry employed 100 hands, turning out an average of more than one machine a day.

Fig.6

THE MANVILLE PATENT SHAPER.

Fig.7

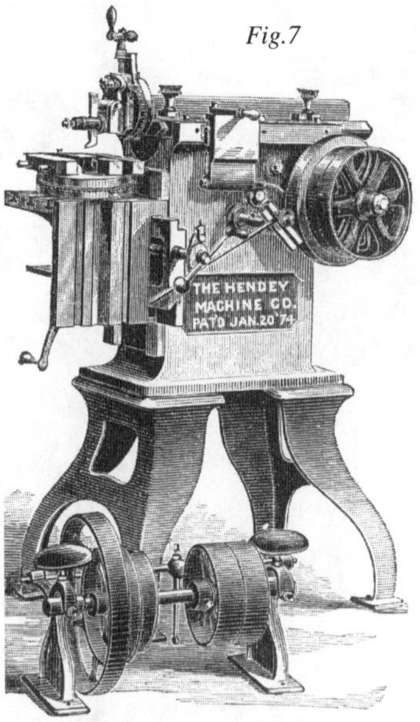

Fig.8

15" FRICTION SHAPER—1876

Fig 9

NEW FIFTEEN-INCH SHAPER.

Fig.10

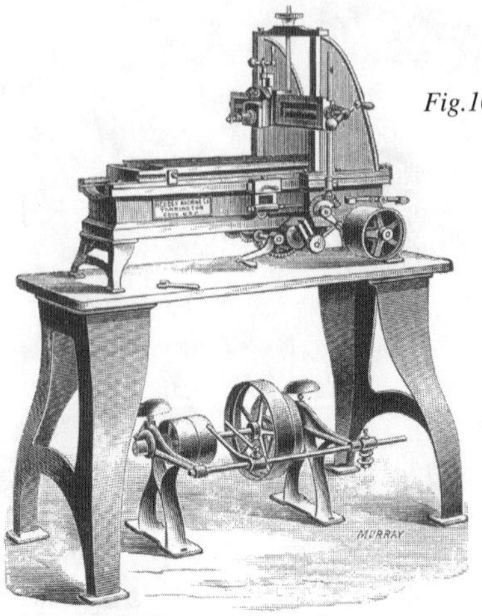

NEW HAND AND POWER PLANER.

Width.	Height.	Length it Planes.	Weight.	Prices.
16	16	4 feet.	2,000 lbs.	$525 00 with Vise.
17	16	4 "	2,200 "	550 00 " "
20	20	5 "	3,000 "	650 00 no "
24	24	6 "	4,400 "	800 00 " "
26	26	6 "	4,800 "	850 00 " " Extra head
24	24	8 "	5,200 "	925 00 " "
26	26	8 "	5,500 "	950 00 " "

NOTE.—All Planers from 3½ ft. to 5 ft. inclusive, have cone-pulleys.

Fig.11

Fig.12

Plane in Width.	Plane in Height.	Plane in Length.	Weight.	Prices.
26 inches.	24 inches.	6 feet.	4,900 lbs.	$800 00
26 "	24 "	7 "	5,300 "	840 00
28 "	28 "	6 "	5,800 "	880 00
28 "	28 "	8 "	6,800 "	970 00
28 "	28 "	10 "	7,800 "	1,060 00
32 "	32 "	8 "	9,000 "	1,200 00
32 "	32 "	10 "	10,000 "	1,300 00
32 "	32 "	12 "	11,000 "	1,400 00
36 "	36 "	8 "	10,500 "	1,400 00
36 "	36 "	10 "	11,600 "	1,500 00
36 "	36 "	12 "	12,800 "	1,600 00
36 "	36 "	16 "	15,000 "	1,800 00
42 "	42 "	8 "	13,000 "	1,860 00
42 "	42 "	10 "	14,500 "	2,000 00
42 "	42 "	12 "	16,000 "	2,140 00
42 "	42 "	16 "	19,000 "	2,420 00

A new, 10" x 10" x 24" combination hand and power planer (Fig.10), weighing 500 pounds, was introduced in 1883. Planers offered in 1884 are listed in Figs.11-12 and included 16" x 16" x 4' (Fig.13) with three speed cone, 20" x 20" x 5' (Fig.14), and 42" x 42" x 12' (Fig.15) sizes. The 8" x 6" x 24" hand planer (Fig.16) also continued in production. By 1885, Hendey was offering a 22" x 22" x 5' geared friction planer (Fig.17) with redesigned reversing mechanism.

Fig.13

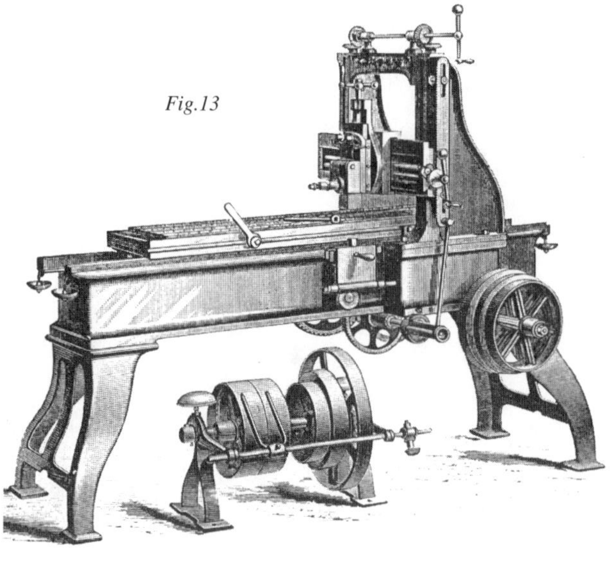

Represents 16 inch Planer.

Fig.14

Fig.15

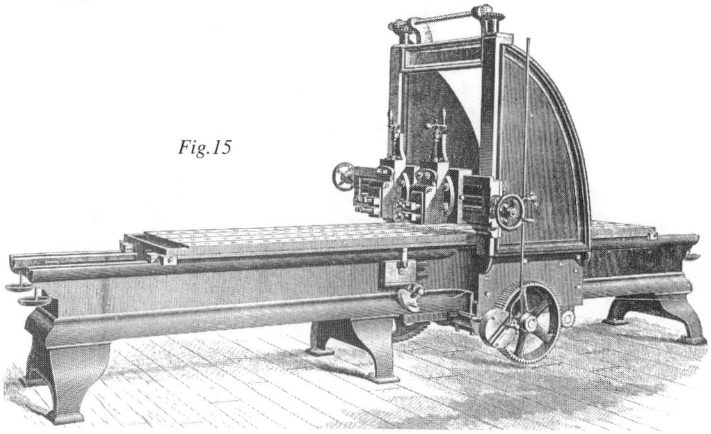

Fig.16

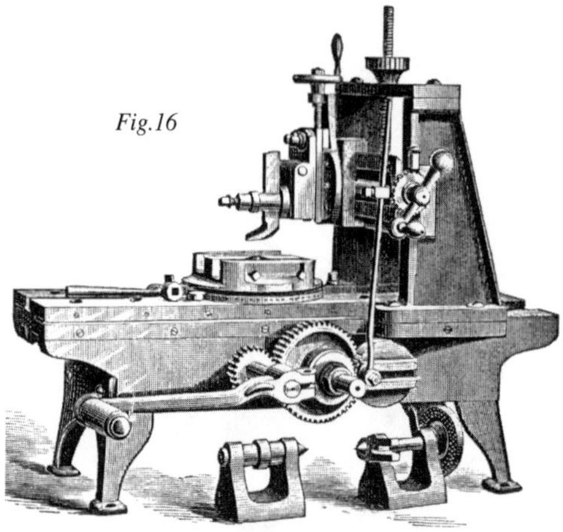

Fig.17

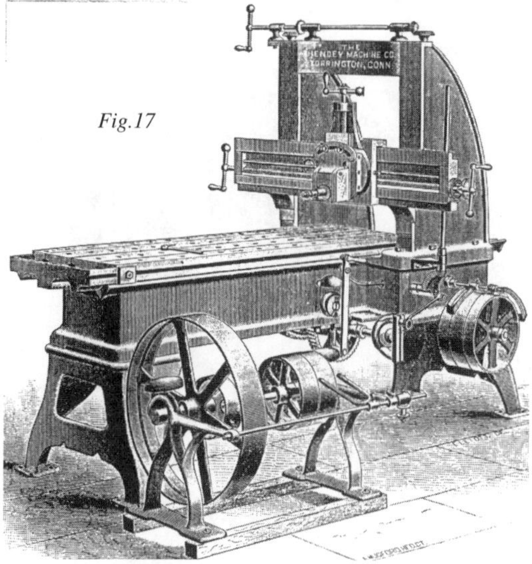

Fig.18

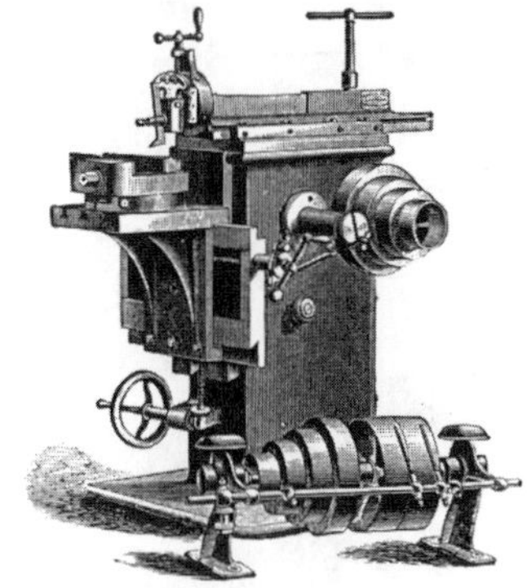

10 AND 6 INCH PILLAR SHAPERS.

Length of stroke (quick return).	Table traverse.	Greatest distance between bottom of slide and top of table.	Weight, with vise and counter-shaft.	Price, with vise and counter-shaft
6 inches. 10 "	8 inches. 16 "	6 inches. 11½ "	600 lbs. 1,700 "	$380 00 550 00

Shapers offered in 1884 included new 6" and 10" stroke models (Fig.18), and a 30"x 72" traverse model (Figs.19-20) weighing 10,000 pounds. In 1885, Hendey introduced new 15" (Fig.21) and 24" (Fig.22) pillar shapers with adjustable angle tables patented September 30, 1884, and new reversing gear patented January 13, 1885; heavy duty 25" shapers (Fig.23) weighing 2700 pounds; and 20" x 60" traverse shapers (Fig.24) weighing 6700 pounds. New 1886 products included a 15" x 36" traverse shaper (Fig.25).

Fig.19

Hendey 30"x72" Shaper. Side View.

Fig.20

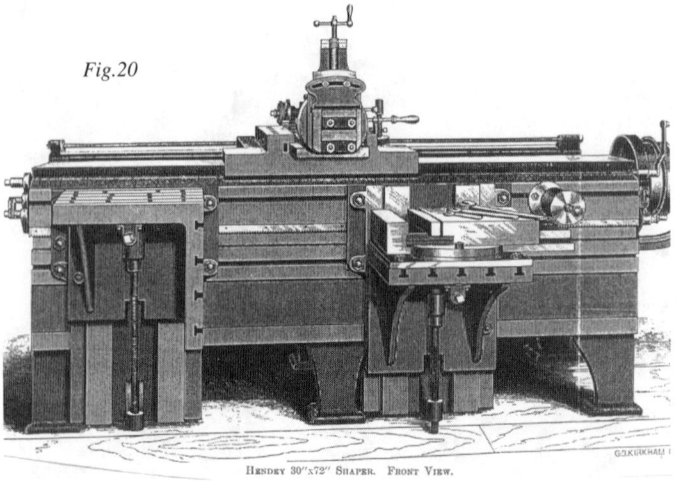

Hendey 30"x72" Shaper. Front View.

Fig.21

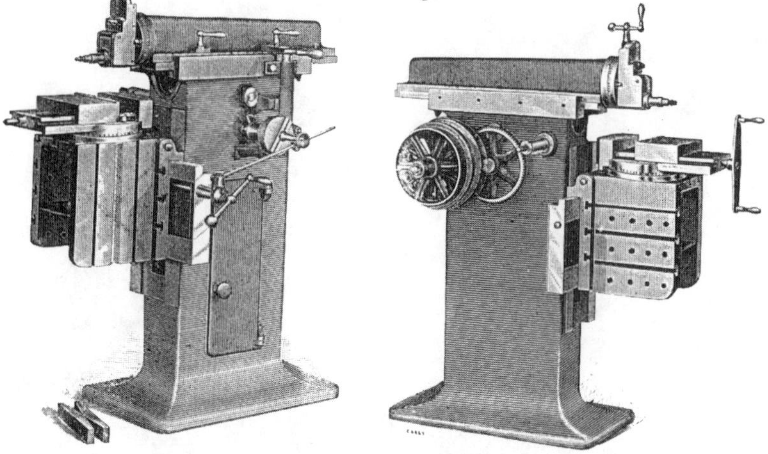

New Fifteen-Inch Shaper.

Fig.22

New 24-Inch Shaper.

NEW 25-INCH SHAPER.

Fig.23

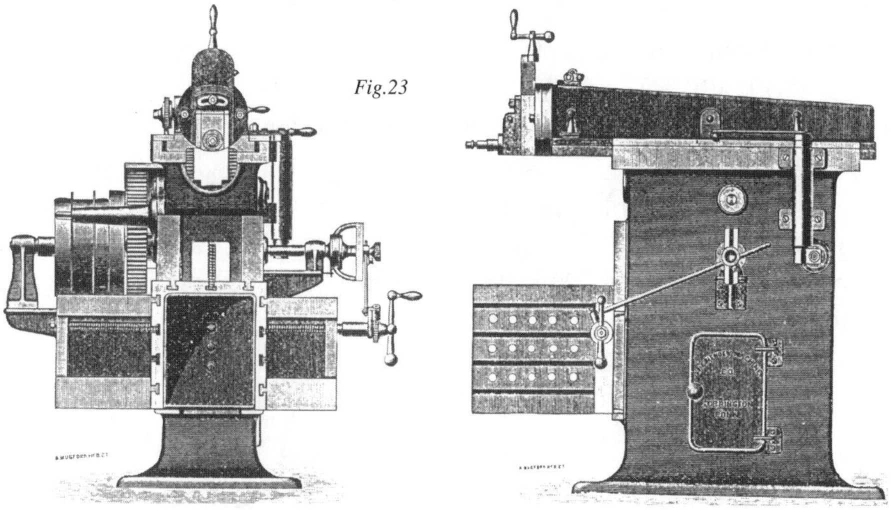

Fig.24

Fig.25

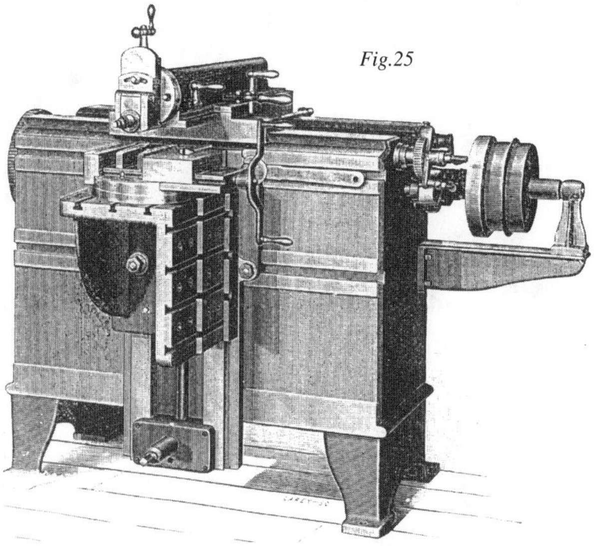

16 X 16 IN. X 4 FT. PLANER.

Fig.26

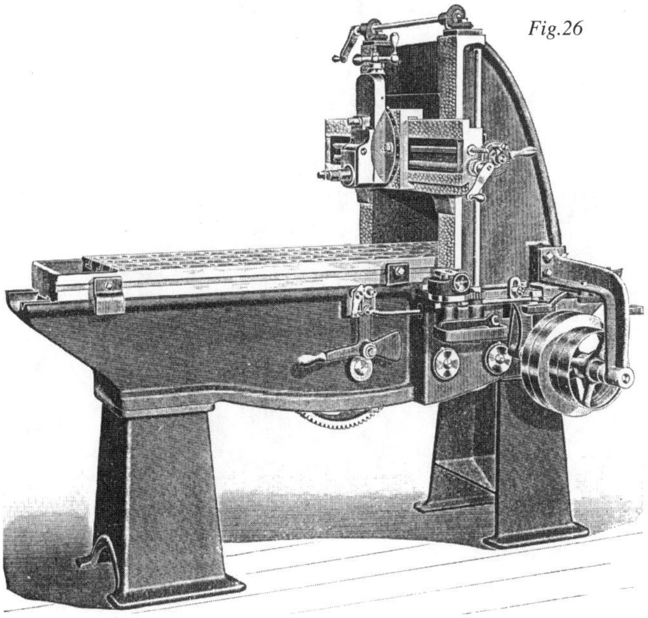

Fig.27

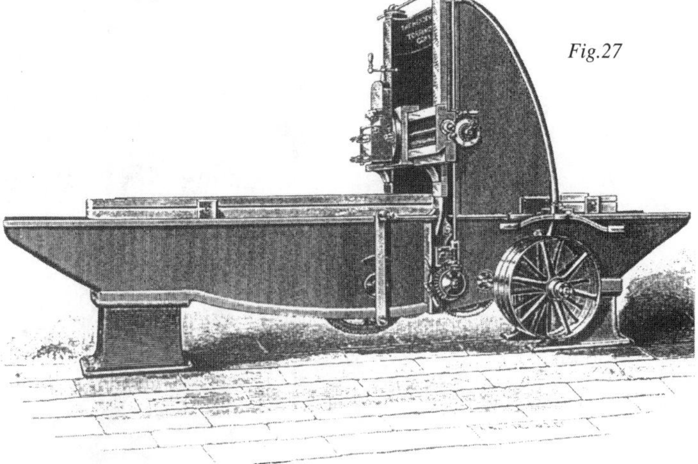

Twenty-seven Inch Planer.

Wendell P. Norton ((1861-?) joined the firm in 1886 as the chief machine designer, leaving in 1889 to start his own firm, W.P. Norton Co., but returned to Hendey in 1892 as superintendent.

A completely new line of planers with much heavier construction was introduced in 1887 and included 16" x 16" x 4' (Fig.26), 27" x 27" x 8' (Fig.27) and 30" x 30" x 10' (Fig.28) sizes. Planer production appears to have ceased about 1900 as the firm concentrated on shapers and lathes.

New 15" friction shapers (Fig.29) were introduced in 1889, followed by an improved 30" x 72" model (Fig.30), and a portable, motor driven shaper (Fig.31) in 1892. A new 24" belt-shifting, 2400 pound, shaper (Fig.32) was introduced in 1893; followed by a 6', 40,000 pound shaper (Fig.33), and 25", 25,000 pound, suspension shaper (Fig.34) in 1894. An improved 15" pillar shaper (Fig.35) was introduced in 1896. Electric motor drive shapers (Fig.36) were offered in 1901.

Fig.28

Thirty Inch by Thirty Inch by Ten Foot Planer.

Fig.29

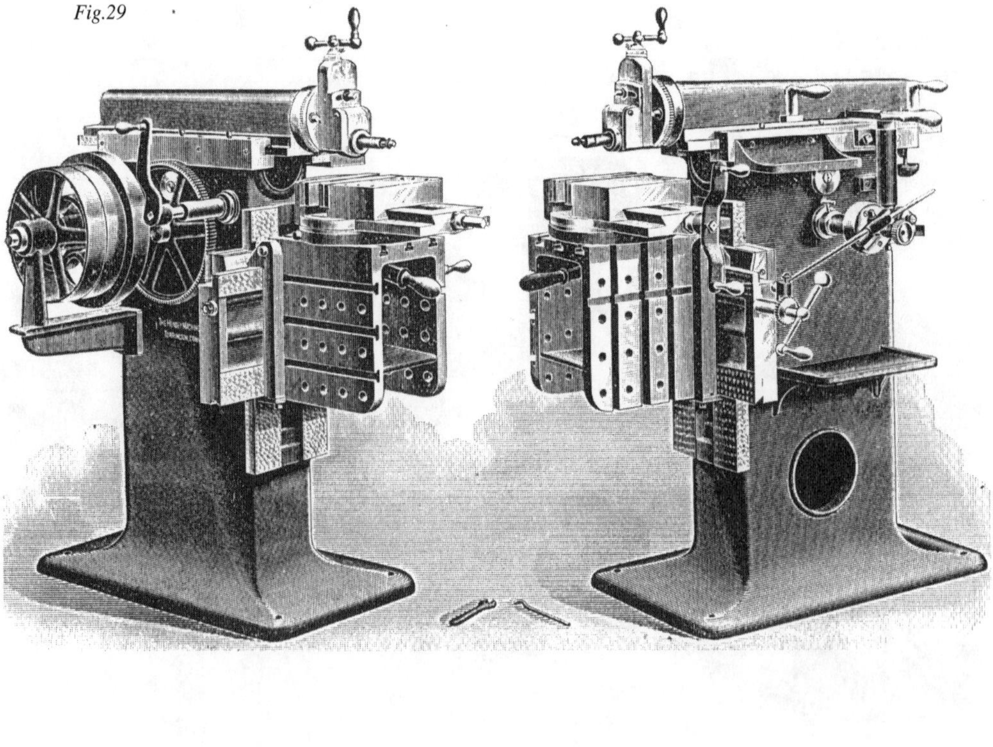

Fig.30

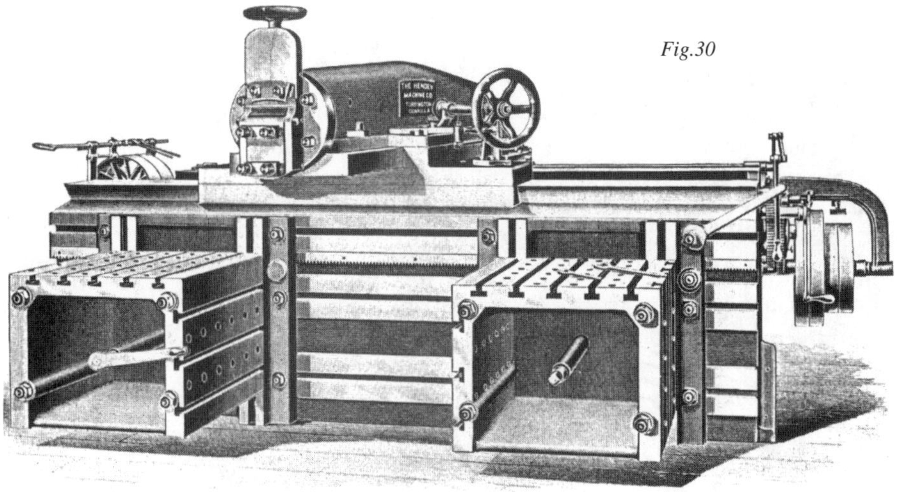

6' STROKE TRAVERSE SHAPER—1892

Fig.31

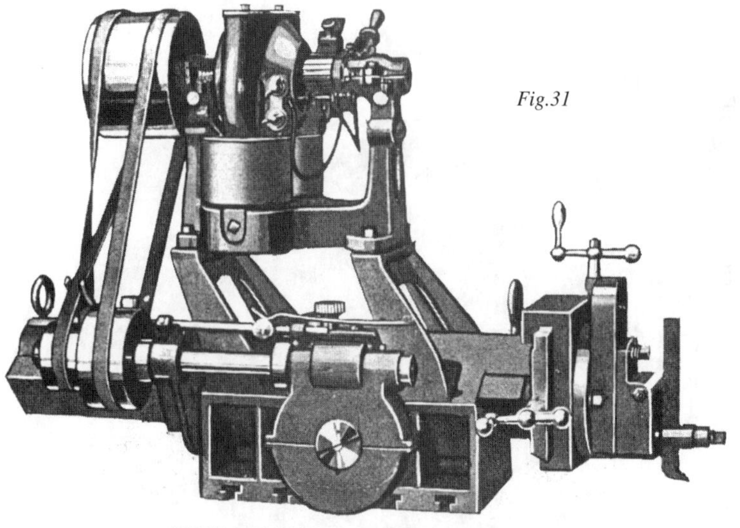

PORTABLE MOTOR DRIVEN SHAPER—1892

Fig.32

Twenty-four-inch Belt-shifting Shaper.

Fig.33

A Six-foot Shaper.

Fig.34

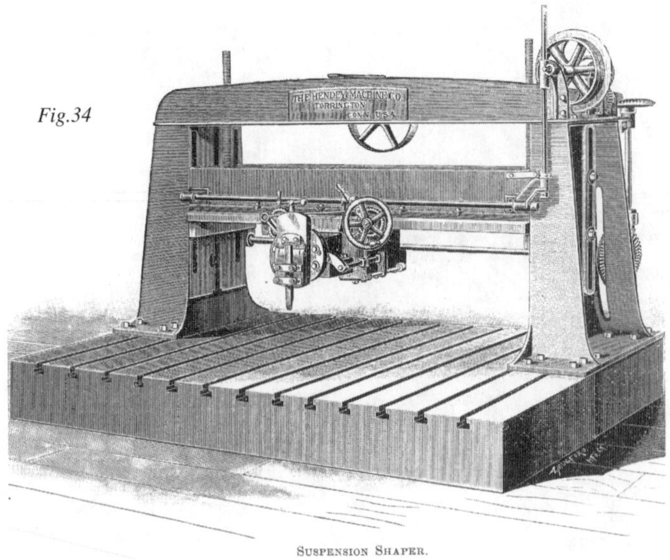

SUSPENSION SHAPER.

Fig.35

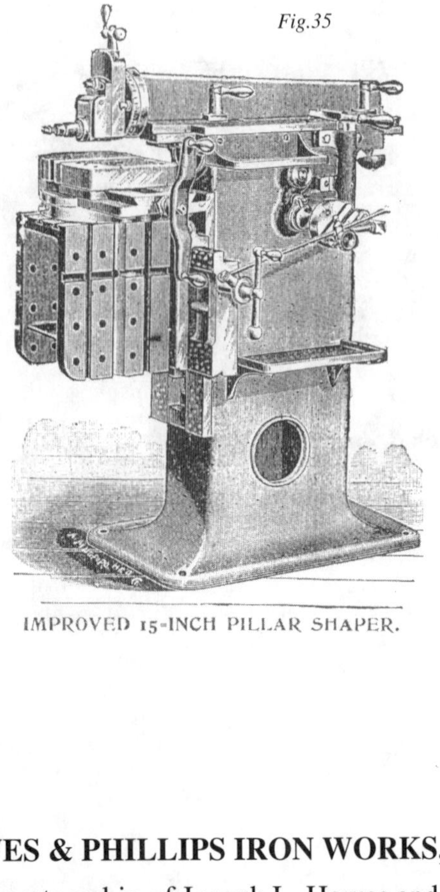

IMPROVED 15-INCH PILLAR SHAPER.

Fig.36

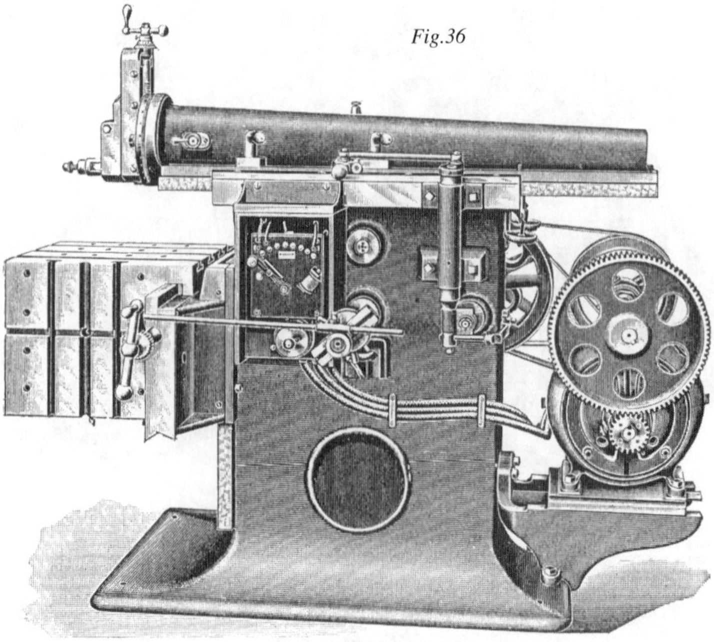

HEWES & PHILLIPS IRON WORKS, Newark, NJ

A partnership of Joseph L. Hewes and John M. Phillips (1817-1884), formed in New York, NY, in 1845 and moved to Newark, NJ, in 1851. Machine tool production began about 10 years after the move to Newark.

Phillips' sons, Edward L. Phillips (1851-1905) and Franklin Phillips (1857-1914) joined the firm, with Edward serving as president from 1884 to 1905 and Franklin from 1905 to 1914.

1869 production included "steam engines and boilers, sugar mills, mining machinery, engine and hand lathes, drill presses, shaping and slotting machines, planing and bolt cutting machines, punching, shearing and drop presses, gear cutters, and machinists' tools of all kinds." *(continued next two pages)*

Shapers included a 9" stroke model (Fig.1) introduced in 1880 and improved in 1882 (Fig.2) and a larger, 15" stroke machine (Fig.3), weighing 4770 pounds, introduced in 1883.

A new line of planers was introduced in 1881 and was offered in seven sizes as shown in Fig.4. The 42" x 42" x 12' model was equipped with bevel gear drive (Fig.5); the 30" x 30" x 8' machine (Fig.6) with a worm drive patented July 21, 1874, by J.L. Hewes (Fig.7). A small, 16" planer (Fig.8) with worm drive and an unusual pedestal bed was offered in 1880.

A planer table cushioning device, patented October 12, 1886, and a new friction feed for planers, patented February 21, 1888, both by Franklin Phillips, were used in later production.

Slotter production included a 12" machine introduced in 1882 (Fig.9) and a large, worm drive model (Fig.10) which could handle work up to 54" high and 12' in diameter.

Machine tool production appears to have ceased prior to 1901, when the catalog listed steam engines and associated equipment only.

Fig.1

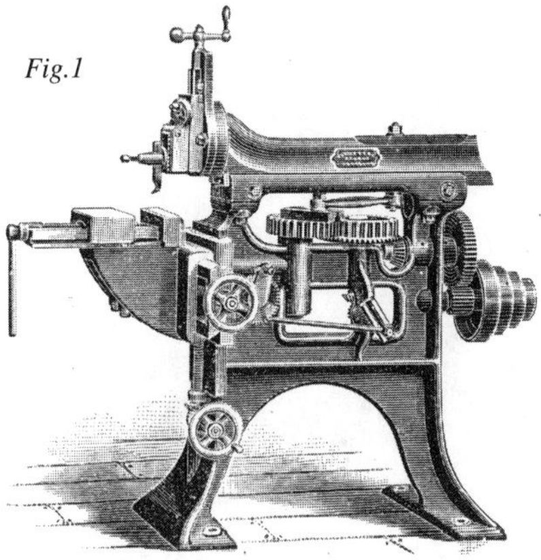

New Shaping Machine.

Fig.2

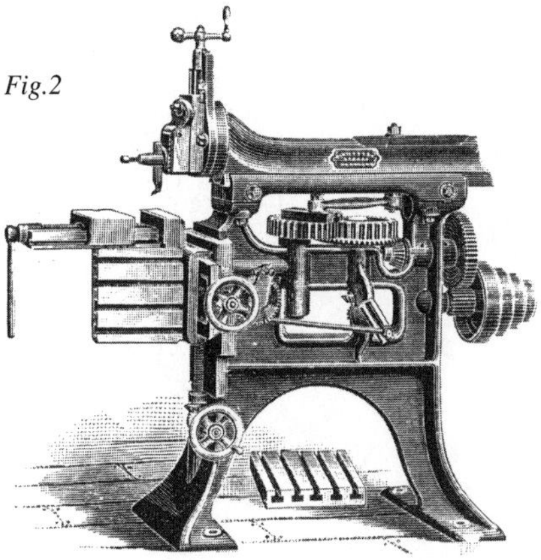

Improved Shaping Machine.

Fig.3

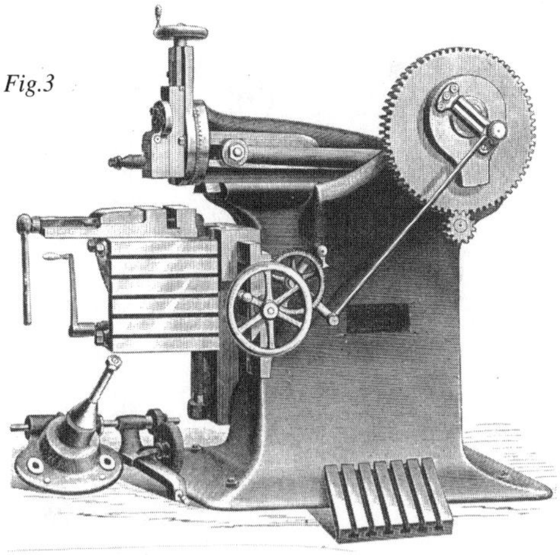

PRICES.

Will Plane In Width.	Will Plane In Height.	Will Plane In Length.	Weight.	Prices.	Per additional foot of Table.	Extra Slide Rest on Cross Head.	Vertical Slide Rest on Upright.
30 inches.	30 inches.	8 feet.	10,500	$1,450 00	$ 60 00	$225 00	$200 00
36 "	36 "	10 "	15,200	1,900 00	70 00	250 00	225 00
42 "	42 "	12 "	19,800	2,500 00	80 00	300 00	250 00
48 "	48 "	12 "	22,500	2,900 00	90 00	325 00	275 00
54 "	54 "	14 "	31,050	3,600 00	100 00	350 00	300 00
60 "	60 "	16 "	36,500	4,600 00	115 00	400 00	325 00
72 "	72 "	20 "	75,000	6,600 00	170 00	425 00	350 00

Fig.4

Fig.5

—Represents 42 inch by 42 inch Planer.

Fig.6

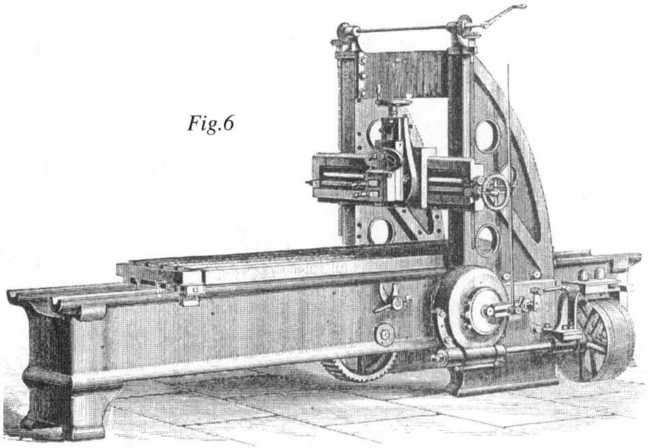

—Represents 30 inch by 30 inch Planer.

J. L. HEWES.

Metal Planing-Machines.

No. 153,254. Patented July 21, 1874.

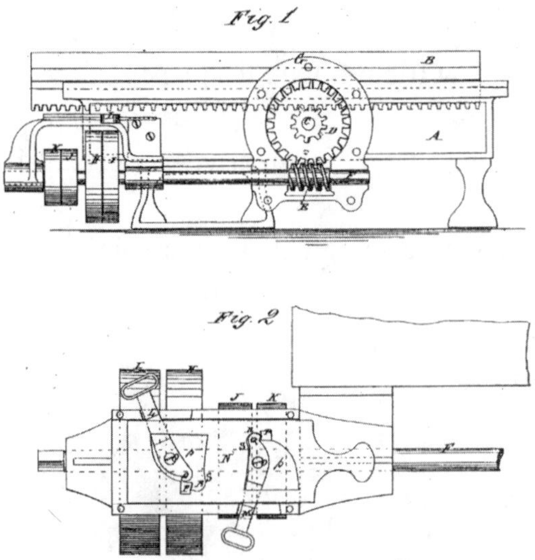

Fig.7

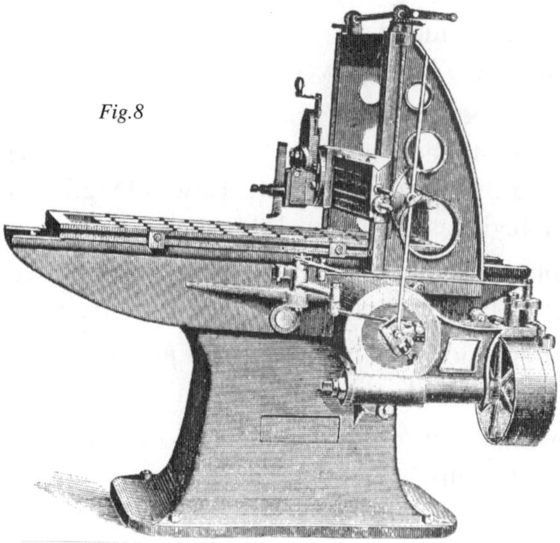

Fig.8

Fig.9

Fig.10

HILLES & JONES, Wilmington, DE

A partnership of William S. Hilles (1823-1876) and Henry C. Jones (1838-1909), formed in 1870 when they bought out Robert H. Barr & Co. and reorganized as HILLES & JONES. The firm continued production of drilling machines developed by Barr.

By 1883, the partners were building screw driven plate planing machines. Early production (Fig.1) could plane 13' 10" long. In 1888, they introduced an improved model (Fig.2) that could plane 18' long and weighed 23,000 pounds.

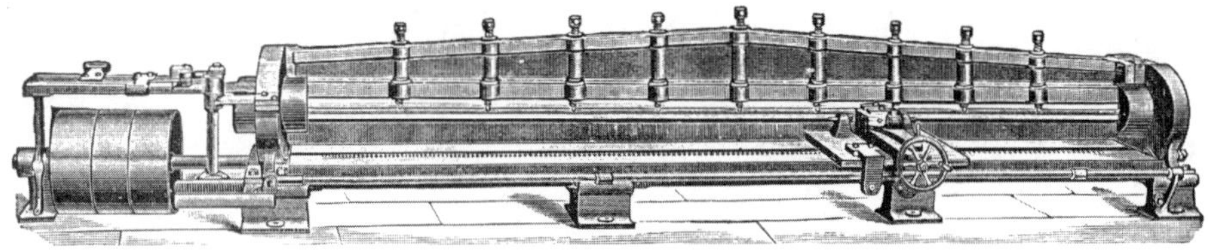

Fig.1

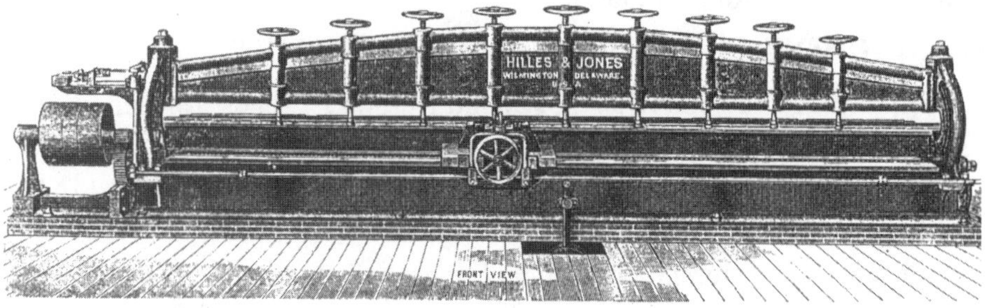

Fig.2

New Plate Planing Machine.

HOWARD, GEORGE C., Philadelphia, PA

Builder of lathes, planers, and drilling machines c1881-1883. Rack drive planers, 36" wide and "any length desired," were offered in 1882. As shown below, the machine was driven through an unusual worm drive from the input pulley to the rack gearing.

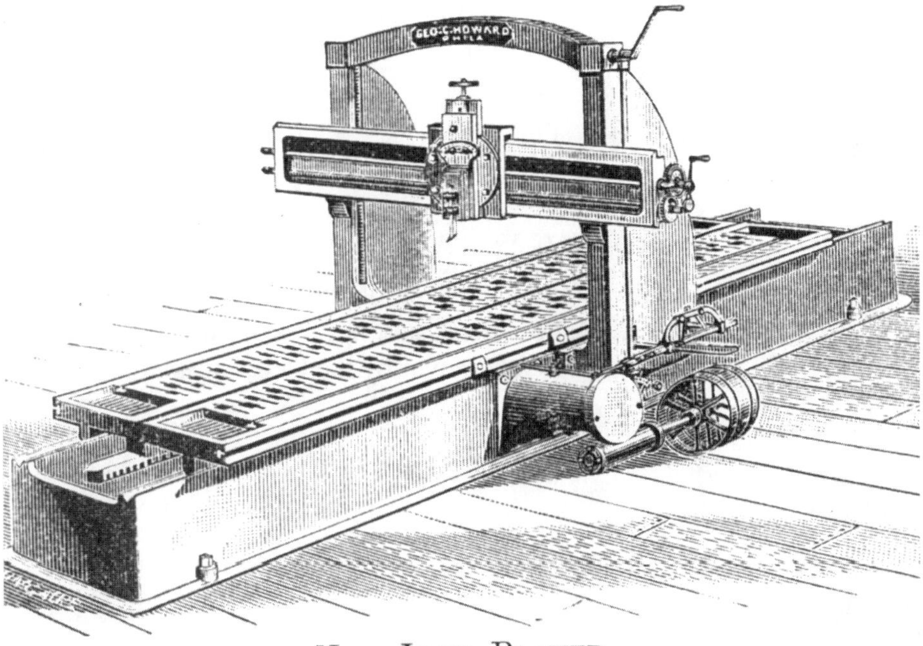

New Iron Planer.

IDEAL MACHINE WORKS, Brooklyn, NY

Builder, in 1906, of the small, bench planer shown right. The machine had a 4" stroke and could plane a piece 5" wide.

Ideal Hand Planer.

INDUSTRIAL WORKS, Philadelphia, PA See WILLIAM B. BEMENT & SON

JONES, LAMSON & CO., Windsor, VT, later

JONES & LAMSON MACHINE CO., Windsor, later **Springfield, VT**

A partnership of Ebenezer G. Lamson (1814-1892) and Russell L. Jones, formed in 1869 as a reorganization of the Windsor Mfg. Co. The firm was a successor to ROBBINS & LAWRENCE CO., whose plant and equipment had been bought by Ebenezer G. Lamson in 1859. Henry D. Stone (1815-1899) continued as superintendent.

Early products included planers, engine lathes, hand lathes, and chucking lathes based on Frederick W. Howe (1822-1891) designs done for Robbins & Lawrence. The firm also made a variety of other machinery, most for quarrying.

In 1876, the machine tool portion of the company was split off and incorporated as the JONES & LAMSON MACHINE CO. Ralph H. Lamson, nephew of Ebenezer G. Lamson, was elected president. On November 18, 1887, Adna Brown (1828-1901) and Amasa Woolson (1811-1891) bought control from Ebenezer G. Lamson. They moved the company to Springfield, VT, in 1888 and increased the capital stock from $50,000 to $60,000. Woolson served as president until his death in 1891.

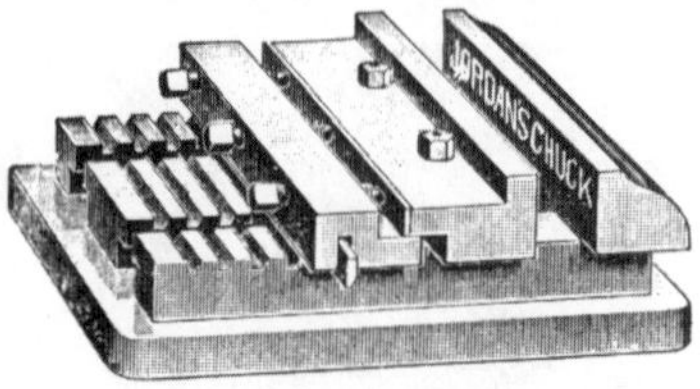

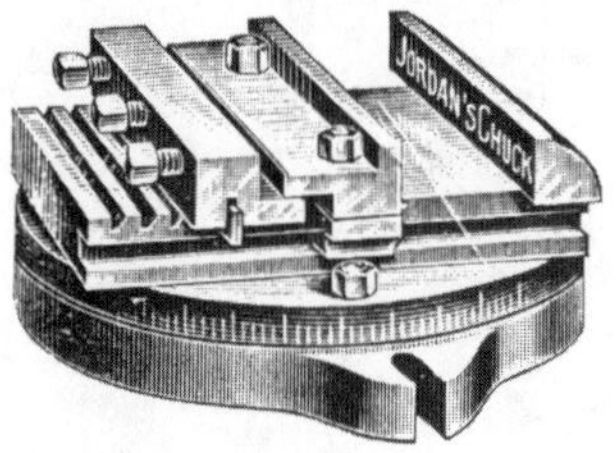

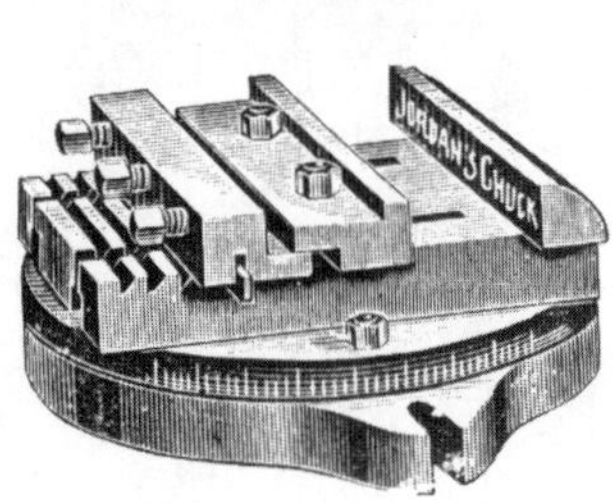

JORDAN, G.W., Worcester, MA

Inventor and maker of the JORDAN planer chuck offered in three styles, as shown left, and in sizes from 8" to 30" jaw length. The chuck business was taken over by the Geo. Burnham Co. in 1892.

JUENGST & SONS, GEO., Croton Falls, NY

Formed about 1884 to build shapers with horizontal cranks patented September 23, 1884, (Fig.1). In 1889, the firm built shapers under contract for the Prentiss Tool & Supply Co., which sold them under the Prentiss name. By 1907 Juengst offered 16", 21" and 26" shapers (Fig.2) under its name.

Fig.1

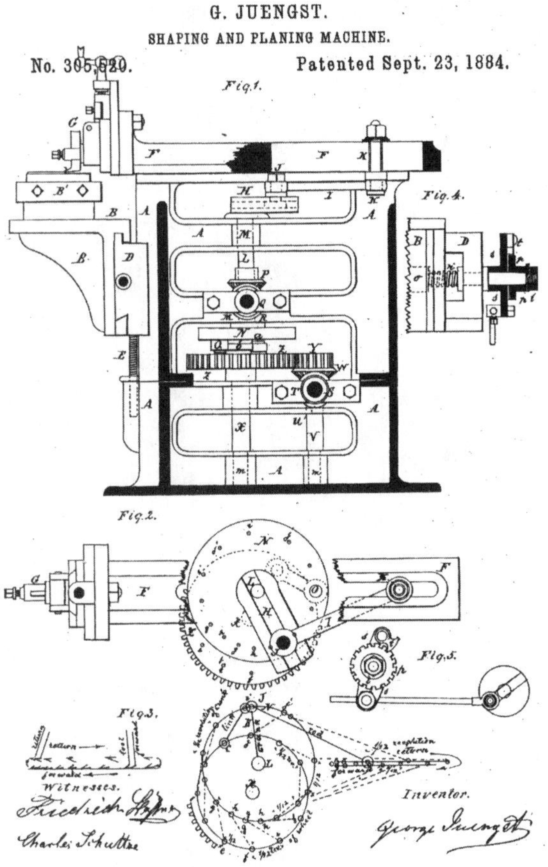

Fig.2

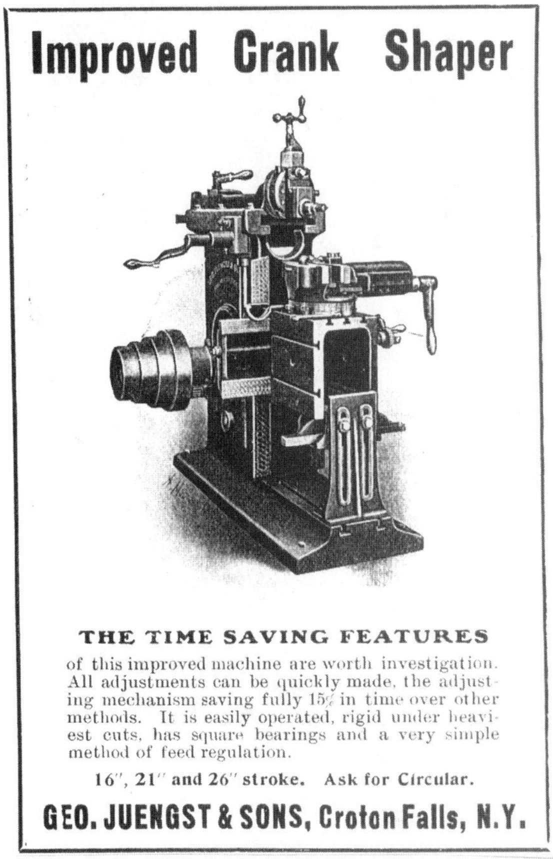

KELLY MACHINE CO., R.A., Xenia, OH, later
KELLY CO., R.A., Xenia, OH

Formed February 1, 1891, by Robert A. Kelly (1838-1892) to make cordage machinery. Kelly's son, James A. Kelly (1871- 1900) and widow, Alice C. Kelly, operated the firm from Kelly's death in 1892 until joined by another son George R. Kelly (1871-1929) in 1895. George R. Kelly reorganized as the R.A. KELLY CO. after his brother died in 1900.

Shaper production began in 1898 when the firm introduced a line of adjustable, quick return, crank shapers in 15" (Fig.1), 16" and 20" (Fig.2) strokes. The largest weighed 2200 pounds. By 1906 the line had expanded to include a 26" back geared crank shaper (Fig.3) and, in 1909, an improved model (Fig.4) with outboard table support. *(continued next page)*

Fig.1

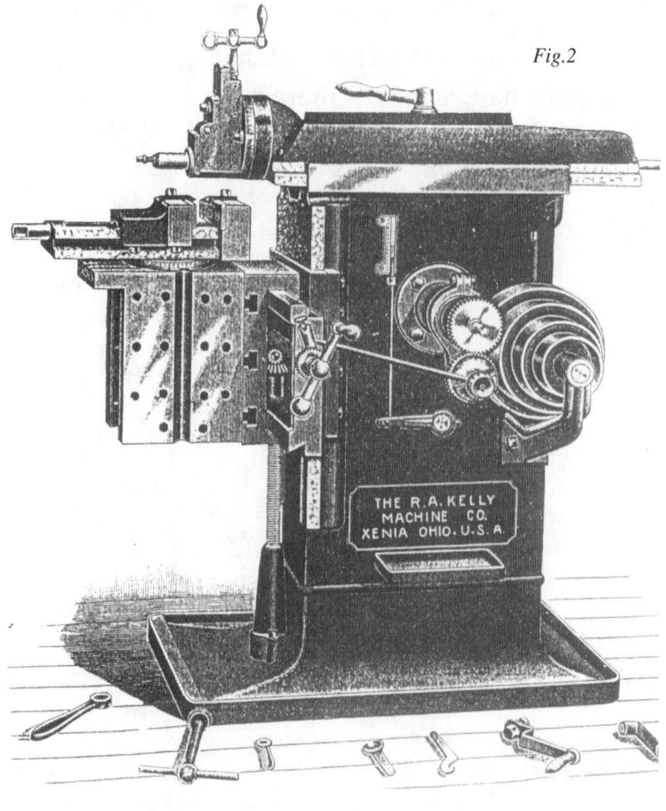

Fig.2

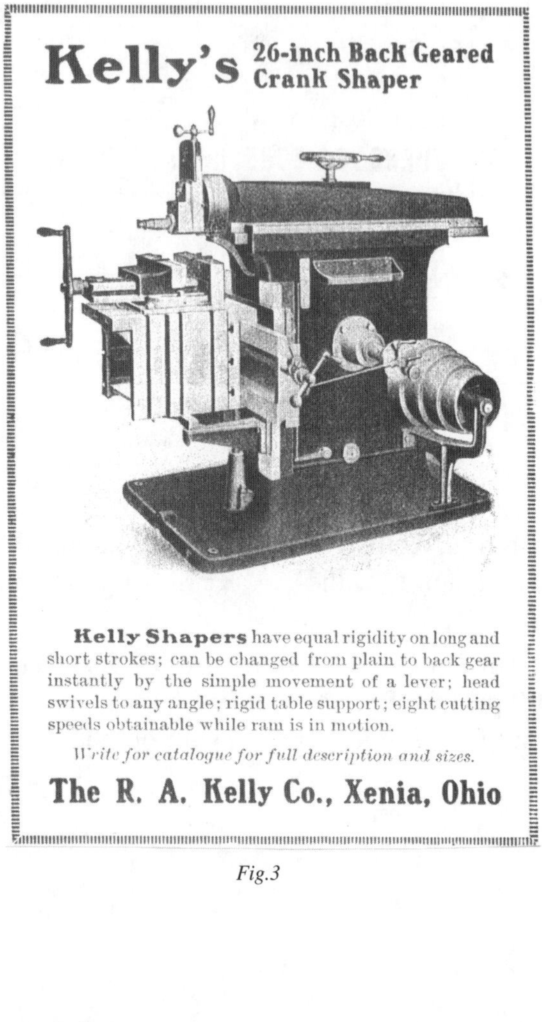

Fig.3

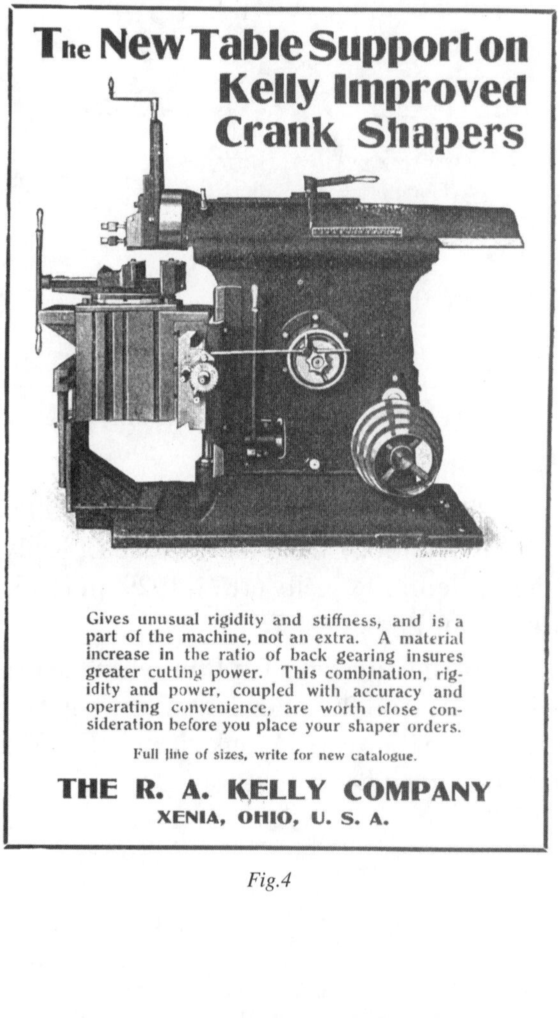

Fig.4

KNECHT PLANER CO., Cincinnati, OH

Formed in 1908 as successor to the Knecht Brothers Co. Charles J. Knecht was president. In 1910, it introduced the RAPID PRODUCTION planer, shown right in 36" x 36" x 12' size. Motor driven, it had a return speed of 150 FPM and variable feeds to 50 FPM.

LAMSON, GOODNOW & YALE, Windsor, VT, later
LAMSON & CO., E.G., Windsor, VT

Formed in 1859 when Ebenezer G. Lamson (1814-1892), Abel F. Goodnow and B. Buchanan Yale bought the plant and equipment of the defunct ROBBINS & LAWRENCE CO. Henry D. Stone (1815-1899). who had worked at Robbins & Lawrence since 1847, was appointed superintendent continuing through the later reorganizations. In 1862, the firm reported employment of "100 men making gun machinery", including planers and lathes. A variety of other machinery was also offered.

Lamson bought out his partners and reorganized as E.G. LAMSON & CO. in 1864. In 1865 he again reorganized, this time as the WINDSOR MFG. CO.

LATHE & MORSE, Worcester, MA, later
LATHE & MORSE TOOL CO., Worcester, MA

A partnership of Martin Lathe and Edwin Morse formed in 1864 as a successor to Shepard, Lathe & Morse. In 1871, the firm reorganized as a stock company, the LATHE & MORSE TOOL CO. Employment in 1882 was 40 to 50 men. The company was defunct in March, 1891, when the assets were sold to William F. Draper, who then formed the Draper Machine Tool Co.

Products included a variety of machine tools, primarily planers and lathes. Its 1872 catalog offered 15" crank planers (Fig.1) weighing 1400 pounds and gear driven planers in 20" x 20"x 4'; 24"x 24"x 5', 6', 8' (Fig.2) or 10'; and 32"x 32" x 8' or 10'. 1891 production included improved 16" x 16" (Fig.3) and 24" x 24" planers (Fig.4).

(continued on next page)

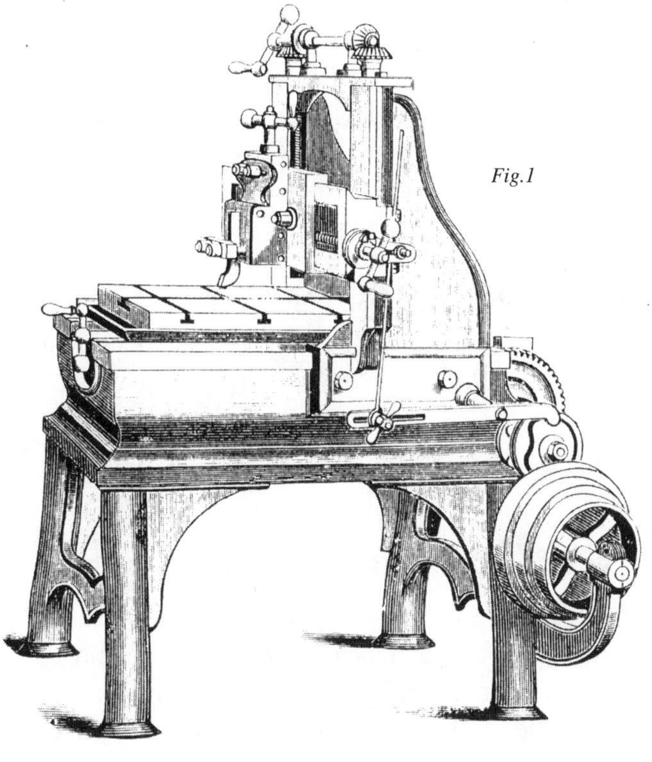
Fig.1

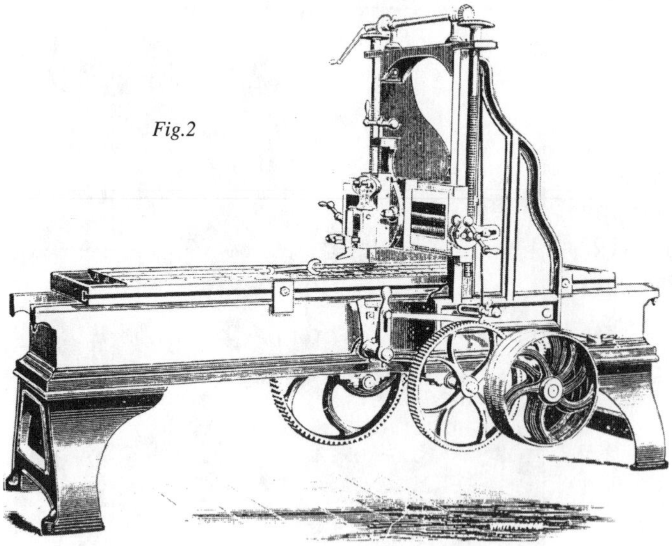

Fig.2

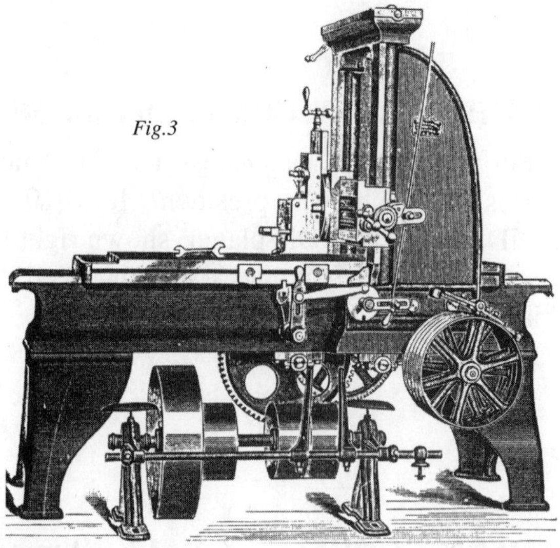

Fig.3

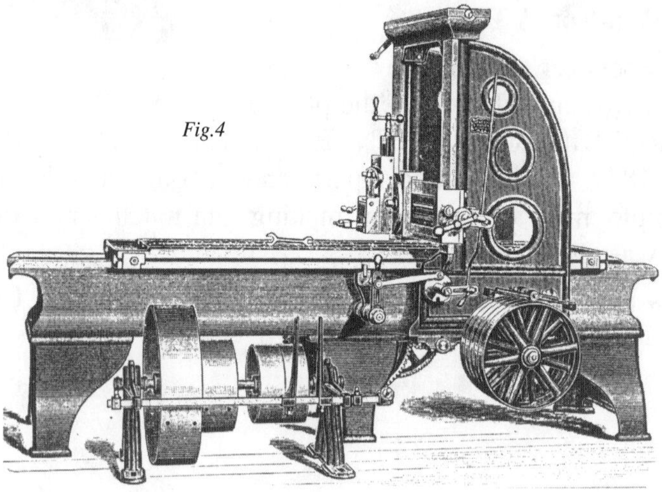

Fig.4

LATTA, A.B. & E., (BUCKEYE WORKS), Cincinnati, OH

Operated by Alexander B. Latta (1821-1865). Maker of "all kinds of lathes and machinists' tools" c1845-1865.

LEONARD & CLARK, New York, NY

Builders, in 1859-1861, of "planers, machinists' tools of all kinds and all sizes of engines lathes, priced from $325 to $1900."

LINCOLN & CO., Hartford, CT See PHOENIX IRON WORKS

LINCOLN IRON WORKS, Rutland, VT

Maker of a variety of quarrying and stone cutting machinery. The firm offered, in 1892, a double head stone planer which could plane 6'6" wide, 3' high, and 12' long at a speed of 25" per minute. Note that the platen, driven by a 5" diameter lead screw, runs in ways only when under the tools and is supported by sets of wheels after passing the tools. The machine was designed to cut both plane surfaces and mouldings. *(Illustration next page)*

THE LINCOLN DOUBLE-HEAD STONE-PLANING MACHINE.

LODGE, BARKER & CO., Cincinnati, OH

A partnership of William Lodge (1848-1917) and William Barker (1853-1915) formed January 1, 1880. Both Lodge and Barker had previously worked for the John Steptoe Co. The firm was reorganized as LODGE, DAVIS & CO. when Charles Davis replaced Barker in January, 1886.

Early production consisted of brassmakers' and engine lathes, but, in 1885, the firm introduced a 24" shaper weighing 2600 pounds (Fig.1) and a 36" rotary planer (Fig.2) for facing iron structural forms.

Fig.1

NEW 24-INCH SHAPER.

Fig.2

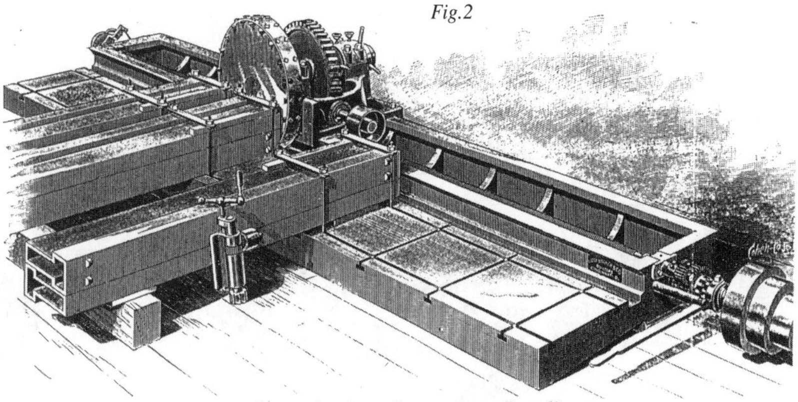

THIRTY-SIX-INCH ROTARY PLANER OR COLUMN FACING MACHINE.

LODGE, DAVIS & CO., Cincinnati, OH, later **LODGE & DAVIS MACHINE TOOL CO., Cincinnati, OH**

A partnership of William Lodge (1848-1817) and Charles Davis (1853-1903) formed in January, 1886, as a reorganization of LODGE, BARKER & CO. In 1889, the firm became a stock company, the LODGE & DAVIS MACHINE TOOL CO. Lodge left the firm in March, 1892, to found the Ohio Machine Tool Works. Davis, who became president when Lodge departed, reorganized as the Davis & Egan Machine Tool Co. September 1, 1896, when Thomas P. Egan bought an interest.

Fig.1

Fig.2

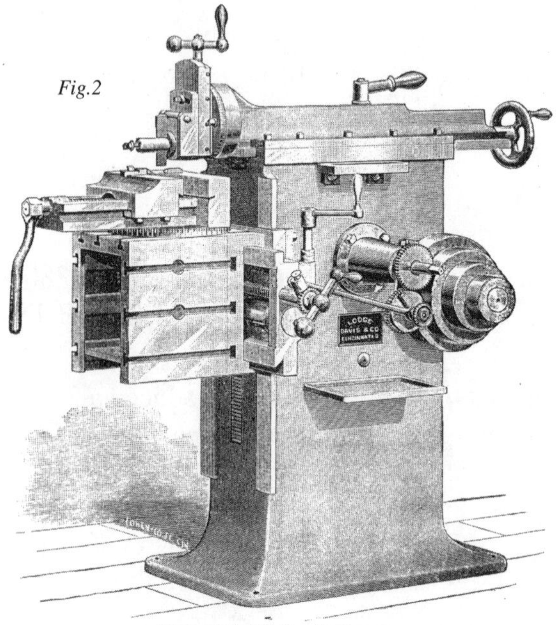

Improved 15″ Crank Shaper.

Fig.3

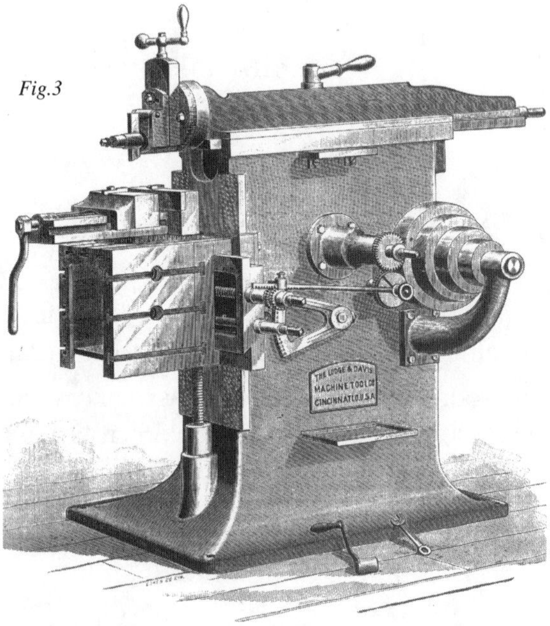

SIXTEEN-INCH SHAPER.

Fig.4

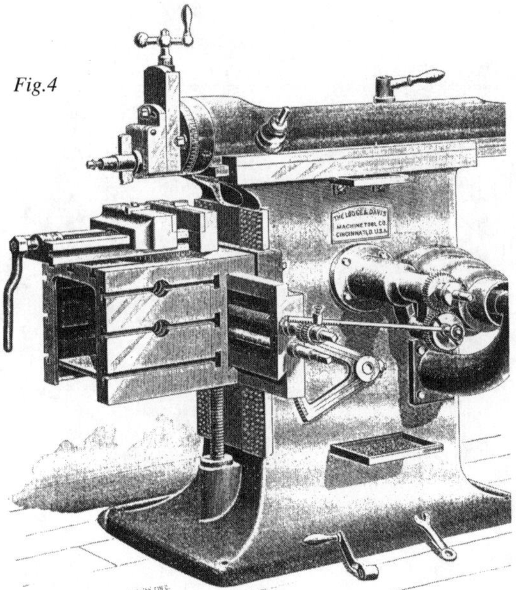

TWENTY-ONE-INCH PILLAR SHAPER.

Fig.5

THE LODGE & DAVIS 26-INCH SHAPER.

Henry Dreses (1854-1930), who had joined the firm in 1883, was chief designer by 1892, serving until 1896 when he left to form Dreses, Mueller & Co.

The new company continued production of most Lodge, Barker & Co. machine tools including the 24" shaper (Fig.1). In 1888, a new line of 15" (Fig.2) and 20" crank shapers was introduced and the geared shaper line was expanded to include 20", 26" and 32" strokes. New 16" (Fig.3) and 21" (Fig.4) pillar shapers were introduced in 1894 and an improved 26" triple geared shaper (Fig.5) in 1895.

Lodge & Davis entered the planer business in 1889 when it introduced a line of 24" (Figs.6-7), 32" and 38" sizes. An improved 36" planer (Fig.8) was introduced in 1892 and a line of extra wide planers (Fig.9) in 42", 48", and 54", with a common height of 38", in 1894. Improved 24" and 26" planers (Fig.10) were offered in 1895.

(continued next page)

Fig.6

Twenty-Four Inch Planer.

Fig.7

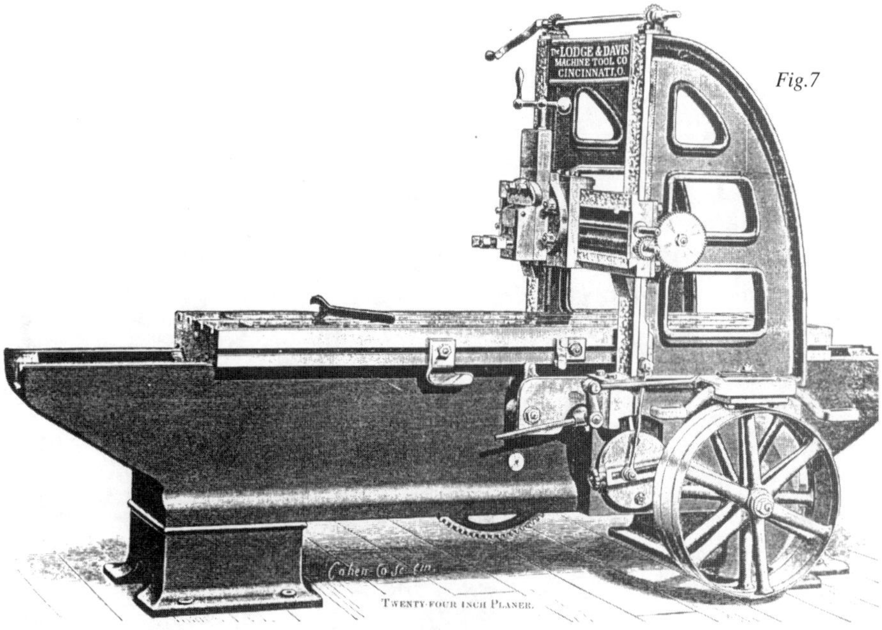

Twenty-Four Inch Planer.

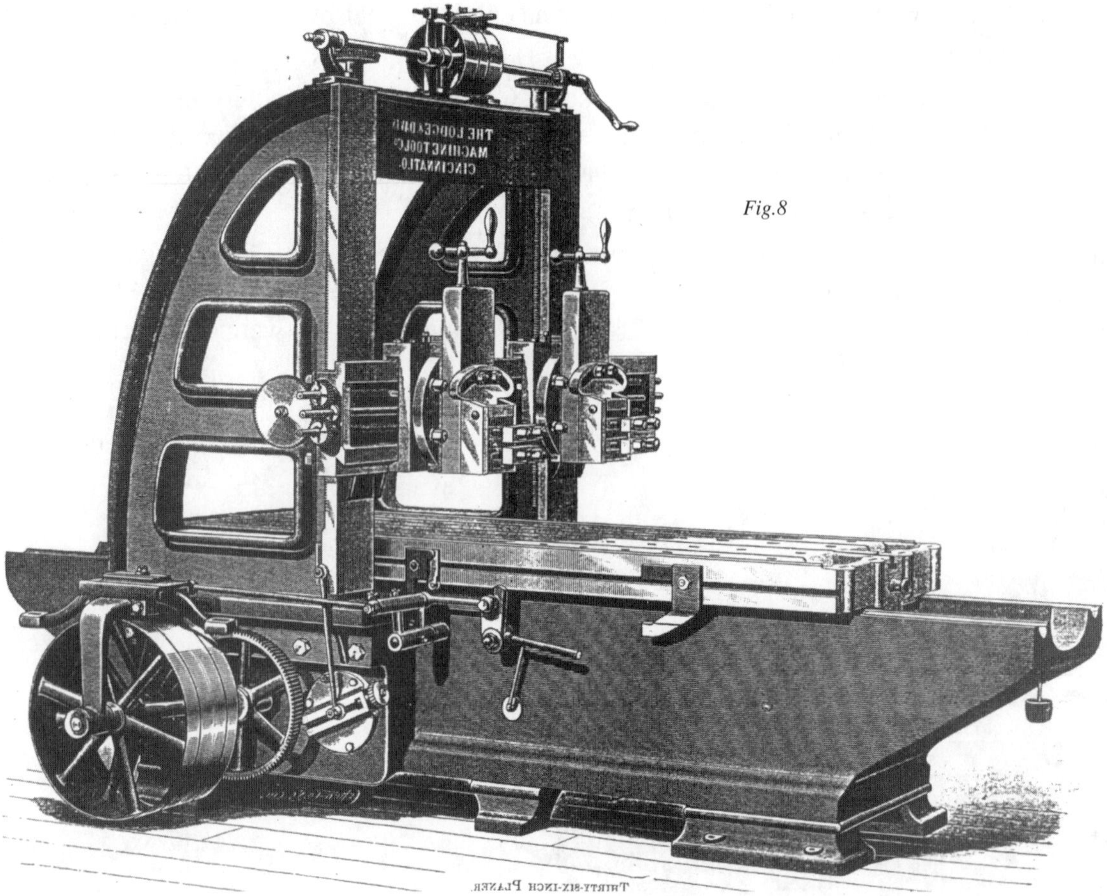

Fig.8

Fig.10

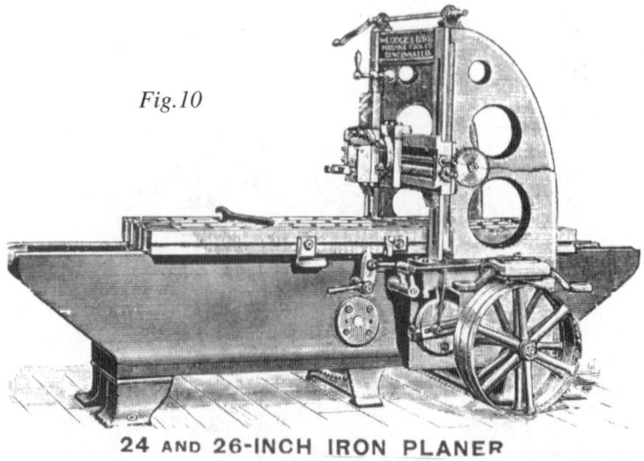

24 AND 26-INCH IRON PLANER

Fig.9

LOVELL, F.S., Fitchburg, MA

Maker, in 1883, of engine lathes, hand lathes, Warren's patent planer chucks, (Fig.1), planer centers (Fig.2) and other machinery. The firm was burned out in 1894.

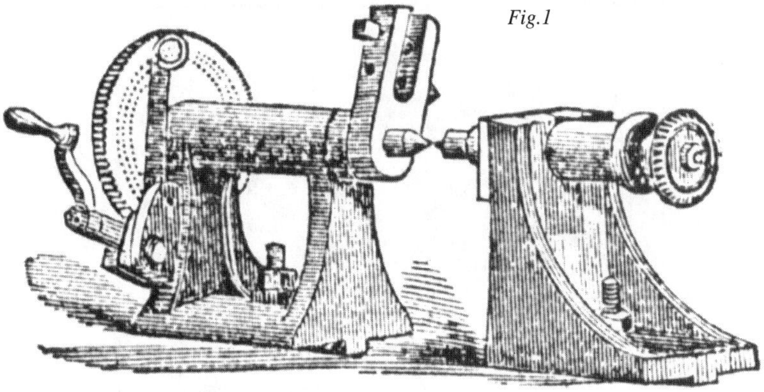

Fig.1

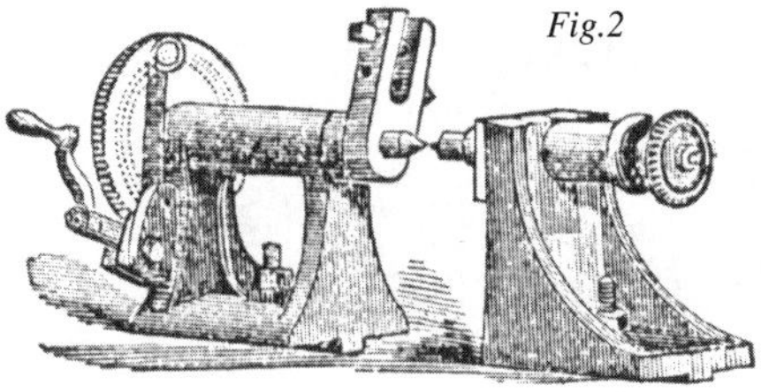

Fig.2

LOWELL MACHINE SHOP, Lowell, MA

Formed in January, 1845, the company was primarily a builder of textile machinery for the Lowell mills. It also built a wide variety of machine tools (Fig.1), most of which were designed by William B. Bement (1817-1897), who joined the firm in 1845, leaving in 1851 to jointly form MARSHALL, BEMENT & COLBY.

Production in 1851 included double table traverse shapers (Fig.2) and bridge type slotting machines (Fig.3). A smaller "slotting and paring" machine is shown in one of Bement's drawings (Fig.4) and a photograph taken of a machine still in use in 1909 (Fig.5). The firm operated until 1897, but the manufacture of machine tools was discontinued in 1867. *(continued next page)*

MACHINISTS' TOOLS.
Engine Lathes, Hand Lathes,
Vertical Drills, Horizontal Drills,
Boring and Reaming Lathes, Slide Rests, Chucks,
Planers, Shaping Machines,
Compound Planers, Bolt Cutters,
Slotters, Gear-cutting Engines,
Portable Engines, &c., &c.,
Of various sizes and numbers, manufactured by the LOWELL MACHINE SHOP, from new and improved patterns. For sale by
STEVENSON & PEIRSON,
20 6mjiaso* No. 48 Kilby street, corner Liberty square, Boston.

Fig.1

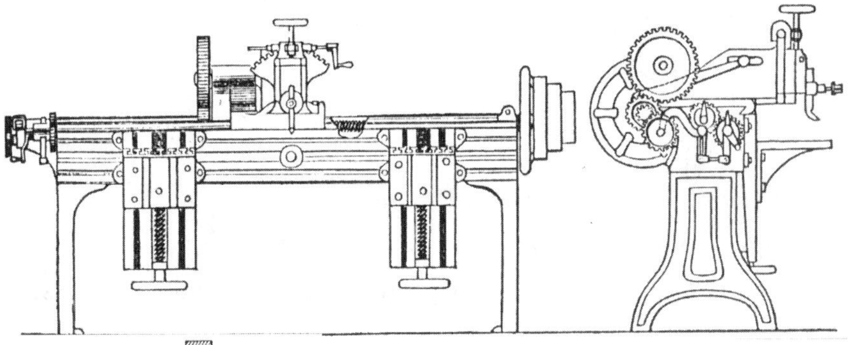

Fig.2

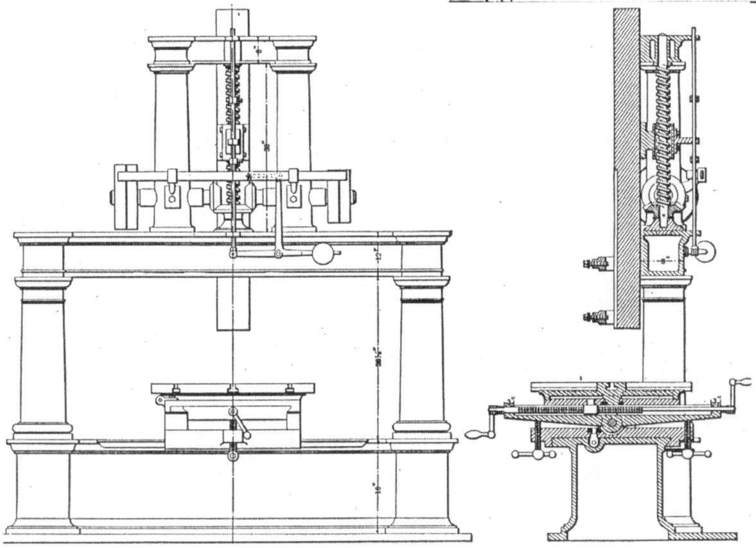

Fig.3

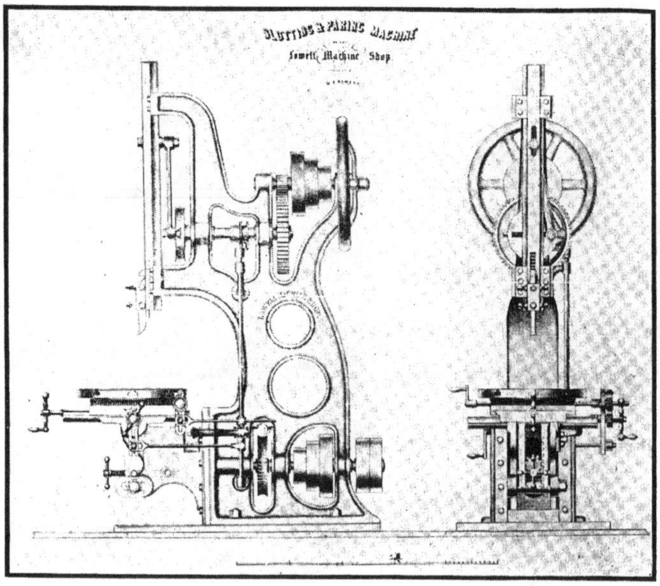

Fig.4

Fig.5

LUTTER & GIES, Milwaukee, WI

A partnership of George M. Lutter (1857-1937) and Ernst A. Gies formed in 1887. The partners incorporated the firm as the Lutter & Gies Co. in 1910. Shaper production began about 1900 and, by 1909, the firm offered the MILWAUKEE crank shaper, shown right, in 16" and 24" sizes.

MacFARREN, LEVY & CO., Chicago, IL

A partnership of J. MacFarren and George Levy. Makers, in 1882, of lathes, planers, shapers, screw machines and drill presses. The firm failed in 1883.

MACHINE TOOL WORKS, Philadephia, PA

Formed in 1880 when Frederick B. Miles and Oscar C. Ferris sold control of Ferris & Miles to James Dougherty, who reorganized as the MACHINE TOOL WORKS. Miles continued as manager.

On May 1, 1885, Dougherty sold out to Frederick B. Miles and the firm merged with William Bement & Son to form BEMENT, MILES & CO.

Products included 10" shapers, slotters, boring machines, and 17" x 17" planers previously made

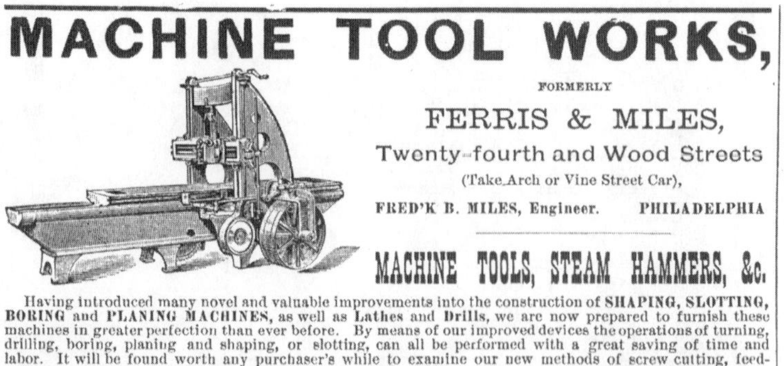

Fig.1

by Ferris & Miles. An example of its planers is shown in an 1880 ad (Fig.1). New design planers were introduced in 1883, based on Miles' patent of May 13, 1883, (Fig.2). The new design was produced by Bement, Miles & Co. for several years after the merger.

Fig.2

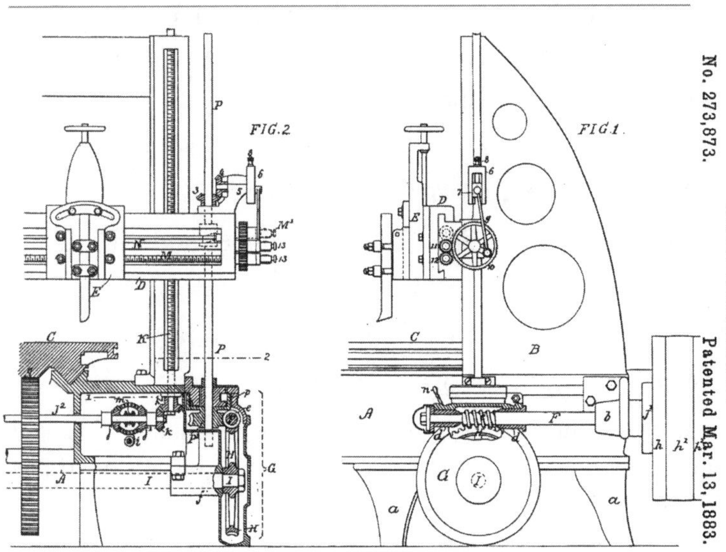

MARSHALL, BEMENT & COLBY, Philadelphia, PA

A partnership of Elijah D. Marshall, William B. Bement (1817- 1897) and Gilbert A. Colby, formed in 1851 to make large machine tools including planers and shapers. Bement had been a machine designer for the Lowell Machine Shop from 1845 to 1851.

The firm reorganized as BEMENT, COLBY, DOUGHERTY & CO. when James Dougherty replaed Marshall in 1853.

MARVEL & CO., C.M., Lowell, MA

Founded c1835 by Caleb M. Marvel to make textile machinery and "machine tools of every description."

MASON, JOSHUA, Paterson, NJ

Inventor and builder of a planer designed to cut on both the forward and reverse strokes, patented July 22, 1856. The machine, shown left, was equipped with a tool head which rocked as the table reversed at either end and presented alternate edges of special, double edged cutting tools.

MASON MACHINE WORKS, Taunton, MA

Operated by William Mason c1850-1870. Builder of locomotives, textile machinery, and machine tools including planers and lathes.

McCONNELL, J.E., Iowa City, IA

Builder, in 1881, of 24"x 20' engine lathes and 26"x 24"x 8' planers.

McMAHON & CARVER, Worcester, MA, later

McMAHON & CO., Worcester, MA

Formed about 1882 as a partnership of Michael F. McMahon and Thomas F. Carver to build planers, lathes and emery grinding machines. By 1888 the firm had been reorganized as McMAHON & CO., which remained active until at least 1895.

MEINHARD, Charles A., Ft. Wayne, IN

Inventor and builder of a combination planer and slotting machine patented in 1868. The machine, shown right, was a standard planer with a head modified to accept a plate that could hold a bar with a slotting tool.

MEINHARD'S COMBINED PLANER AND SLOTTING MACHINE.

MOORE HALL FOUNDRY & MACHINE CO., Phoenixville, PA

In 1881, the firm announced that they "are about to commence the manufacture of drill presses and planers, in addition to their well known line of lathes."

MORRIS & CO., I.P., Philadelphia, PA

Founded about 1840 to make a variety of machinery, including some machine tools. In 1862, the firm reorganized as Morris, Towne & Co.

The only known machine tool product is a slotting machine dated 1852, shown right as photographed in 1906.

Fig.1

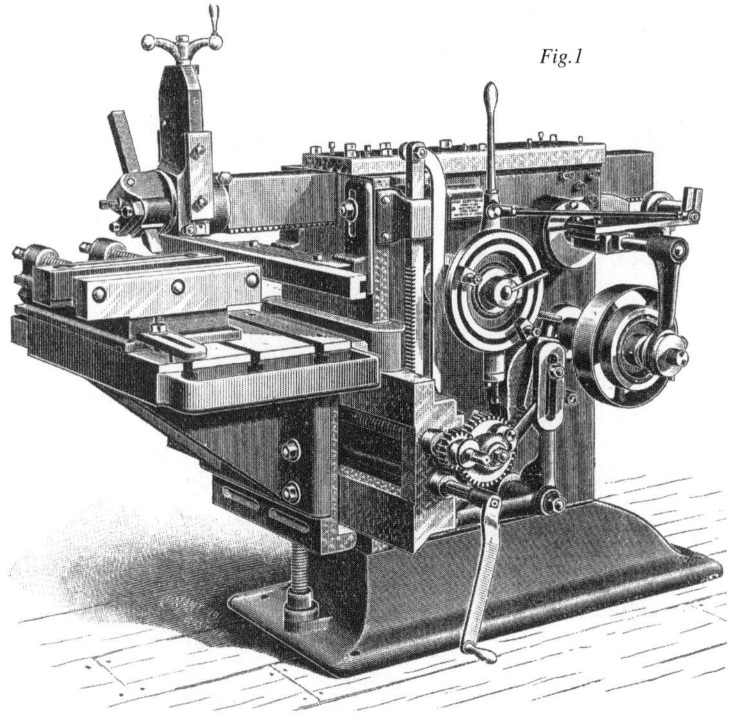

THE MORTON "DRAW-CUT" SHAPING MACHINE.

MORTON MFG. CO., Romeo, later Muskegan Heights, MI

Founded by Matthew Morton (1836-1909) in 1878 as the Morton Valve Co. Morton reorganized as the MORTON MFG. CO. when he began building keyseating machines in 1883. He moved to Muskegan Heights and incorporated in July, 1891. Morton, who was granted 35 machine tool related patents from 1884 to 1895, served as president until his death in 1909.

In 1893, Morton exhibited a 24" rack feed shaper of unique design at the Columbian Exposition. Called the "Draw-Cut" shaper (Fig.1), it was shown taking unusually heavy cuts and was offered in strokes from 14" to 72". Morton claimed the cutting ability was a result of cutting on the return stroke rather than the forward stroke. Cutting forces in a draw-cut were into the column rather than tending to push the table away from the column. This extra cutting ability may also have been due to the heavier than usual construction and the enclosure of the ram on all four sides. The only other known example of a draw-cut shaper was offered by the Cincinnati Shaper Co. in 1904, so it appears that the industry was not convinced of the draw-cut merits.

In 1900, Morton offered an improved model (Fig.2) in five sizes; 20", 24", 30", 42" and 48"; and a motor driven traveling head shaper (Fig.3) mounted on a 9'x 10' floor plate, with 48" stroke, 48" vertical feed, 78" longitudinal feed, and weighing 32,000 pounds.

1909 production included an improved motor driven 26" draw- cut shaper (Fig.4) and an improved version of the traveling head shaper (now called a planer) with 48" stroke, 48" vertical feed and 108" of horizontal feed (Fig.5).

Fig.2

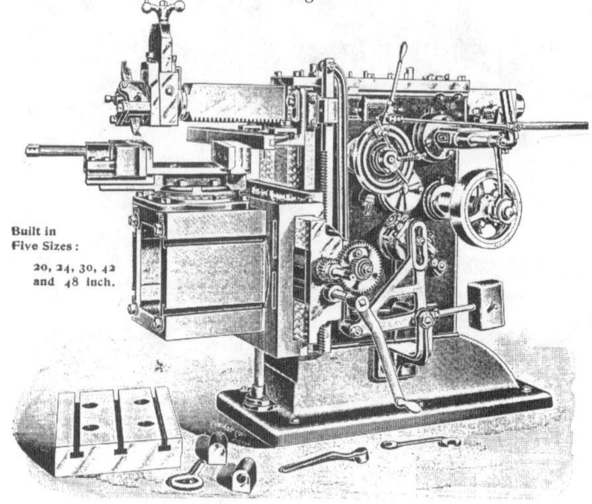

Fig.3

Fig.4

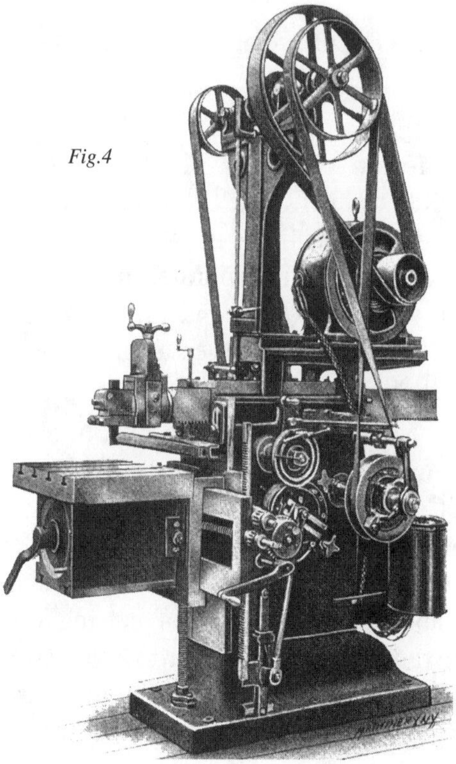

The Morton Traveling Head Planer

is the most modern and up-to-date tool for machining castings in heavy engine building and general machine shop practice.

Fig.5

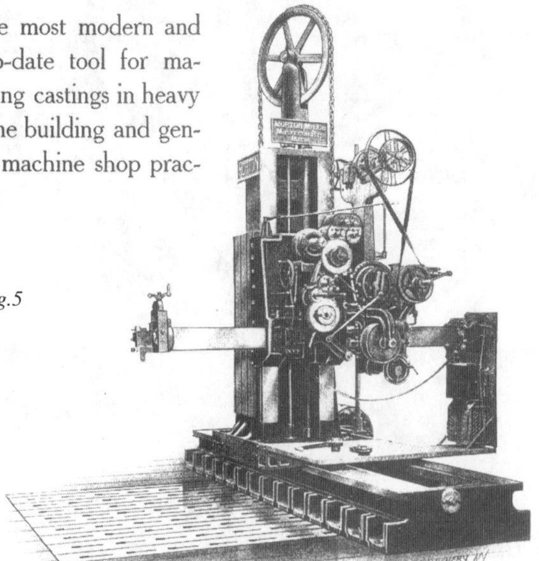

NASHUA MFG. CO., Nashua, NH

Founded in 1824 to build a variety of machinery, including engine lathes and planers. Ira Gay was superintendent.

NATIONAL TOOL CO., Williamsport, PA

Builder of 30" and 36" iron planers, patented November 8, 1870, by William M. Barr and September 26, 1871, by Seth W. Paine. The illustration below shows the machine as offered in 1882-1885.

NEW IRON PLANER

NEW HAVEN MFG. CO., New Haven, CT

Founded in 1850 by Asahel Pierpont who had moved to New Haven from Springfield, MA. Very early products are unknown, but by 1860 the firm offered iron planers, lathes, four spindle drilling machines and milling machines. A New Haven planer built about 1865 (Fig.1) was photographed, still in use, in 1920. Note the ornate castings.

By 1882, the firm's production had reached a value of $300,000, indicating a large firm for the time. R.A. Brown was president but the firm was operated by Leslie Moulthrop, secretary, and Alexander Thayer, superintendent. Thayer had previously been associated with THAYER, HOUGHTON & CO. and the NEW YORK STEAM ENGINE CO.

Beginning about 1877, machine design appears to have been done by Albert B. Bean and George W. Bean, both of whom assigned several planer, lathe, and drilling machine patents to the firm during the period 1879-1886. About 1890, Oscar E. Perrigo was put in charge of machine design, serving until moving to Pratt & Whitney Co. in 1917.

(continued next four pages)

Traverse shapers with 14 1/2" stroke (Fig.2), weighing 5000 pounds and priced at $1250 were offered by 1870. An improved version of the traverse shaper (Fig.3) and heavy crank shapers (Fig.4) were offered by 1880.

Its 1886 catalog offered planer centers (Fig.5); planer chucks (Fig.6); 9" slotters weighing 4600 pounds (Fig.7); No. 1, 16" traverse shapers with 4 1/2' lateral travel, weighing 5000 pounds (Fig.8); No. 2, 12" crank shapers weighing 2400 pounds (Fig.9); iron planers in 48" x 48" x 16', 40" x 36" x 12' (Fig.10), 32" x 30" x 8', 26" x 24" x 5' (Fig.11), 22" x 20" x 4', and 18" x 18" x 3' (Fig.12) sizes.

1904 production included 40" x 40" planers with 16' or 20' beds (Fig.13), and 10" back geared slotters (Fig.14), weighing 5300 pounds.

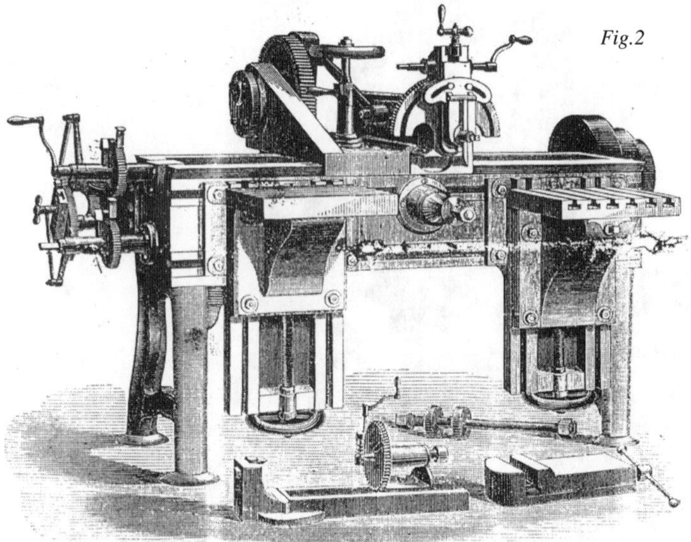

Fig.2

DESCRIPTION

14½ INCH SHAPING MACHINE.

The Cutting Bar has 14½ inch stroke, and will cut or plane a piece 14½ inches by 5 feet long; has quick return mo
ınd improved with two adjustable tables for folding work; each table is provided with centres, chucks, and vises;
:ountershaft and hangers; wrenches; and all wrought iron work is case-hardened. This is a most perfect and com
nachine, and is particularly adapted to all kinds of locomotive work, and is also very useful in large jobbing shops.

Weight about 5.000 lbs. Price, $1.250

MADE BY NEW HAVEN MANUFACTURING COMPANY, AND FOR SALE BY

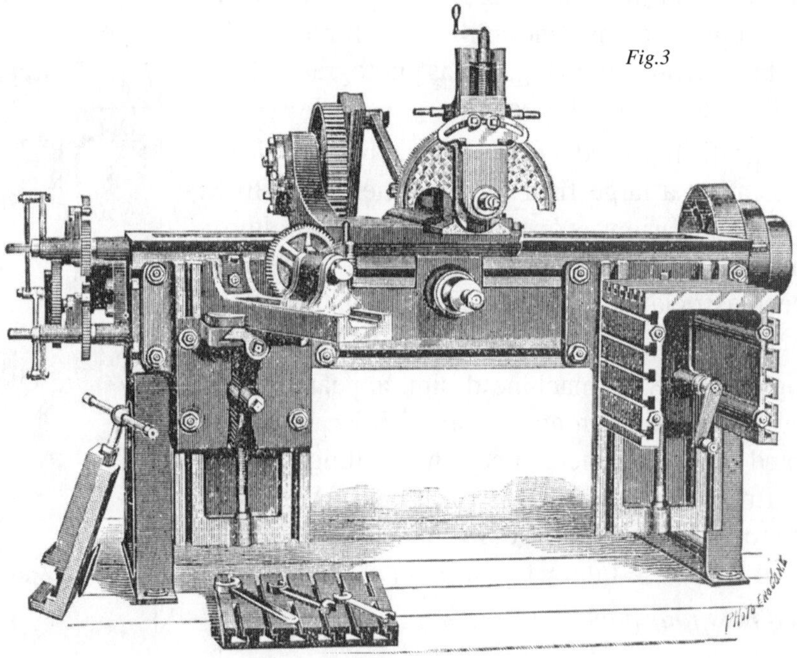

Fig.3

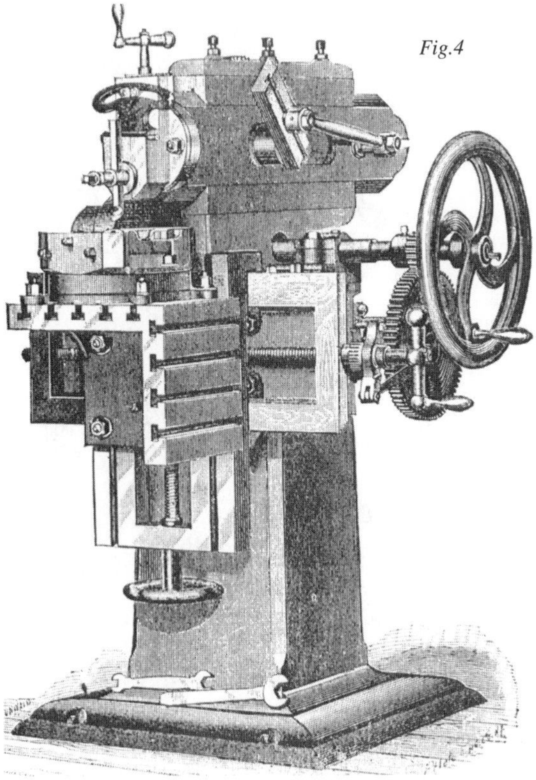

Fig.4

PLANER CENTERS.

Fig.5

PLANER CHUCKS.

Fig.6

Fig.7

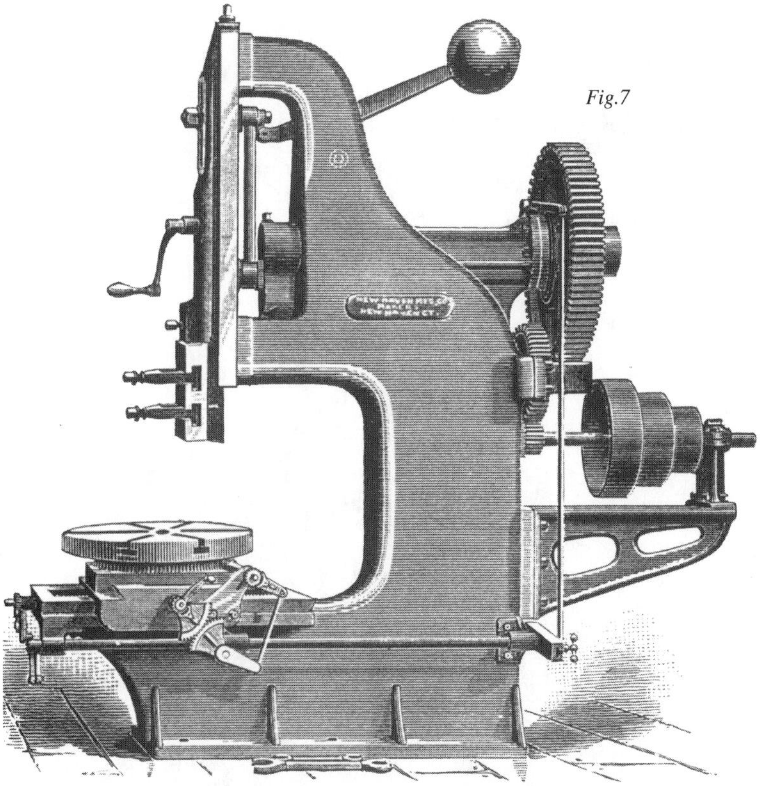

Fig.9

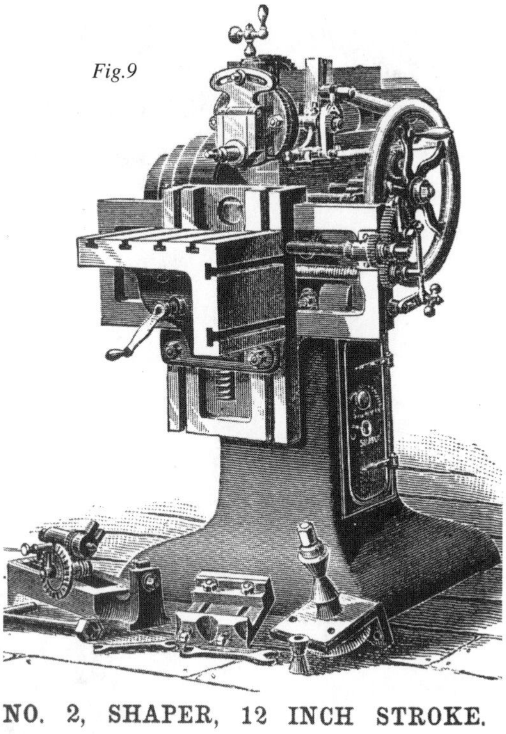

NO. 2, SHAPER, 12 INCH STROKE.

Fig.8 on next page

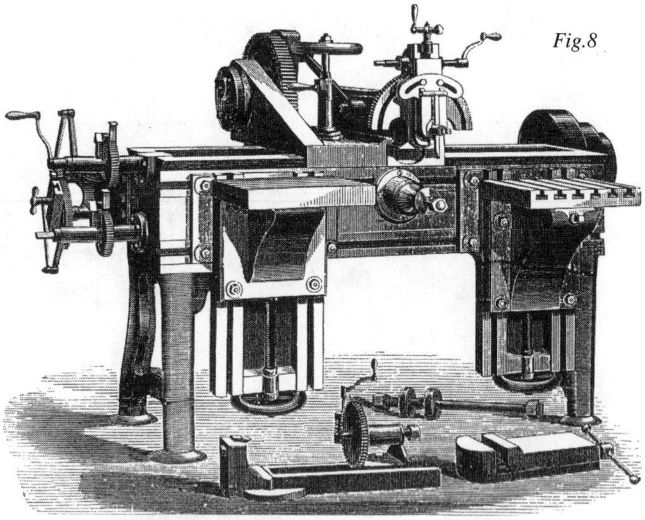

Fig.8

NO. 1 SHAPER, 16 INCH STROKE.

Fig.9

NO. 2, SHAPER, 12 INCH STROKE.

Fig.10

IRON PLANER, 10 FEET × 40 INCHES WIDE.

Fig.11

IRON PLANERS, 5 FEET × 26 INCHES WIDE.

Fig.13

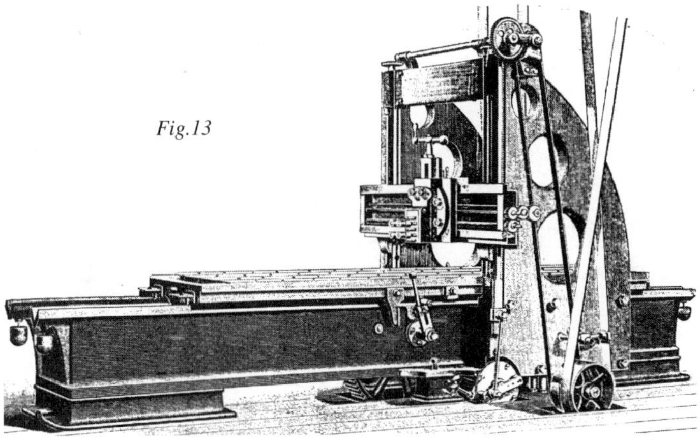

Fig.12

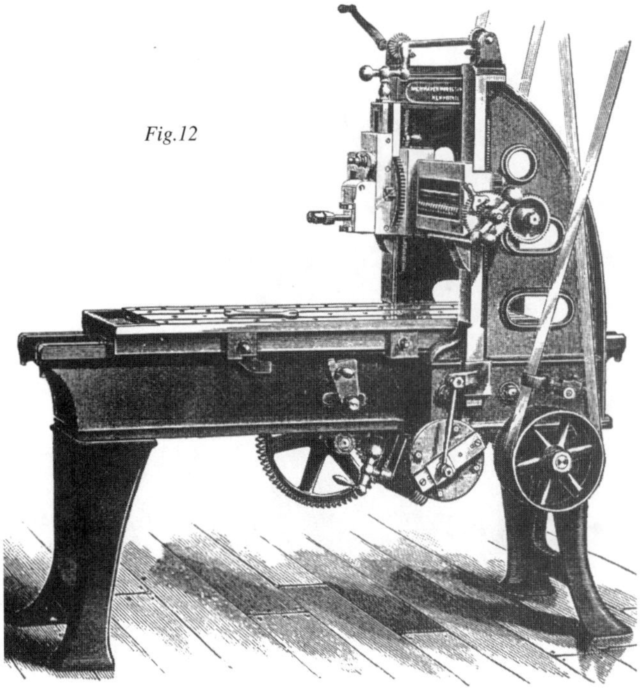

IRON PLANER, 3 FEET × 18 INCHES WIDE.

Fig.14

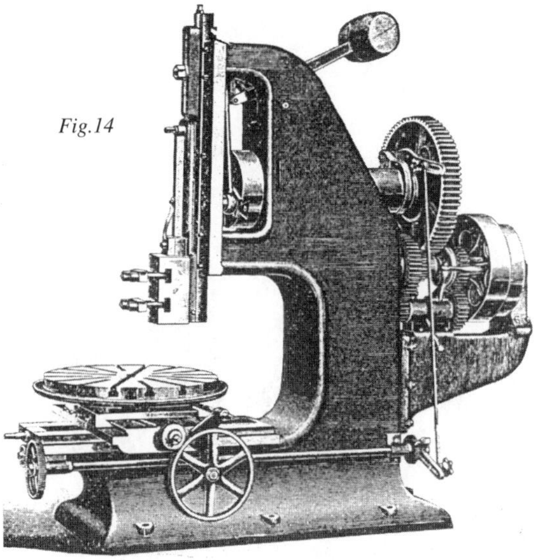

NEW YORK STEAM ENGINE WORKS, New York, NY, and Worcester, MA

Formed about 1860 to make steam engines, the firm began the manufacture of lathes and other machine tools in 1862 when it purchased the assets of THAYER, HOUGHTON & CO. Production of the Thayer, Houghton line of machine tools, including crank shapers (Fig.1), continued under the management of Alexander Thayer (1812-1895).

Thayer left in 1864 to join the NEW HAVEN MFG. CO. Alfred B. Couch (1829-1888) was then appointed superintendent and general manager. An improved line of Couch designed planers (Fig.2), patented February 1, 1870, and Couch designed shapers (Fig.3), patented May 17, 1870, was introduced in 1870. Couch left in 1871 to join Wm. B. Bement & Son as a machine designer.

1874 production included improved crank shapers in pillar (Fig.4), and two table traverse (Fig.5) styles; slotting machines with 8" stroke and 16" x 16" table travel (Fig.6), 12" stroke (Fig.7), and a heavy duty, back geared model (Fig.8). The firm also offered tool holders for cutting two slots simultaneously, patented May 5, 1874, (Fig.9).

The Worcester factory was closed in 1871 and production moved to its Passiac, NJ, factory. Machine tools were produced in Passiac until the factory closed in 1877.

(continued next two pages)

Fig.1

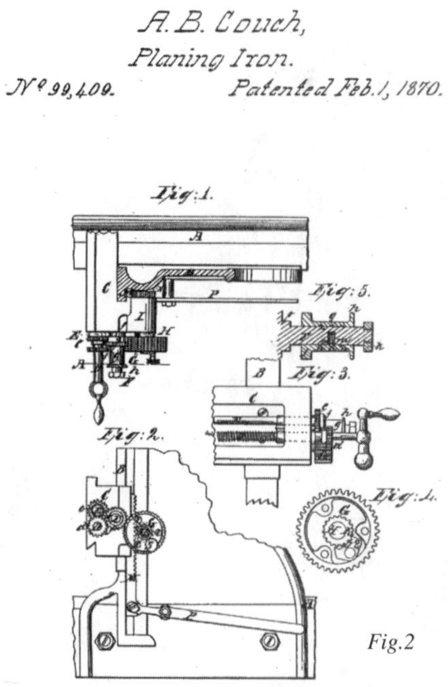

Fig.2

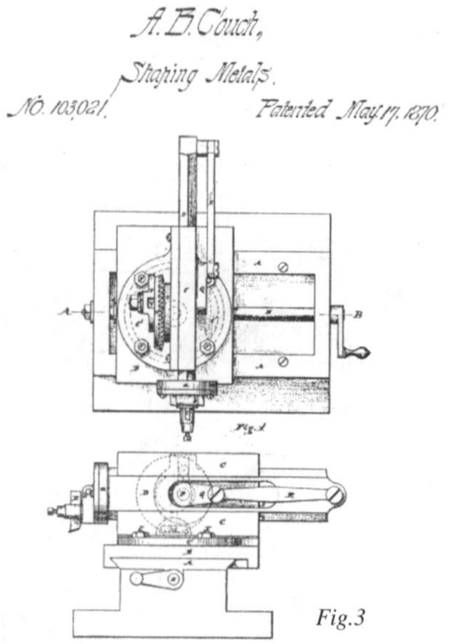

Fig.3

Fig.4

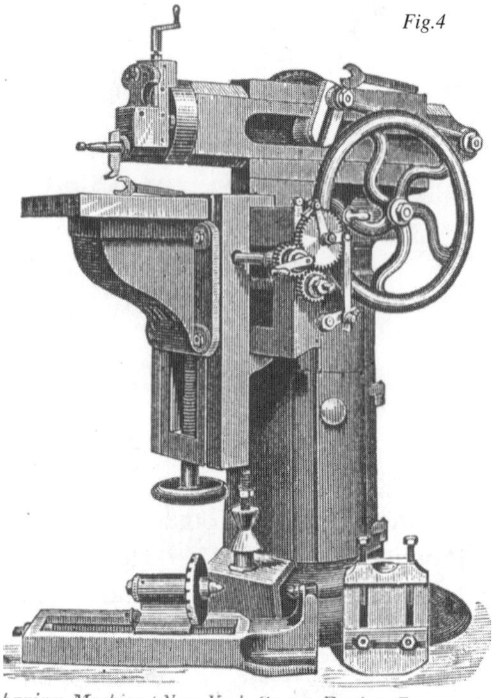

haping-Machine (New York Steam-Engine Company).

Fig.5

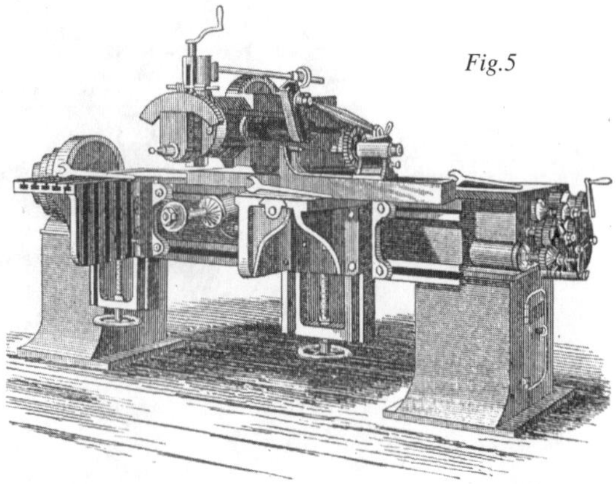

Shaping-Machine (N. Y. Steam-Engine Co.), with Two Tables.

Fig.6

Fig.7

Fig. 5209.

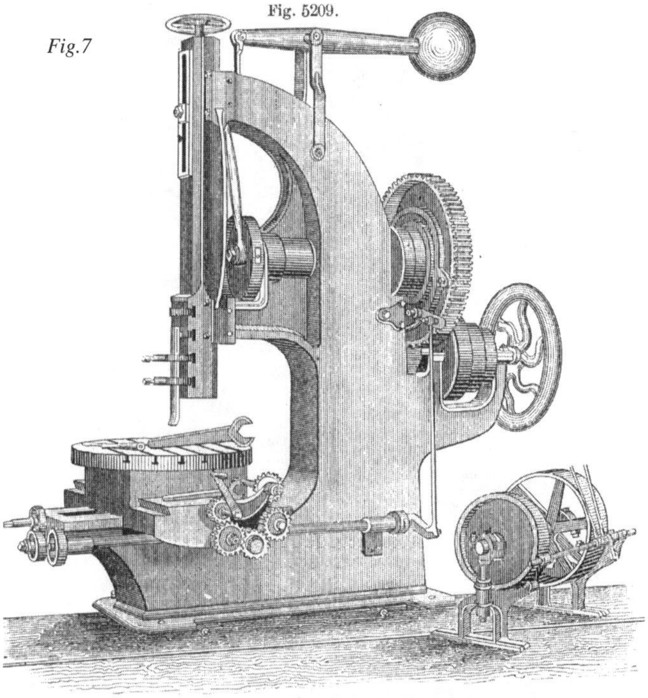

Slotting-Machine (New York Steam-Engine Company).

Fig.8

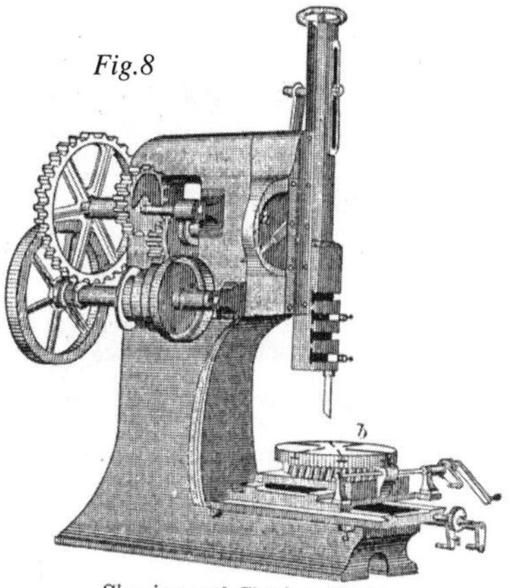

Shaping and Slotting Machine.

J. C. CHAPMAN.
Slotting and Planing Tools.

No. 150,395. Patented May 5, 1874.

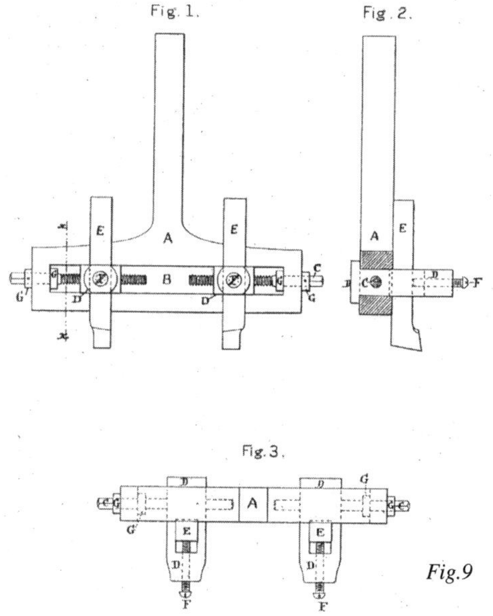

Fig.9

MACHINE TOOLS

For Immediate Delivery.

1 42 in. x 18 ft. bed, treble-geared **LATHE.**
1 32 in. x 18 ft. bed, treble-geared "
1 36 in. x 36 in. x 9 ft. stroke **PLANER.**
1 40 in. x 36 in. x 12 ft. stroke **PLANER.**
1 48 x 48 x 22 ft. stroke **PLANER.**
These planers are held at very low prices.
1 72 in. Pulley **TURNING MACHINE.**
1 72 in. " **BORING MACHINE.**
1 13 in. **SLOTTER.**
1 42 in. Cam Milling Machine for Printing Press Cam.

THE NEWARK MACHINE TOOL WORKS,
Newark, N. J.

NEWARK MACHINE TOOL WORKS, Newark, NJ

Formed in 1886 by Henry B. Binsse as the successor to the business of George A. Ohl & Co. Builder of engine lathes, planers, slotters, drilling and boring machines 1886-1888 (Fig.1). About 1889 the firm began to specialize in slotters and horizontal drilling and boring machines.

Production included 13" slotters that could slot to the center of a 57" diameter circle (Fig.2) introduced in 1887, and an improved 13" slotter (Fig.3) with Whitworth quick-return, introduced in 1891.

In 1901, the firm reorganized as the Binsse Machine Co. which appears to have continued only the horizontal drilling and boring machines. *(continued next page)*

Fig.2

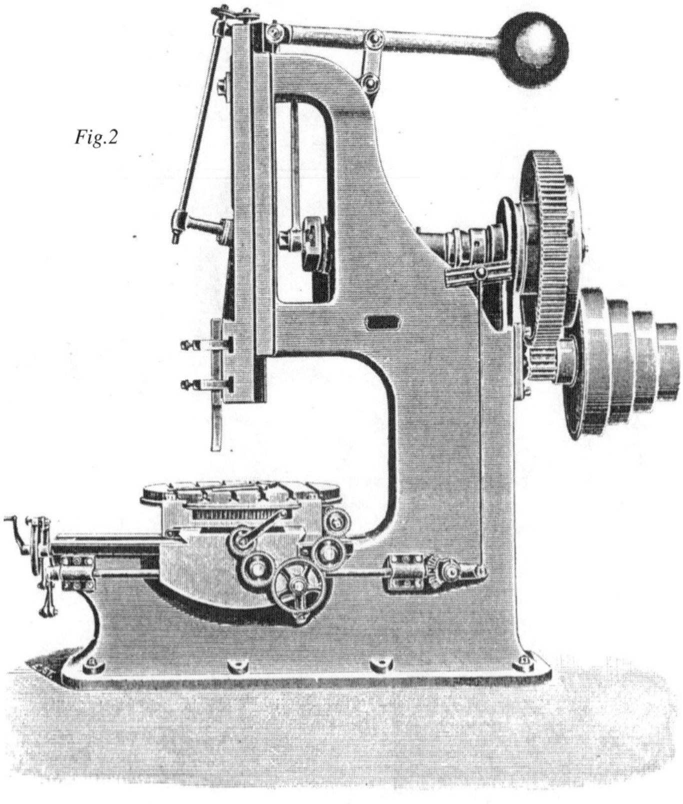

THIRTEEN-INCH SLOTTING MACHINE.

Fig.3

NEWTON MACHINE TOOL WORKS, Philadelphia, PA

Formed in 1880 by Charles C. Newton (1846-1906) to build milling machines when the partnership of Newton & Cox, a twist drill maker, was dissolved. Newton acted as sole proprietor until incorporating July 14, 1897, and served thereafter as president and treasurer until his death in 1906.

About 1890, Newton began building crank drive slotters (Fig.1) in 6", 8", 10", 12", 14", 16", and 18" strokes and rack and spiral pinion drive slotters in 20", 25" and 30" (Fig.2) strokes. By 1900, portable slotters were offered in 48" stroke x 30" crossfeed, weighing 18,000 pounds (Fig.3) and 60" stroke x 48" crossfeed, weighing 33,000 pounds (Fig.4). The portable slotter was designed to work on floorplates on which very large workpieces were secured along with the machine tools. Capacity was restricted only by the size of the floorplate.

A 6 1/2" “frog and switch” slotter (Fig.5) was introduced in 1901. The slotter was aimed at railroad frog and switch makers who demanded a simple and heavy duty machine. Extra heavy, motor driven, 33" slotters, weighing 35,000 pounds (Fig.6) were introduced in 1906.

Production of rotary planing machines began about 1895 in vertical (Fig.7) and horizontal (Fig.8) styles. By 1901, vertical rotary planers were offered in No. 1, 18" cutter, weighing 9000 pounds; No. 2, 24" cutter, weighing 13,500 pounds (Fig.9); No. 3, 30" cutter, weighing 16,000 pounds; and No. 4, 36" cutter, weighing 23,000 pounds. Horizontal rotary planers were offered in No. 1, 24" cutter, weighing 10,000 pounds (Fig.10); No. 4, 42" cutter, weighing 28,000 pounds (Fig.11); No. 5, 48" cutter, weighing 32,000 pounds; and No. 6, 60" cutter, weighing 40,000 pounds.

(continued next three pages)

Rotary planers were also offered, in 1901, mounted on a revolving bed (Fig.12) for use in facing long work on an angle; as duplex models (Fig.13) for facing both ends of a workpiece; and in a motor driven, bridge style, vertical spindle model (Fig.14).

The only known shaper built by Newton is an extra heavy 18" model (Figs.15-16), weighing 30,000 pounds and equipped with power elevation of the table.

Slotting Machine.

Fig.1

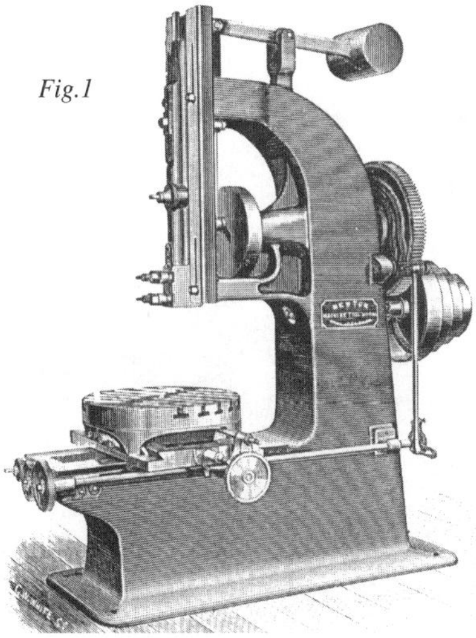

Fig.2

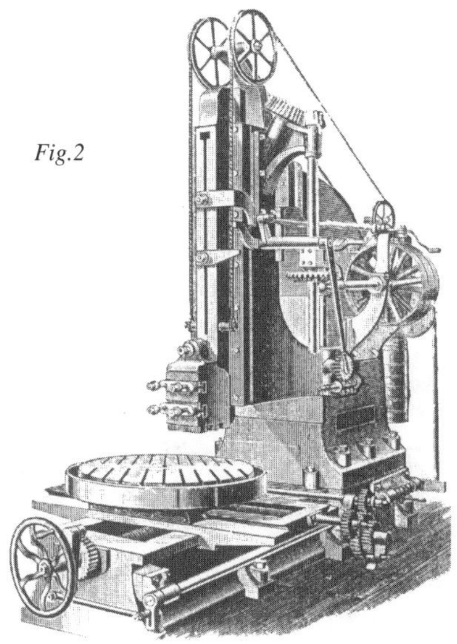

Fig.3

Fig.4

Fig.5

Frog and Switch Slotter.

Fig.6

Fig.7

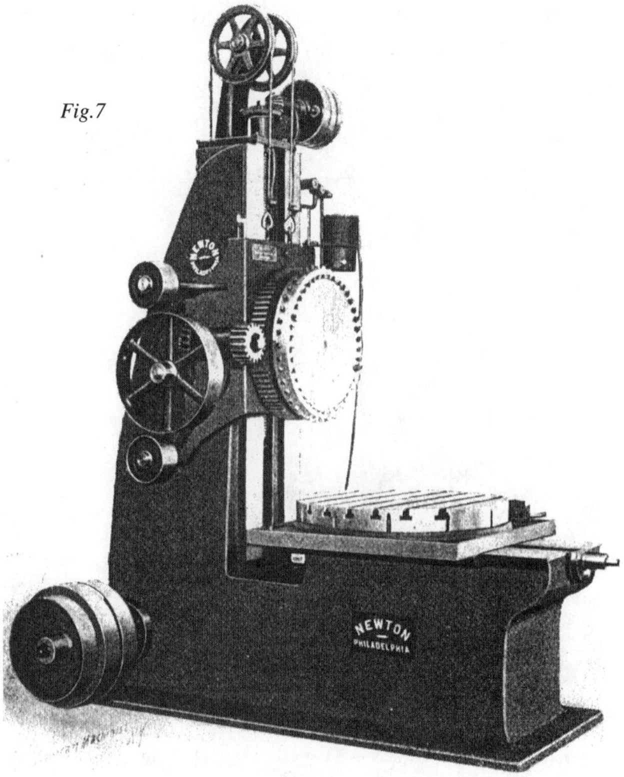

Fig.8

VERTICAL ROTARY PLANING MACHINE.

Fig.9

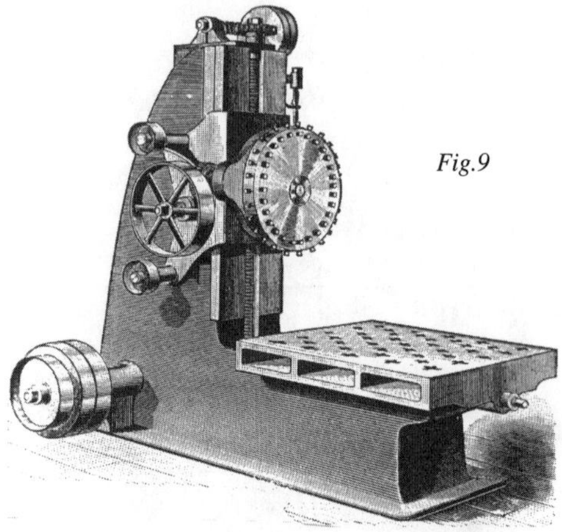

Fig.10

Fig.11

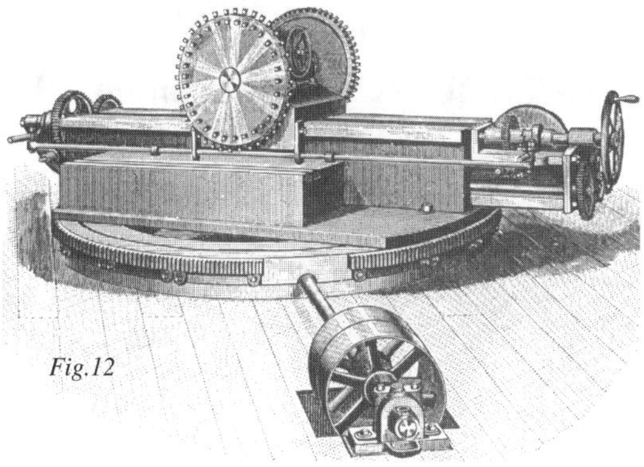

Fig.12

Fig.13

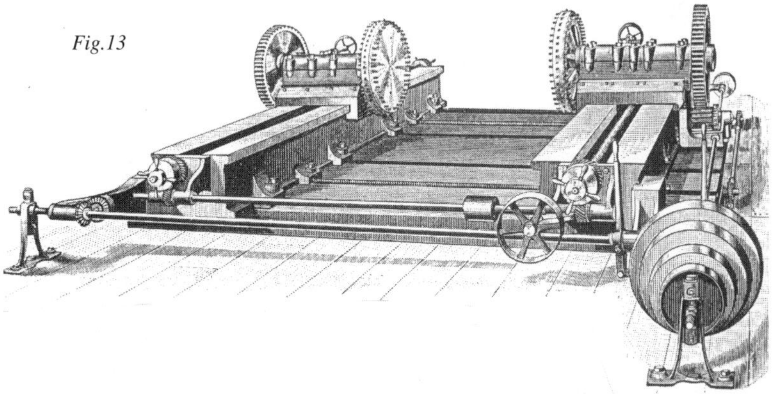

Fig.14

Fig.15

Fig.16

NILES & CO., Cincinnati, OH, later
NILES TOOL WORKS, Hamilton, OH

A partnership of James Niles (1809-1881) and his brother Johnathon Niles (1804-1878) formed in 1845. The brothers were reported to employ 150 hands making steam engines, locomotives, and sugar mill machinery. Machine tool production began about 1859 and by 1868 included engine lathes, planers, drilling machines and boring mills. In 1868, the Niles brothers, who had moved to Hartford, CT, in 1860, sold out to Alexander Gordon (1839-1910), George A. Gray, Jr. (1839-1905) and James W. Gaff. *(continued next eight pages)*

Width	Length	Price	Weight
18"	3'	$450	
18"	4'	$465	
24"	5'	$650	3800 pounds
24"	6'	$690	
30"	6'	$800	6000 pounds
36"	8'	$1140	8600 pounds
36"	10'	$1240	9800 pounds
40"	10'	$1320	
40"	12'	$1420	
40"	14'	$1530	
44"	14'	$1800	
44"	16'	$1900	18,000 pounds
48"	16'	$2800	
48"	20'	$3000	20,000 pounds
60"	20'	$4500	30,000 pounds
72"	20'	$6000	40,000 pounds
84"	24'	$7800	58,000 pounds
96"	24'	$8300	65,000 pounds
96"	30'	$10200	
120"	24'	$10000	
120"	30'	$12200	

Planers offered in 1868

Niles Tool Works,
CINCINNATI, OHIO.
MACHINISTS' TOOLS OF THE BEST descriptio·, at reasonable prices.
Gaff, Gray & Gordon
Have purchased the entire interest of the
NILES WORKS,
In this branch of their business, and will continue the manufacture of
MACHINISTS' TOOLS,
with increased facilities.
IRON-WORKING MACHINERY
is a SPECIALTY with us.

The partnership of Gaff, Gordon & Gray (Fig.1) was formed to operate the company as the NILES TOOL WORKS. Gaff, an Indiana distiller, was the money man, Gordon the manager, and Gray the machine designer and superintendent. The new firm specialized in large machine tools for the railroad and steamboat machinery industries. Its first catalog, dated 1868 and showing George A. Gray, Jr. as superintendent, offered planers as shown in the table on the previous page and in Fig.2:

The factory was moved to Hamilton, OH, in 1873 and the firm incorporated in 1874. Gray left the firm in 1877 to form G.A. Gray, Jr. & Co. Gaff died in 1879 and his son, James W. Gaff, Jr. succeeded his father as president. George T. Reiss (1849-1915) was appointed chief engineer in 1879 and was responsible for machine design for Niles and, later, Niles-Bement-Pond, until his death. Employment had risen to 400 hands by 1881.

A new planer line, incorporating a worm drive patented June 22, 1886, by J.K. Cullen (Fig.3), was introduced in 1884. The new line included 26" x 26" , 30" x 30" (Fig.4), 36" x 36" and 44" x 44" (Fig.5) sizes. In 1889, planers with an improved feed mechanism (Fig.6) were introduced. These were offered in 18 sizes (Fig.7) including 60" x 60" (Fig.8). Plate planers with compound rest (Fig.9) were offered in 1891.

Fig.2

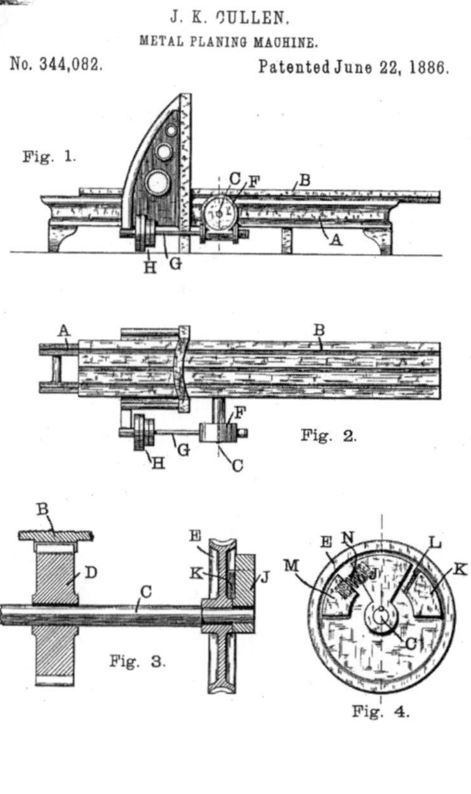

Fig.3

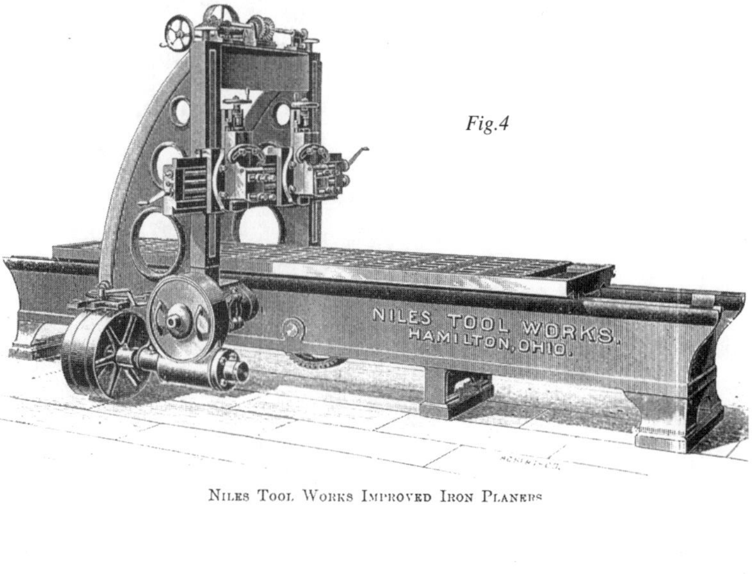

Fig.4

NILES TOOL WORKS IMPROVED IRON PLANERS

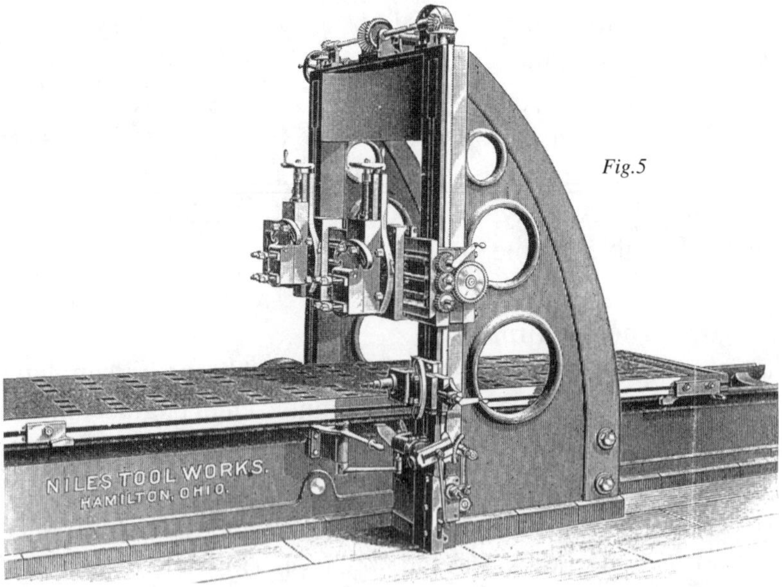

Fig.5

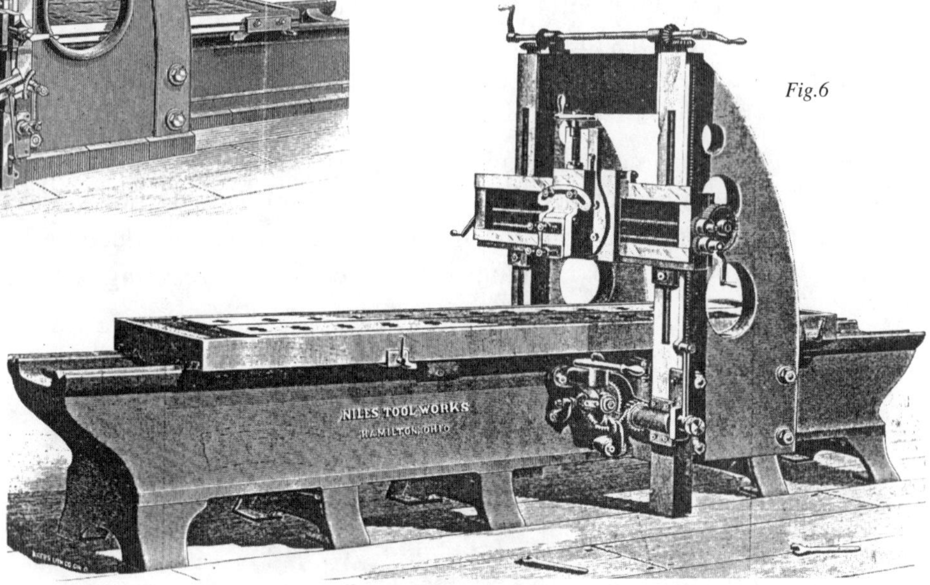

Fig.6

In 1897, Niles brought out a radical new planer design in which the reversal was accomplished by pneumatic clutches (Fig.10) that did not require belt shifting or pulley reversal. Machine tool builders, at that time, had begun to realize that problems in reversing planer tables were far more a result of inertia of rotating parts rather than inertia of the table itself.

Shaper production appears to have begun about 1878 when two-table traverse shapers (Fig.11A) were offered. By 1889 shapers were available in 16", 18" (Fig.11) and 24" strokes.

Slotters were offered in 1882 in 9", 13" (Fig.12) and 18" strokes; in 1888 from 9" to 48" strokes; and in 1892 from 6 1/2" to 54" (Fig.13) strokes, including an 18" size (Fig.14).

Fig.7

Sizes as Follows:

To plane	26 in.	wide,	26 in.	high,	6 ft.	or more	long.	
“	32 “	“	32 “	“	6 “	“	“	
“	36 “	“	36 “	“	6 “	“	“	
“	38 “	“	38 “	“	6 “	“	“	
“	42 “	“	42 “	“	8 “	“	“	
“	44 “	“	44 “	“	8 “	“	“	
“	48 “	“	48 “	“	10 “	“	“	
“	54 “	“	54 “	“	10 “	“	“	
“	54 “	“	54 “	“	10 “	“	“	Ex. heavy.
“	60 “	“	60 “	“	10 “	“	“	
“	60 “	“	60 “	“	10 “	“	“	Ex. heavy.
“	72 “	“	72 “	“	12 “	“	“	
“	72 “	“	72 “	“	12 “	“	“	Ex. heavy.
“	84 “	“	84 “	“	14 “	“	“	
“	96 “	“	96 “	“	14 “	“	“	
“	120 “	“	120 “	“	20 “	“	“	
“	144 “	“	120 “	“	20 “	“	“	
“	144 “	“	144 “	“	20 “	“	“	

Fig.8

60-INCH PLANING MACHINE.

Fig.9

NO. 1 PLATE-PLANING MACHINE, COMPOUND REST.

Fig.10

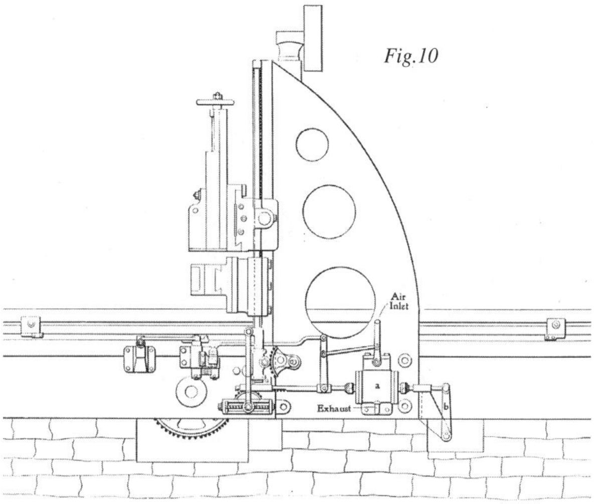

Fig.11A

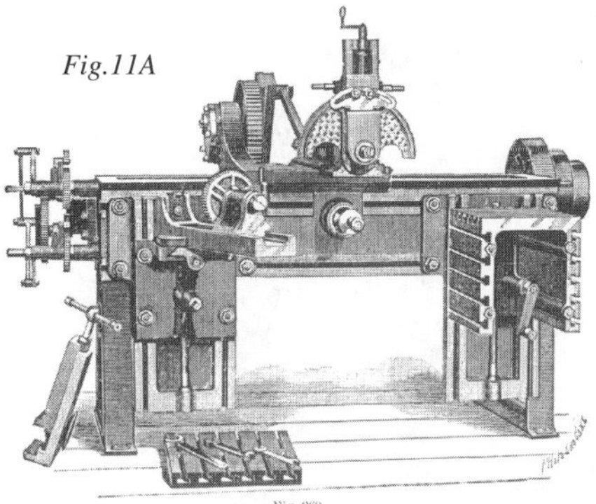

Fig. 260.

Fig.11

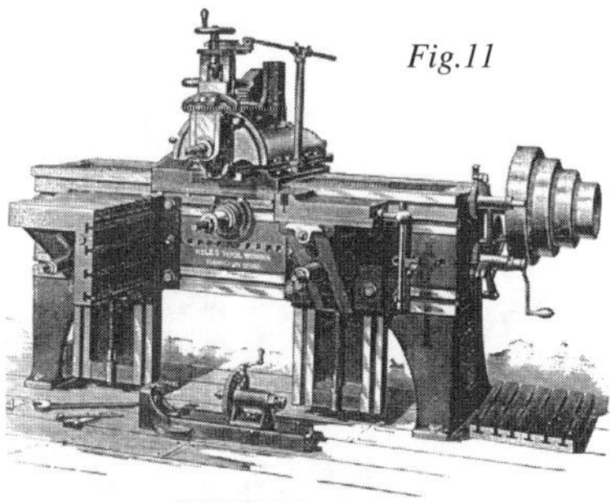

18-INCH SHAPING MACHINE.

Fig.12

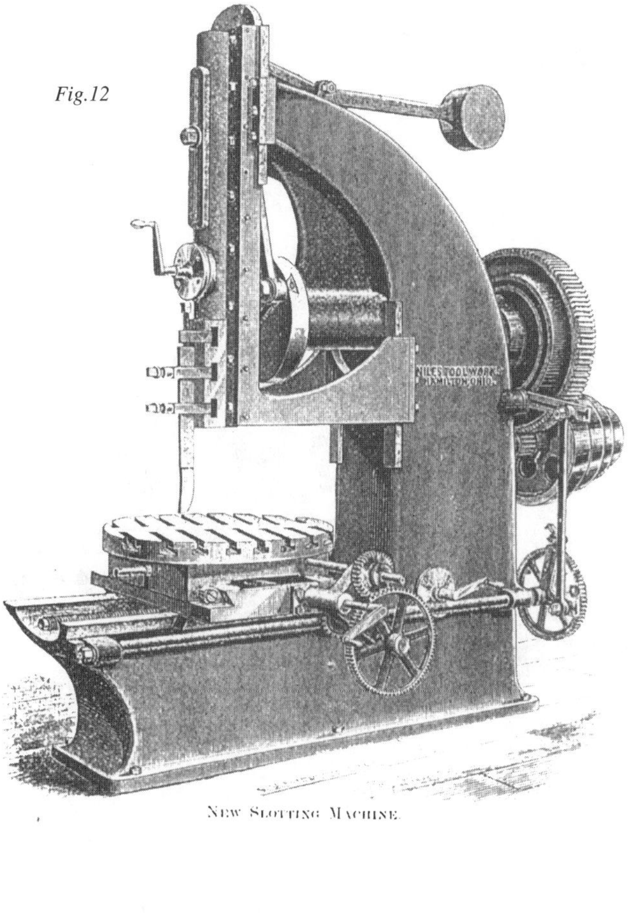

NEW SLOTTING MACHINE.

Fig.13

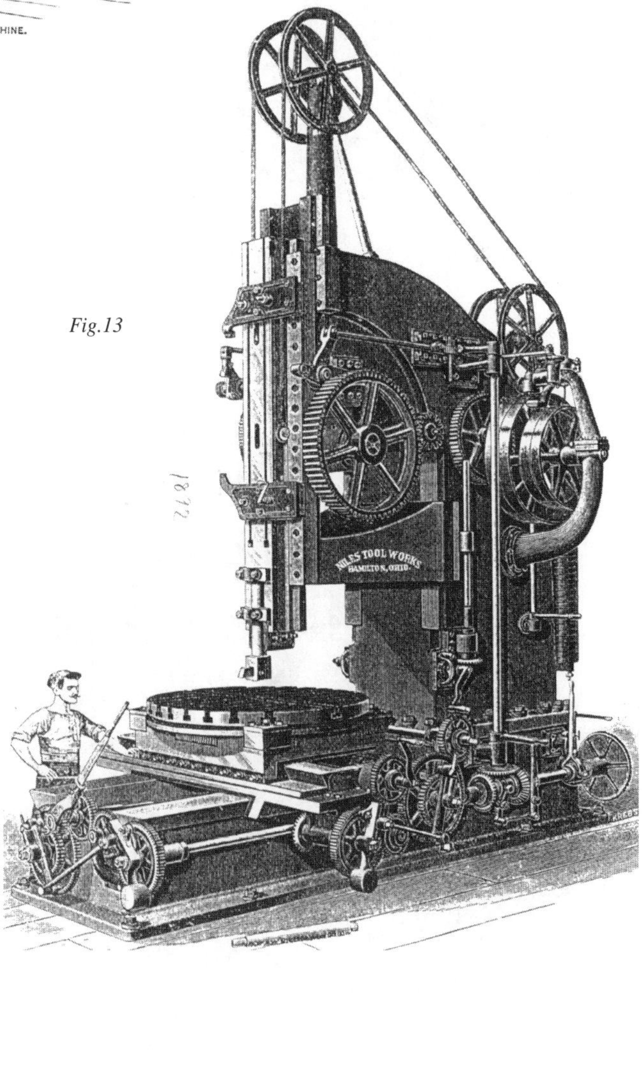

In 1892, the firm was reorganized and incorporated with a capital of $1,000,000. Alexander Gordon was elected president, Robert C. McKinney (1852-1916) treasurer and general manager. Gordon served until August 15, 1899, when he orchestrated a merger of Niles Tool Works, Bement, Miles & Co. and the Pond Machine Tool Co., forming the Niles-Bement-Pond Co. with Gordon as chairman and McKinney president. The Niles Tool Works continued operation as a division of the Niles-Bement-Pond Co.

Its 1903 catalog listed planers in 26" (Fig.15), 32" (Fig.16), 54" (Fig.17), 72" (Fig.18), 96" (Fig.19), and 12' extra heavy (Fig.20) sizes; frog and switch planers in 36" x 12" (Fig.21) and 36" x 36" (Fig.22) sizes; slotters in 6 1/2" (Fig.23), 10" (Fig.24), 12" (Fig.25), 16" (Fig.26), 18" (Fig.27), 26" (Fig.28), 30" (Fig.29) and 54" (Fig.30) strokes; geared shapers in 24" (Fig.31), 36" (Fig.32), and 40" (Fig.33) strokes. In 1907, Niles offered a 75 HP motor driven, pit planer (Fig.34) for planing the edges of armor plate up to 24' long, 12' wide and 12" thick.

Fig.14

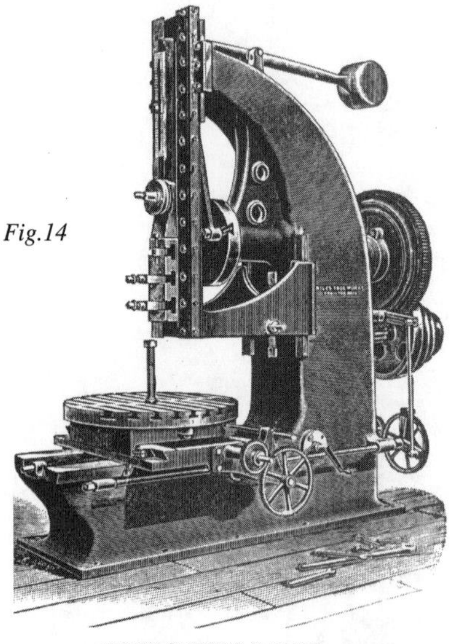

18-INCH SLOTTING MACHINE.

Fig.15

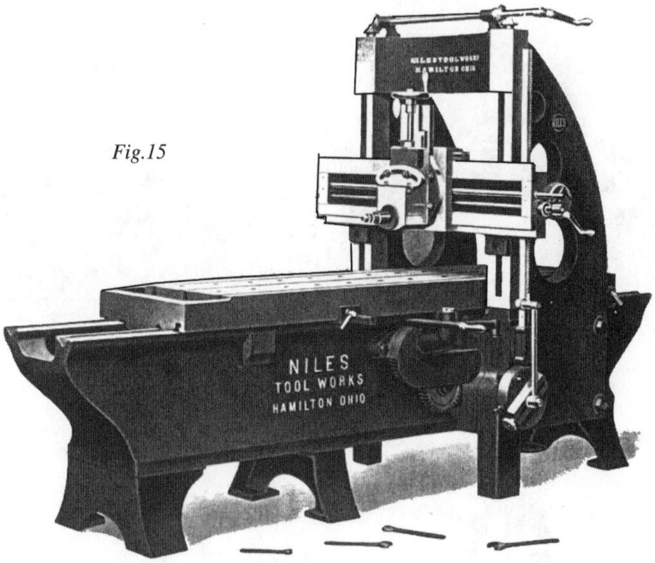

Fig.16

Fig.17

Fig.18

Fig.19

Fig.20

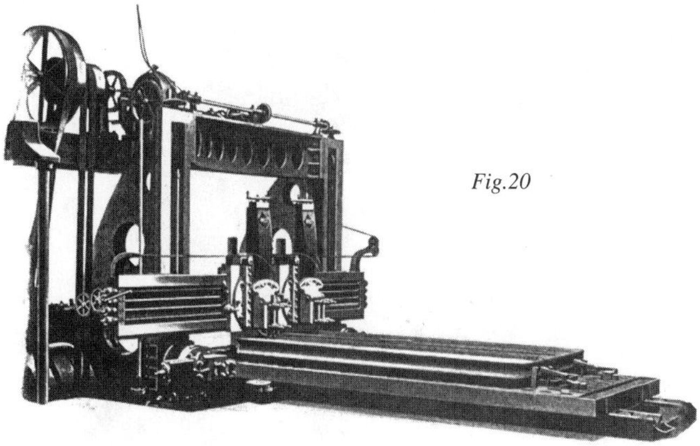

Fig.21

Fig.22

Fig.23

Fig.24

Fig.25

Fig26

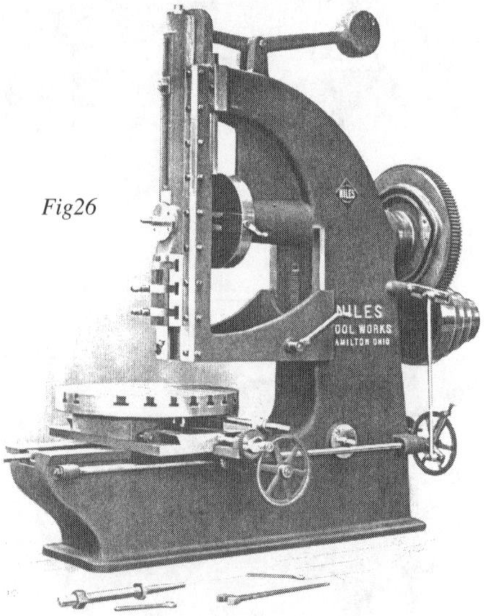

Fig.27

Fig.28

Fig.29

Fig.30

Fig.31

Fig.32

Niles Tool Works

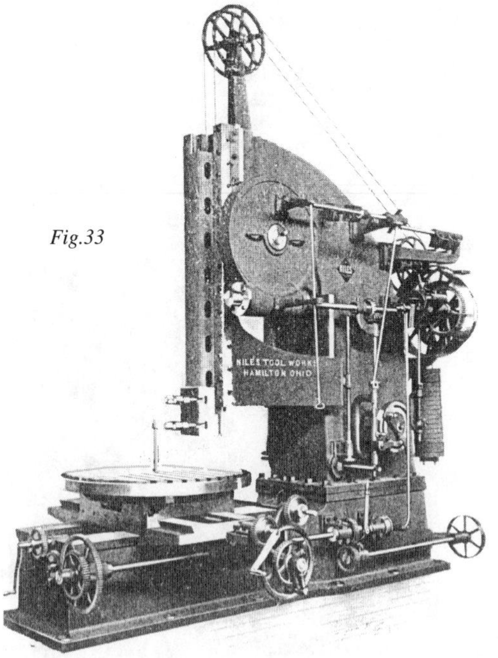

Fig.33

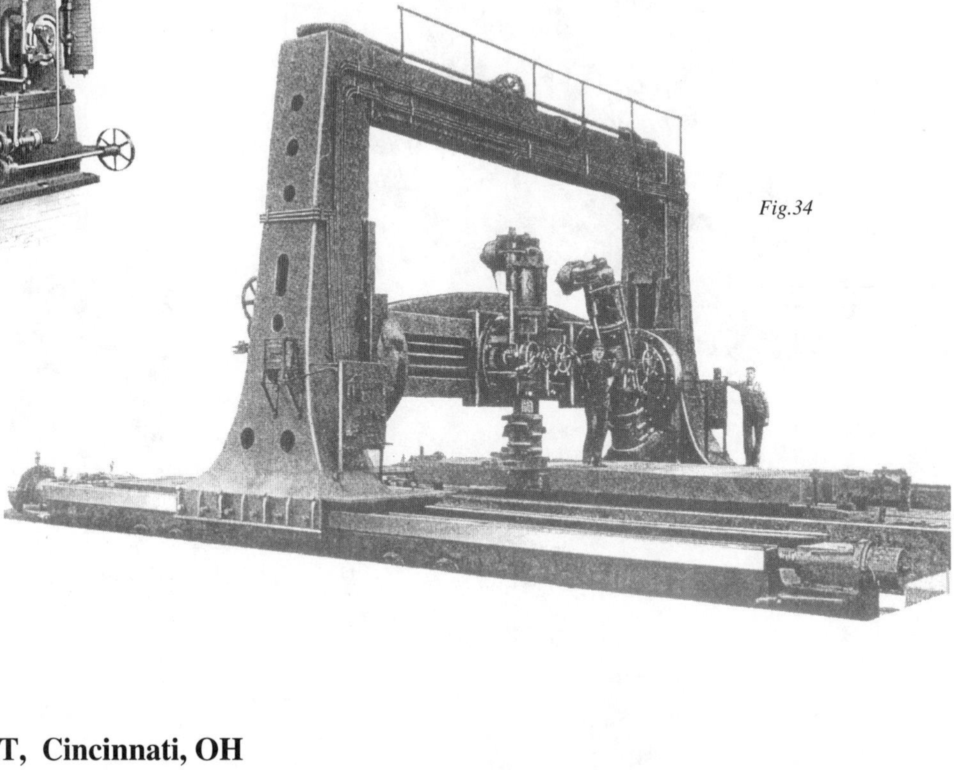

Fig.34

OESTERLEIN & BERNHARDT, Cincinnati, OH

Founded by William Oesterlein (1848-1920) c1878. The only known product is an 23" x 24"x 6' iron planer that sold for $500 in 1884 although he advertised "other machinist tools at proportionally low prices." Oesterlein's factory was destroyed in the flood of 1884 but he was back in business in 1886, operating as William Oesterlein & Co.

OHIO MACHINE TOOL CO., Kenton, OH

Formed in 1897 as a reorganization of SMITH & SILK MACHINE TOOL CO. William D. Smith (1860-1939) remained in control of the firm until selling out to Walter D. Sayle in 1911.

Initial production included planers and shapers (Fig.1). By 1904, the firm offered OHIO, 21" and 28" triple geared shapers, weighing 2000 pounds and 2700 pounds respectively (Fig.2). *(continued on next page)*

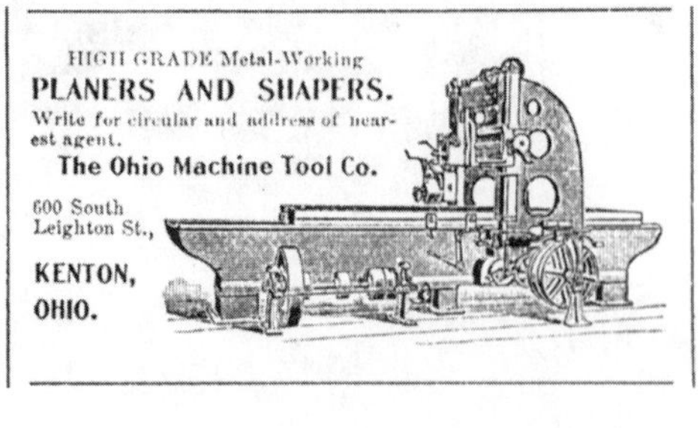

Ohio Machine Tool Co.

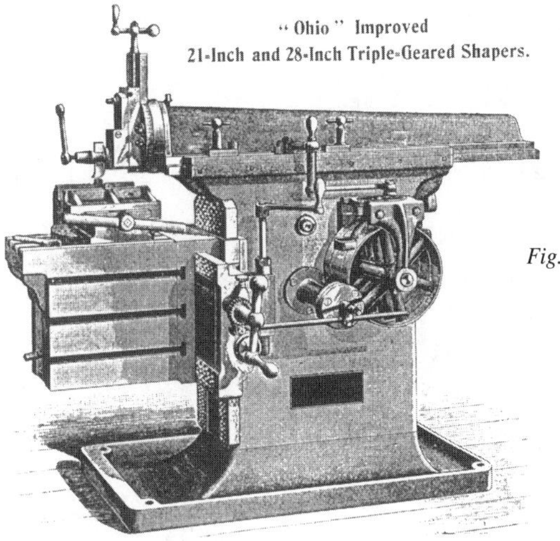

Fig.2

OSBORN & CO., L.E., New Haven, CT

Builder, in 1866, of "very superior iron planers," 4 1/2' x 2'; 6 1/2' x 2 1/2'; and 8 1/2' x 3'.

PARKER BROS., Meriden, CT

A large manufacturer of shotguns and a variety of hardware, the firm announced, in 1882, that they "have gone into the manufacture of machinists' tools and are already turning out small planers." The *American Machinist* magazine noted that the the planers resembled those made by Pratt & Whitney Co.

PARMELEE & MIX, New Haven, CT

A partnership of Andrew Y. Parmelee and William B. Mix formed about 1850. One of its planers, dating about 1855, was still in use in Milwaukee, WI, in the 1920s.

PARSONS TOOL CO., Cleveland, OH

Incorporated in 1894 with capital of $50,000 for "operating, manufacturing, and selling the double tool head for iron planers and shapers patented by F.W. and E.P. Parsons."

The tool head, patented March 22, 1892, *next page*, was one of many devices designed to allow planers to plane in both directions.

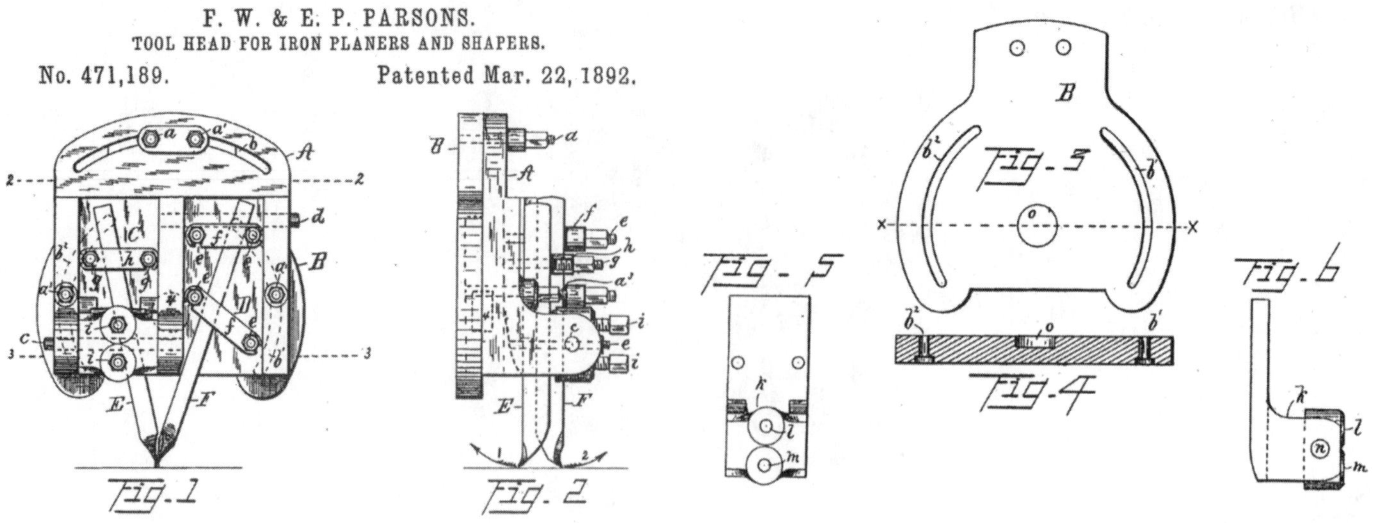

PATCH MFG. CO., Rutland, VT

Builder, in 1895, of a stone planing machine (Fig.1). The machine could plane 12' long, 6' wide and 3' high, weighed 40,000 pounds and was driven by a 5" diameter screw. The V ways were only under the tools; outside the tool area, the table was supported by friction wheels. See Lincoln Iron Works for a very similar machine.

In 1898, Patch introduced a circular stone planing machine (Fig.2) designed to plane circles with radii of one to 15 feet. The platen was rotated, as it reciprocated, by a series of curved bars shown on the left of the bed.

Fig.1

THE PATCH STONE PLANING MACHINE.

Fig.2

Front View.

THE PATCH CIRCULAR STONE PLANING MACHINE.

PEASE & CO., H.C., Worcester, MA

Formed about 1870 by Henry C. Pease. In 1872 the firm offered Long's patent (October 2, 1860) slide valve seat planers, and "the best hand planer in use." A conventional planer (Fig.1), weighing 3400 lbs., was introduced in 1882 and an improved model, patented October 22, 1889, (Fig.2) 16" to 36" wide "by any length" was offered in 1890.

The firm failed in 1892 and was reorganized as the Pease Machine Tool Co. to make lathes under contract for the Prentiss Tool & Supply Co.

Fig.1

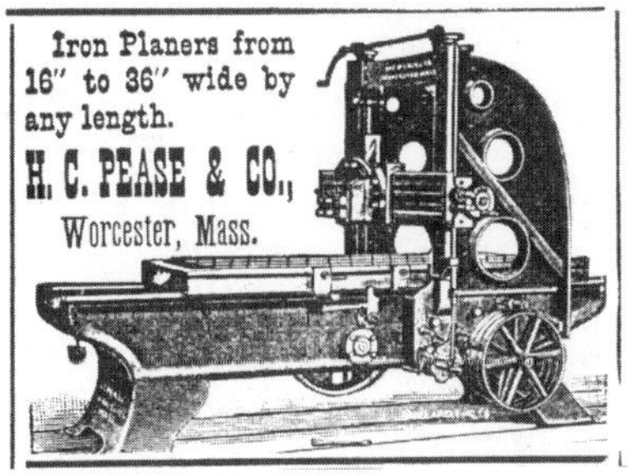

Fig.2

PEDRICK & AYER, Philadelphia, PA

A partnership of Daniel W. Pedrick (1840-1926) and Henry C. Ayer, formed in 1881 to operate the L.B. Flanders Machine Works. In 1886, the partners dropped the Flanders name, reorganized as Pedrick & Ayer, and continued production of Flanders products including Greenwood's universal Planer Chuck (Fig.1) and a radius link planer attachment (Fig.2).

In 1890, the partners began building the Richards Patent (May 18, 1882 and March 6, 1888) open-side planing and shaping machine (Fig.3), also made by E.A. Walker. Figs.4-7 show several ways in which odd shaped workpieces could be handled on the Richards machine.

A variation of the Richards shaper was introduced in 1891. Called the STANDARD shaper (Fig.8), it could plane 12" wide and 30" long. A DUPLEX model (Fig.9), which consisted of two Richards shapers tied together with a heavy table, was also introduced in 1891.

In 1894, the firm incorporated as the Pedrick & Ayer Co. with capital of $100,000. The machinery sales firm of Manning, Maxwell & Moore, which was to be the selling agent and business manager, was the majority stockholder. *(continued on next page)*

GREENWOOD'S UNIVERSAL PLANER CHUCK.

For Straight, Curved (Concave or Convex), or Angle Work Used on any Planer with Cross-Feed for Links, Wedges, Keys, etc. Indispensable for Locomotive Builders and Master Mechanics.

PEDRICK & AYER, 1025 Hamilton St., Philadelphia, Pa.

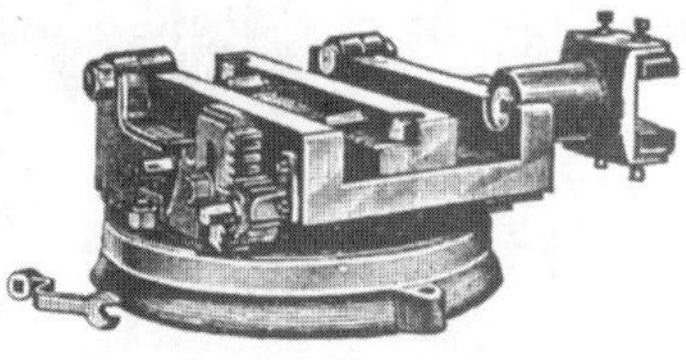

Fig.1

Radius Link Planer Attachment.

For Planing Links, Blocks and Circular Work, on ordinary Planer. Quickly Attached. Easily Operated. Does Accurate Work.

CIRCULARS ON APPLICATION.

PEDRICK & AYER, Philadelphia, Pa.

Fig.2

Fig.3

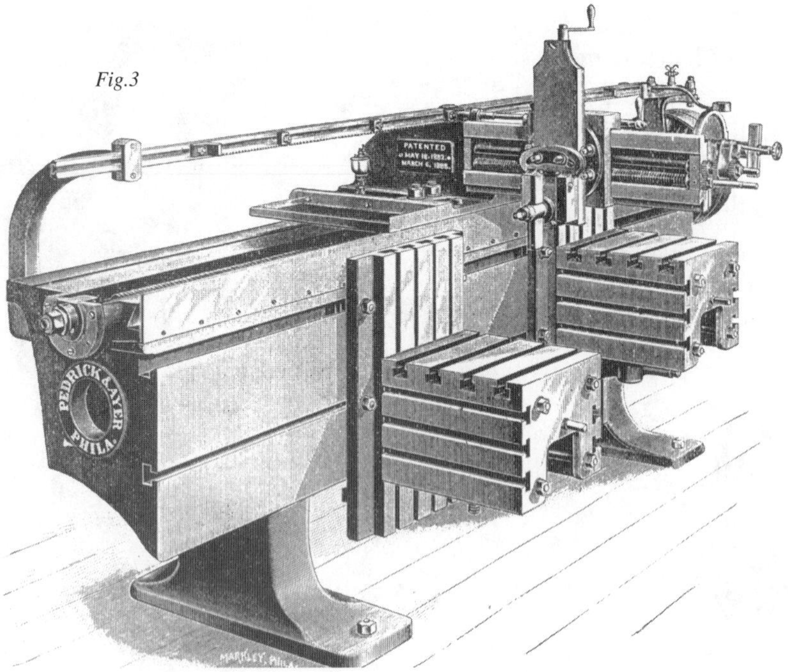

Fig.4

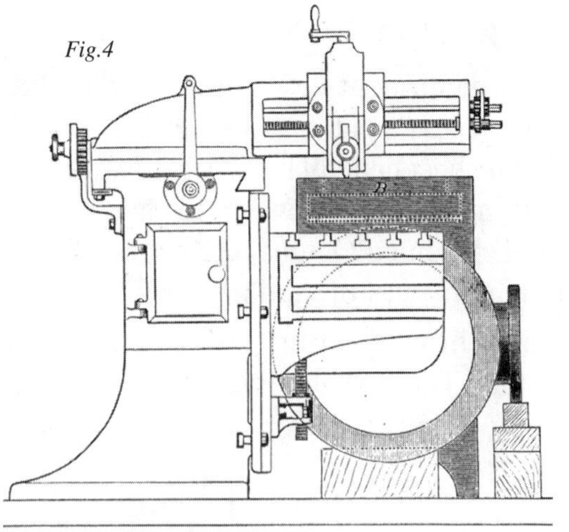

—*Planing Steam-Engine Valve Seat.*

Fig.5

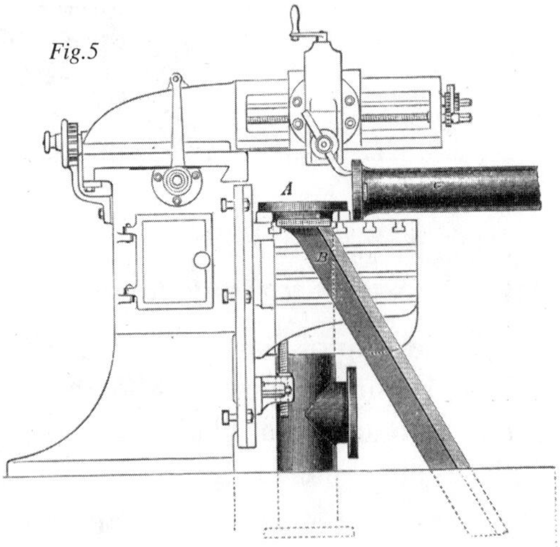

—*Planin; Difficult Pieces.*

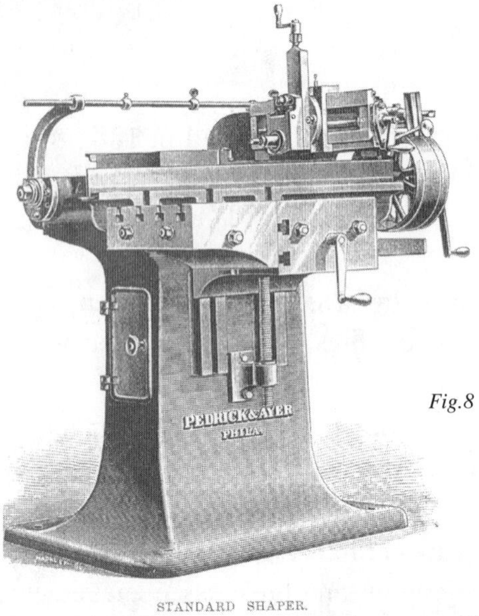

Fig.8

STANDARD SHAPER.

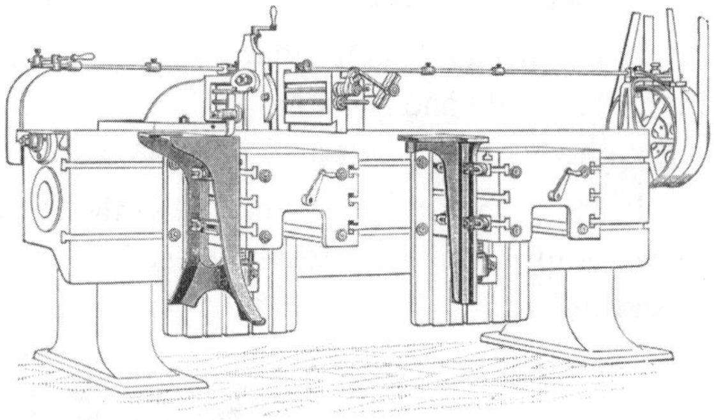

Fig.6 —*Machine Doing Double Work of Same Character.*

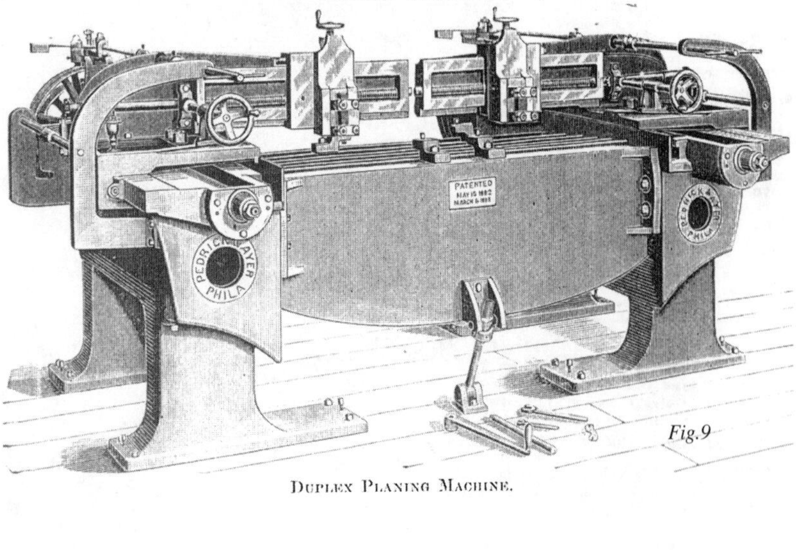

Fig.9

Duplex Planing Machine.

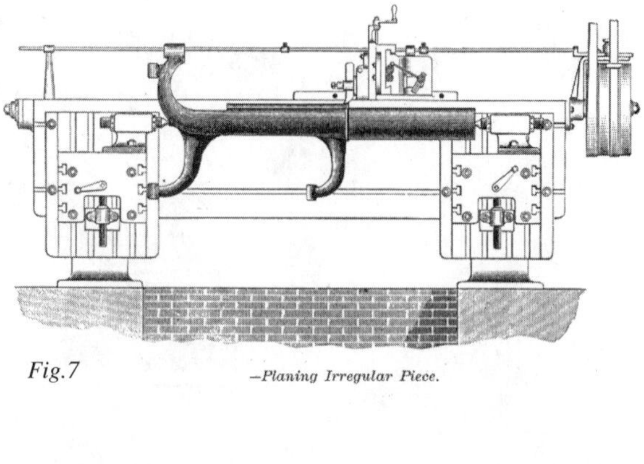

Fig.7 —*Planing Irregular Piece.*

PERKINS MACHINE CO., Boston, MA

Formed in 1896 by Fred Perkins and his sons Bertram D. Perkins and Charles A. Perkins to build presses and other metalforming machinery. In 1899, the firm introduced a 20" friction shaper (Fig.1) and, in 1901, an 18" snagging shaper (Fig.2) designed for very rough work on raw castings. They claimed it could "take a chip as large as you can give it" and told of a case where a 250 lb. man uses a 3 foot wrench with a pipe 10 feet long to tighten the chuck. (Not much has changed since 1901.)

The firm reorganized in 1902 and moved to Warren, MA, in 1904. Bertram D. Perkins was president when he died in 1935.

Fig.1

THE PERKINS FRICTION SHAPER.

Fig.2

PHOENIX IRON WORKS, Hartford, CT

Operated by George S. Lincoln & Co., a partnership of George S. Lincoln (1819-1894), and his brother Charles L. Lincoln (1825-1908), formed in 1846 to make a variety of large machine tools, but specializing in lathes, planers, and milling machines. The firm reorganized as Lincoln & Co. when George S. Lincoln retired in 1885 and again as the Phoenix Iron Works Co. when Lincoln's grandson, Charles L. Taylor took over in 1901.

A rack-driven planer built prior to 1854 (Fig. 1) shows the light contruction of the period. A larger, double belt, planer (Fig.2), offered about 1864, clearly shows heavier construction. By 1870, its planers were equipped with a feed mechanism patented by H.B. Weaver, April 5, 1870, (Fig.3). *(continued next page)*

Fig.1

Fig.2

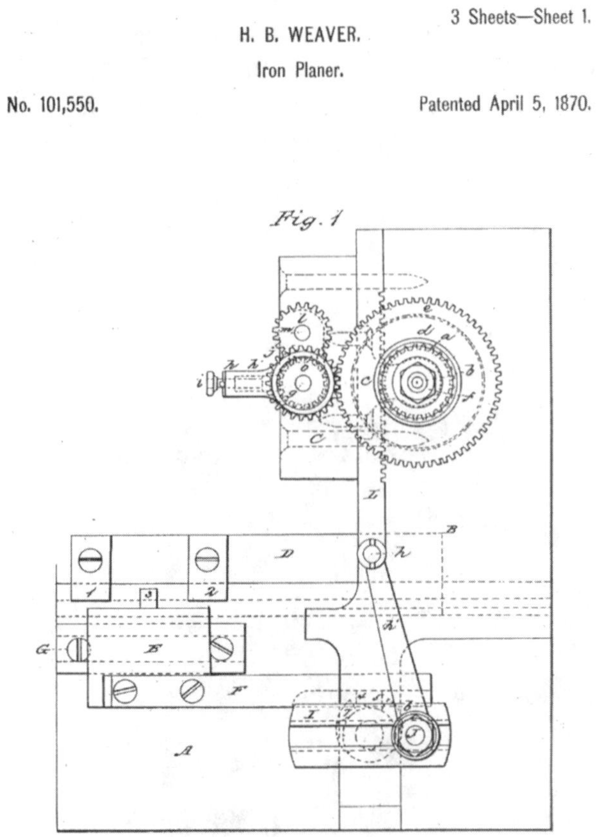

Fig.3

PITTSBURG MACHINE TOOL CO., Pittsburgh, PA

Formed in 1899 to take over the lathe and planer lines previously built by the GLEASON WORKS. Frank Moore was president and F.J. Curtis secretary and general manager. Capital was $250,000.

POND, D.W., Worcester, MA, later

POND MACHINE TOOL CO., Worcester, MA, later **Plainfield, NJ**

Founded by David W. Pond (1848-1897) in 1872 after leaving a partnership with his father Lucius W. Pond. Early production was almost entirely engine lathes and vertical drilling machines.

Pond bought out his father's creditors when L.W. Pond failed in 1875, merged the firm with his own company and operated for a time as D.W. POND, SUCCESSOR TO L.W. POND. In 1882 Pond was the largest machine tool builder in Worcester, employing 240 men.

The firm was incorporated February 1, 1883, as the POND MACHINE TOOL CO. with D.W. Pond as president and Albert C. Stebbins (1844-1917), secretary and treasurer. The company moved to Plainfield, NJ, in 1887 with Pond now serving as superintendent and Stebbins as vice president and general manager. Pond sold his interest to Manning, Maxwell & Moore in 1894 and shot himself August 4, 1897.

On August 15, 1899, the company merged with the Niles Tool Works and Bement, Miles & Co. to form the Niles-Bement-Pond Co. The POND MACHINE TOOL CO. continued to operate as a division. *(continued next six pages)*

Products offered in 1878 included engine lathes. planers, boring mills, upright drills, gear cutters, index machines, etc. The planers (Fig.1) were L.W. Pond designs taken over in 1875.

A new planer design, patented February 17, 1880, by Samuel E. Hildreth led to an improved, heavier, line introduced in 1882, which included 26" x 26" (Fig.2), 38" x 38" (Fig.3) and 42" x 42" (Fig.4) sizes. By 1884, the line had expanded to include new 22" planers (Fig.5) in five sizes, and larger planers in ten sizes (Fig.6), including 26" x 26" (Fig.7), 32" x 32" (Fig.8), 38" x 38" (Fig.9), 42" x 42" (Fig.10), 54" x 54" (Fig.11), 60" x 60" (Fig.12) and 84" x 84" (Fig.13). A still heavier line of planers (Fig.14), dubbed the 1891 pattern, was introduced in 1891.

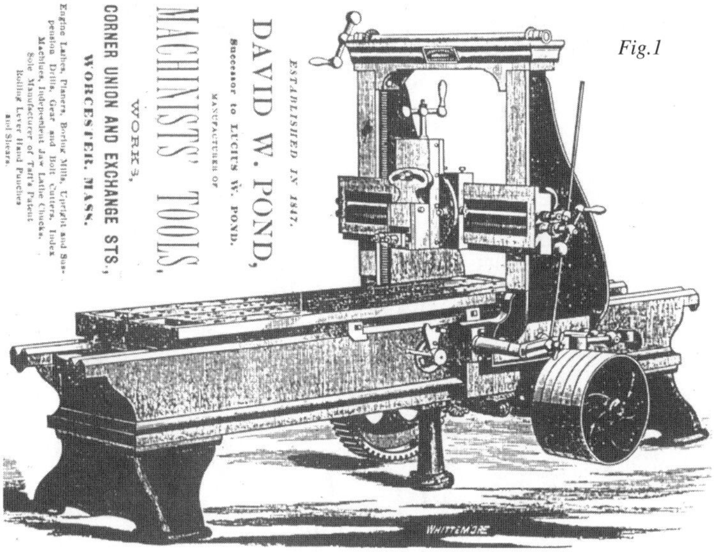

Fig.1

Fig.2

Pond's New Iron Planer.

Fig.3

New Iron Planer.

Fig.4

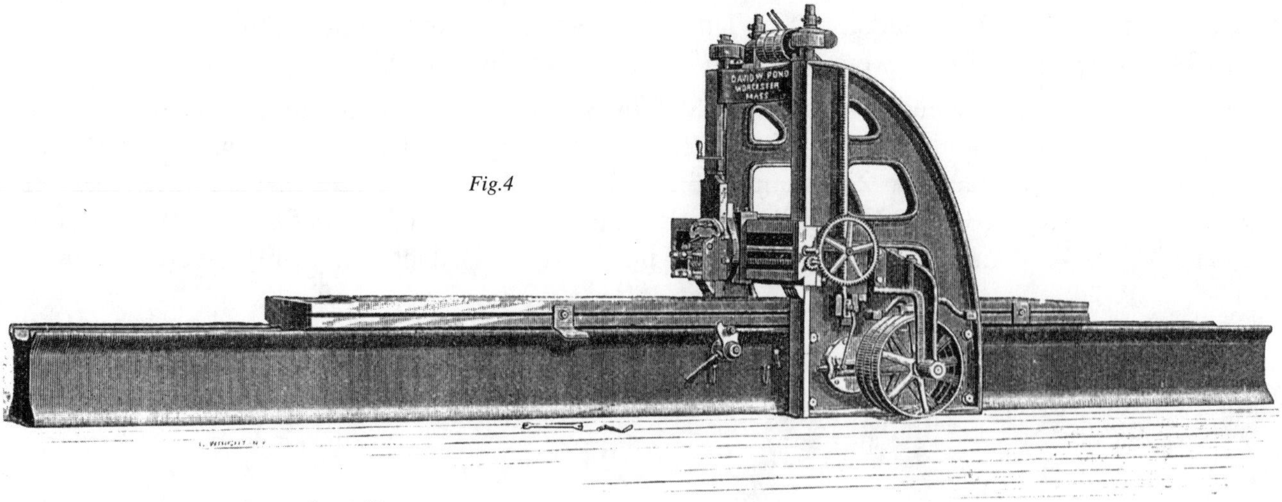

Iron Planer to Plane 42 Inches High by 42 Inches Wide.

Fig.5

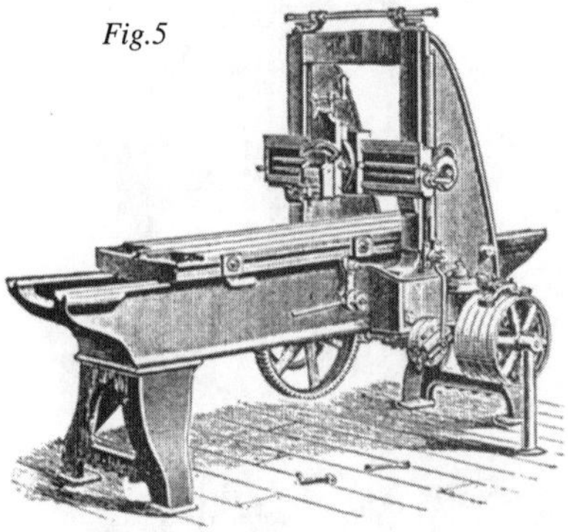

22-INCH PLANER.

This Planer is made from entirely new designs and patterns, is extra heavy and well proportioned in all its parts; has large shafts, long bearings, &c., accurately fitted. Gears and racks are cut from solid stock. Bearings and sliding surfaces are accurately hand scraped. Table is of unusual thickness, and all slots are planed and pin holes drilled and hand reamed from the solid.

All shafts, screws, rods and pinion gears, are made from steel.

Wrenches, and the necessary countershaft, are furnished.

Countershaft has one tight and one loose pulley, each 12 inches diameter and 3½ inches face, and should make 216 revolutions per minute.

Plane in Width.	Plane in Height.	Plane in Length.	Weight.	Price. Fig. 557 B.
22 inches.	22 inches.	5 feet.	4,100 lbs.	$625.
22 "	22 "	6 "	4,400 "	650.
22 "	22 "	7 "	4,700 "	675.
22 "	22 "	8 "	5,000 "	700.
22 "	22 "	9 "	5,300 "	725.

Fig.6

Figures.	Plane in Width.	Plane in Height.	Plane in Length.	Weight.	Weight per foot.	Price.	Price per foot	Extra Saddle on cross-head.	Extra Saddle on uprights.
553	84 inch.	84 inch.	12 feet.	56,000 lbs.	2,670 lbs.	$6500.	$200.	$600.	$550. each.
553	72 "	72 "	12 "	52,000 "	2,000 "	6000.	175.	600.	550. "
553A	60 "	60 "	12 "	45,000 "	2,000 "	5000.	150.	500.	500. "
554	54 "	54 "	12 "	30,000 "	1,375 "	3200.	110.	300.	350. "
554	48 "	48 "	10 "	25,525 "	1,300 "	2700.	100.	275.	325. "
555	42 "	42 "	10 "	23,000 "	1,100 "	2400.	90.	250.	300. "
556	38 "	38 "	8 "	19,800 "	920 "	1750.	80.	250.	300. "
557	36 "	36 "	6 "	10,000 "	725 "	1500.	75.	200.	....
557	32 "	32 "	6 "	9,400 "	700 "	1300.	75.	200.	....
557A	26 "	26 "	5 "	5,500 "	500 "	850.	50.	200.	....

26-INCH SQUARE.

Fig.7

36 AND 32-INCH SQUARE.

Fig.8

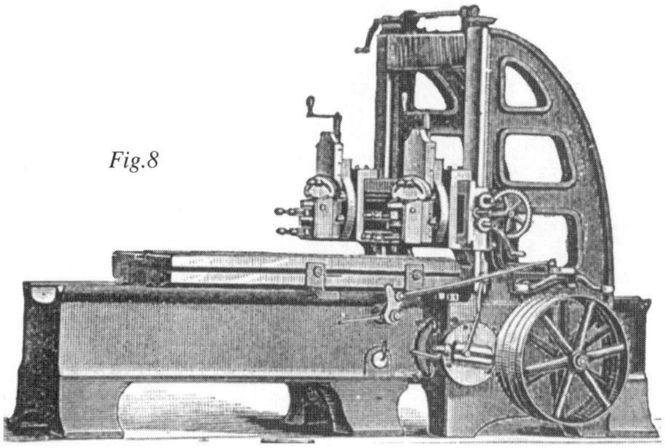

38 INCH SQUARE.

Fig.9

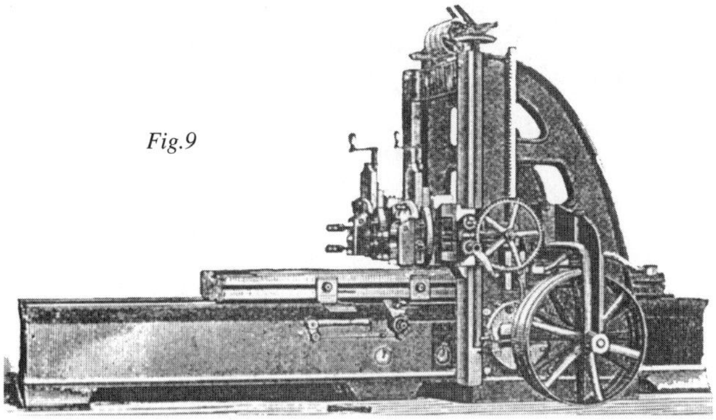

42 INCH SQUARE.

Fig.10

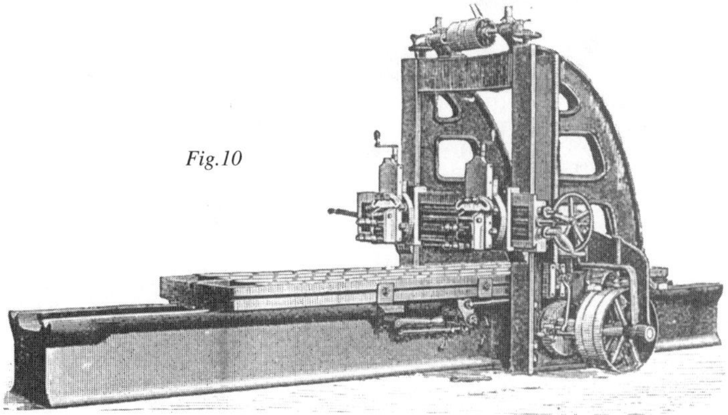

54 AND 48 INCH SQUARE.

Fig.11

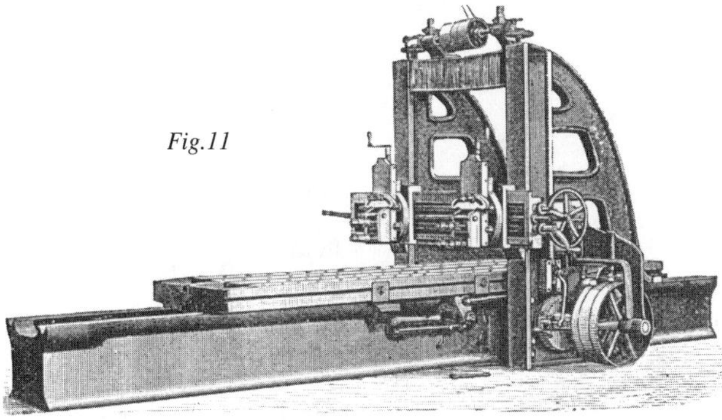

60 INCH SQUARE.

Fig.12

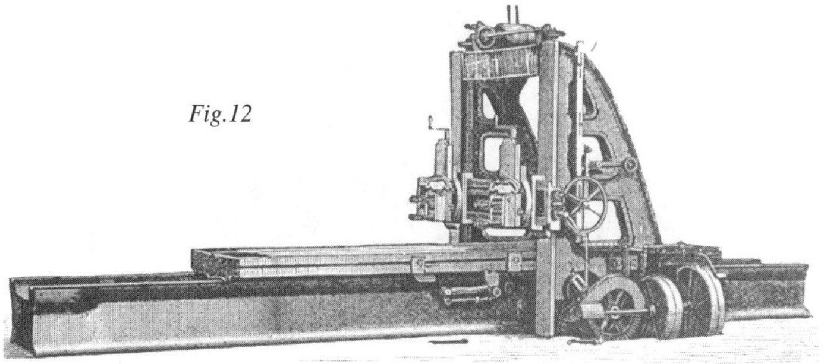

84 INCH SQUARE.

Fig.13

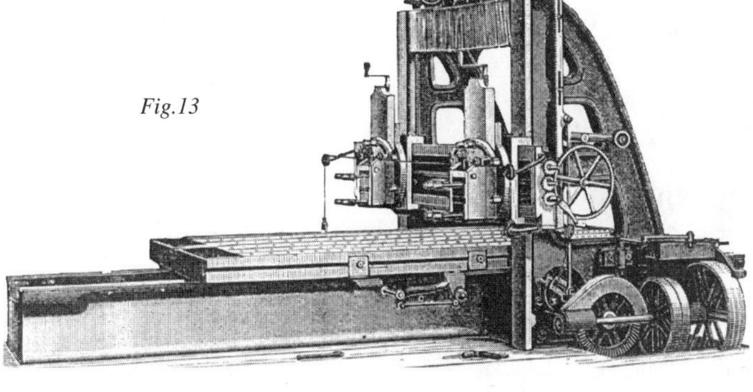

Fig.14

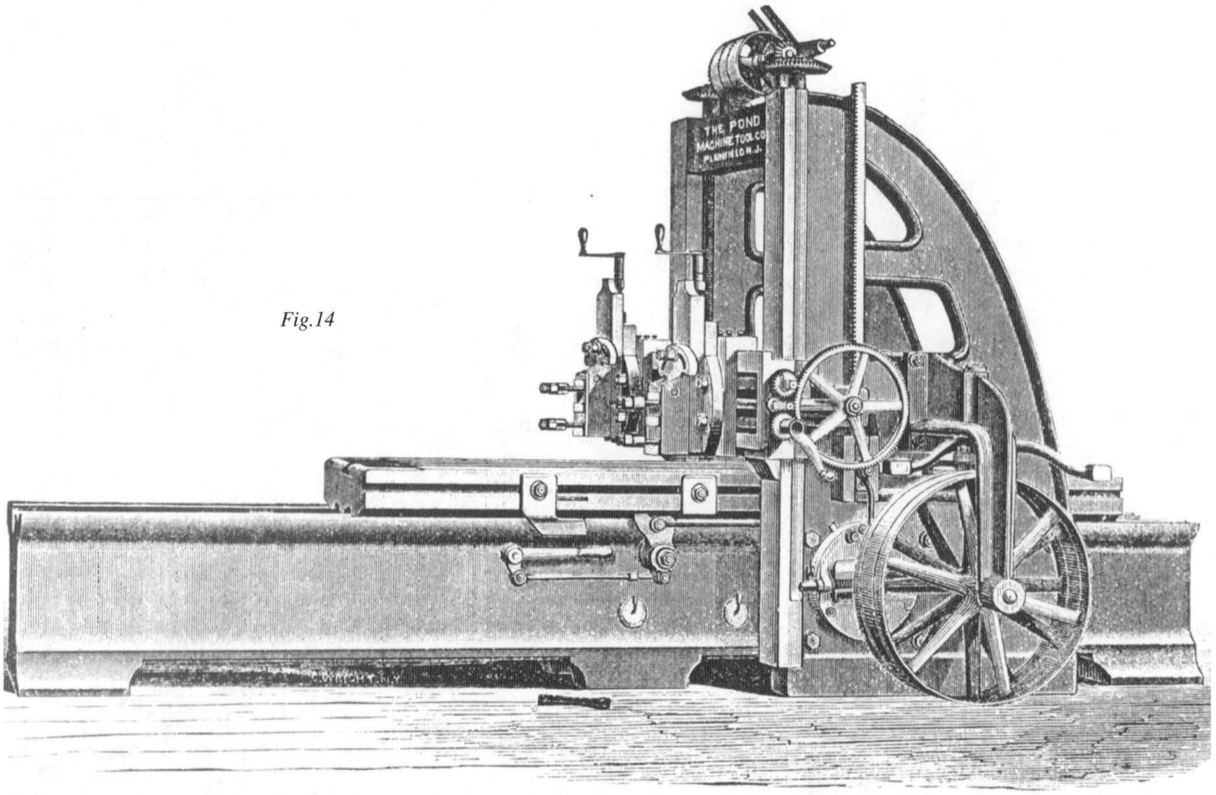

Heavy Planer, 1891 Pattern—Pond Machine Tool Company.

1903 production included 30" planers in countershaft (Fig.15) and motor (Fig.16) drive, 36" planers (Fig.17), 42" planers in countershaft (Fig.18) and motor (Fig.19) drive, 48" planers in countershaft (Fig.20) and motor (Fig.21) drive, 54" planers (Fig.22), 60" planers (Fig.23), and 96" planers (Fig.24).

Fig.15

Fig.16

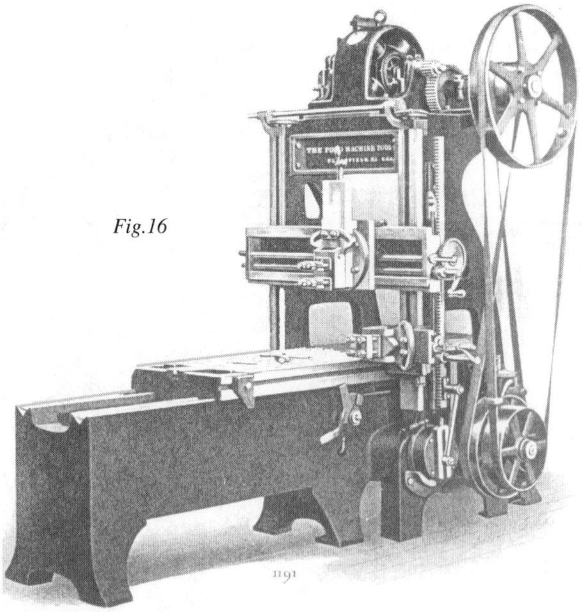

Fig.17

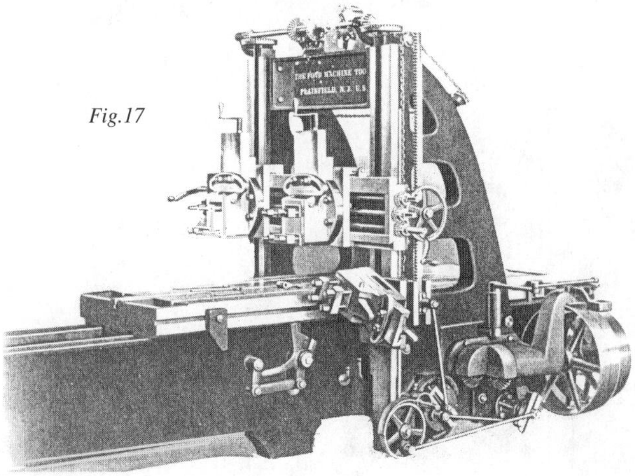

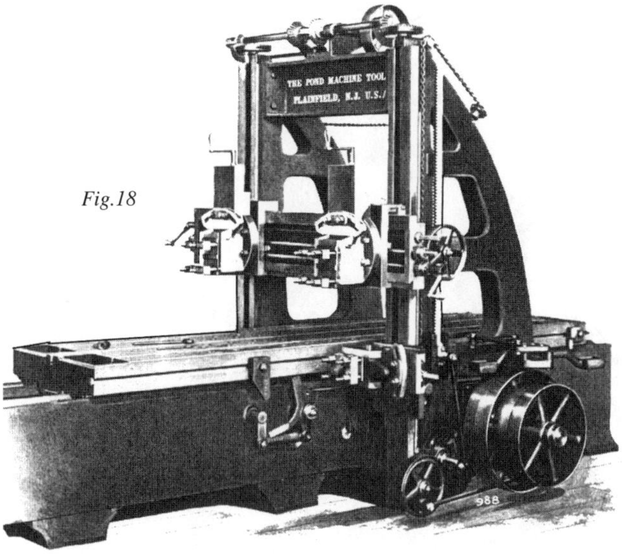

Fig.18

Fig.19

Fig.20

Fig.21

Fig.22

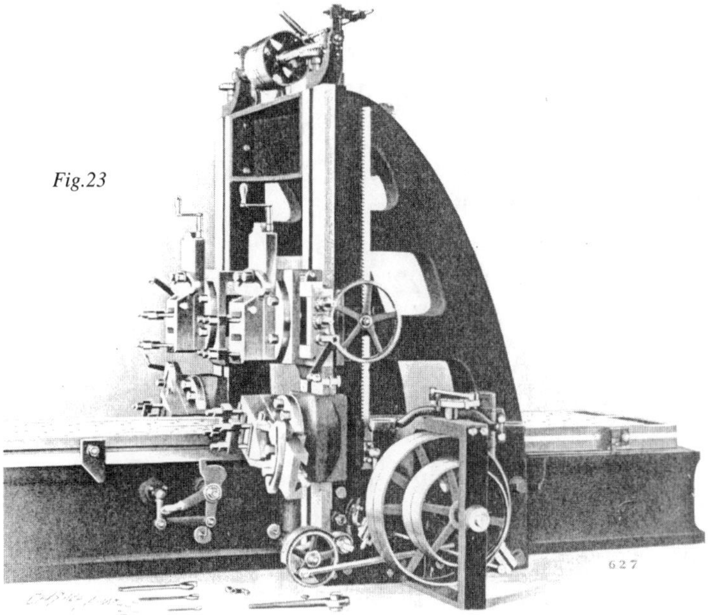

Fig.23

Pond Machine Tool Co.

Fig.24

POND, L.W., Worcester, MA

Formed in 1856 by Lucius W. Pond (1826-1889) as a successor to Samuel Flagg & Co., where Pond had been a partner. Samuel E. Hildreth (1829-1893) served as superintendent and machine designer until leaving in 1873 to join P. Blaisdell & Co.; Gardner Light was master mechanic. By 1858, Pond was offering "planers from 2 to 36 feet, engine lathes, and upright drills."

Pond took his son, David W. Pond, as a partner about 1869 but David Pond left to form his own company in 1872. L.W. Pond's business was taken over by his creditors in 1875 when he pleaded guilty to three counts of forgery and was sentenced to 15 years in prison. His son bought the firm from the creditors and merged it into D.W. POND.

Products offered in Pond's 1874 catalog included 14" x 8"x 30" hand planers (Fig.1) weighing 675 pounds; a new 17" x 12" x 12" adjustable stroke crank planer (Fig.2) weighing 1325 pounds; and iron planers from 22" to 72" (Fig.3), including 25" x 22" (Fig.4), 36" x 32" (Fig.5), and 60" x 60" (Fig.6). Accessories included Sherwood's patent chucking jaws (Fig.7) in seven sizes, Warren's patent planer chuck (Fig.8) in five sizes, and improved planer centers (Fig.9) in three sizes.

A new planer design, patented February 17, 1874, (Fig.10) was assigned to L.W. Pond, but appears not to have been used before the failure.

(continued next two pages)

Fig.1

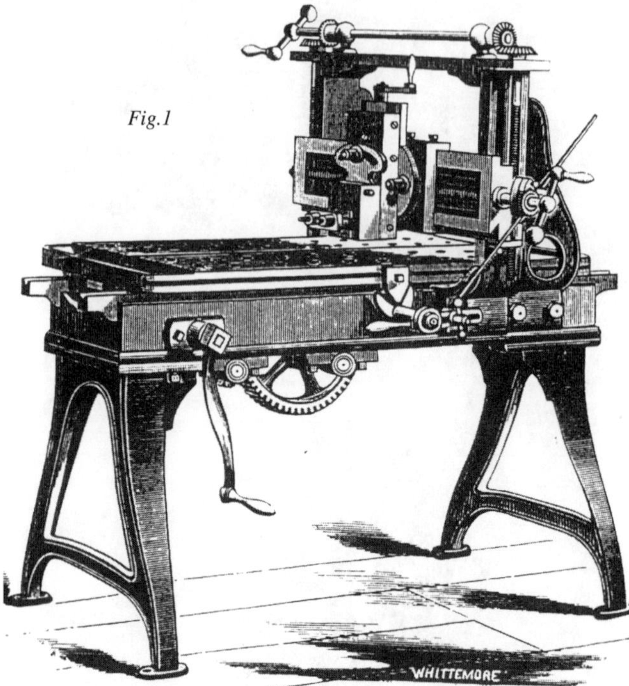

HAND PLANER.

Fig.2

NEW CRANK PLANER.

Fig.3

Plane in Width.	Plane in Height.	Plane in Length.	Weight.
22 inches.	20 inches.	3 feet.	2,400 lbs.
22 "	20 "	4 "	2,600 "
25 "	22 "	4 "	3,050 "
25 "	22 "	5 "	3,400 "
25 "	22 "	6 "	3,750 "
30 "	26 "	5 "	4,800 "
30 "	26 "	6 "	5,200 "
30 "	26 "	8 "	6,000 "
30 "	26 "	10 "	6,800 "
36 "	32 "	6 "	6,700 "
36 "	32 "	8 "	7,700 "
36 "	32 "	9 "	8,200 "
36 "	32 "	10 "	8,700 "
42 "	36 "	8 "	11,400 "
42 "	36 "	10 "	12,900 "
42 "	36 "	12 "	14,400 "
42 "	36 "	14 "	15,900 "
42 "	36 "	16 "	18,000 "
52 "	48 "	12 "	18,000 "
52 "	48 "	16 "	22,000 "
52 "	48 "	18 "	24,000 "
60 "	60 "	12 "	23,000 "
60 "	60 "	16 "	29,000 "
60 "	60 "	20 "	35,000 "
72 "	72 "	36 "	80,000 "

Fig.4

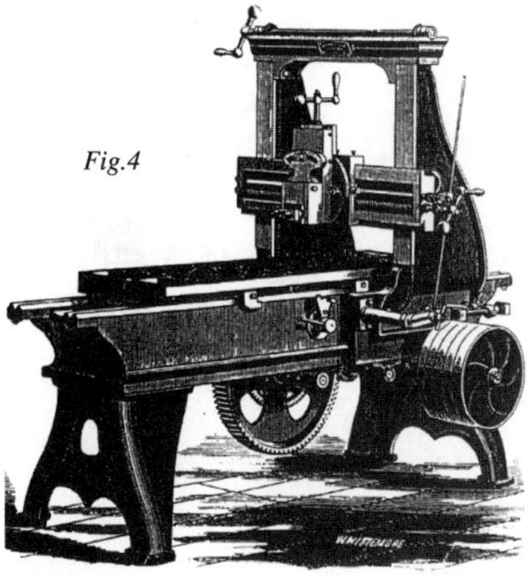

Fig.5

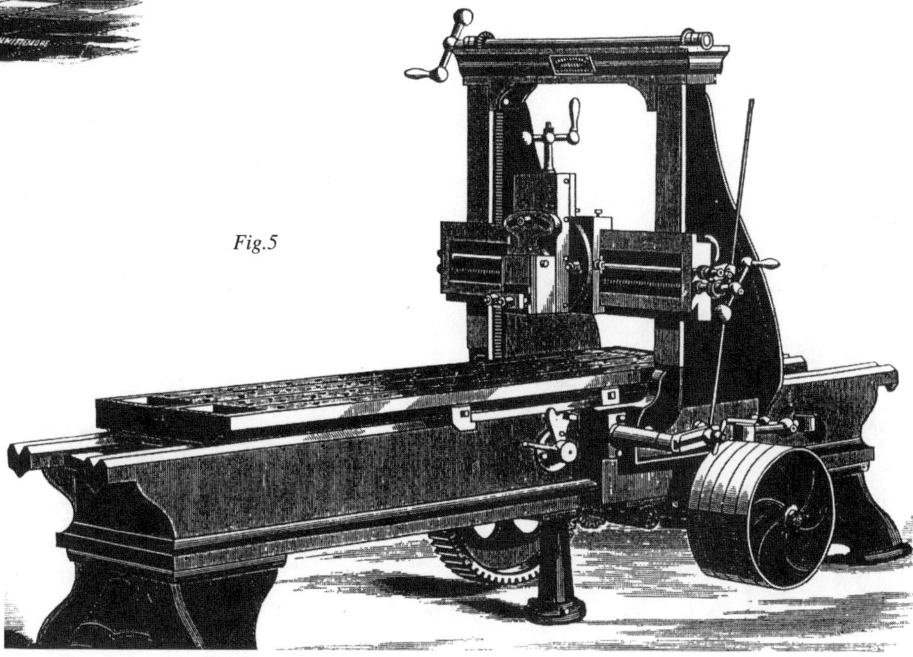

Fig.6

Fig.7

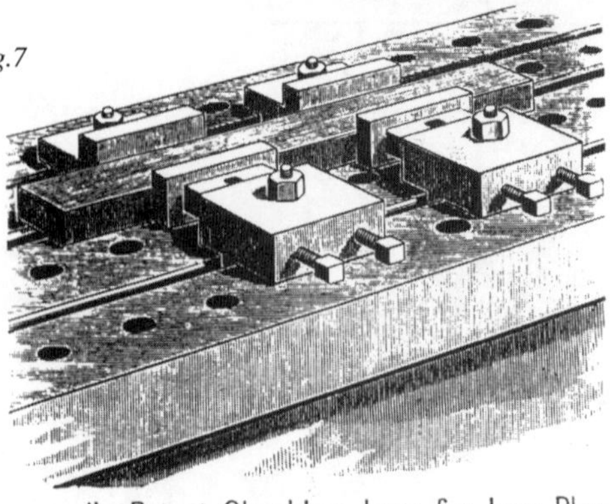

Sherwood's Patent Chucking Jaws for Iron Planers.

PRICES.

No. 1, 3 Inch Jaws, Malleable Iron, ... $
" 2, 3½ " " Cast Iron, ...
" 3, 4 " " " . . . .
" 4, 5 " " " . . . .
" 5, 6 " " " . . . .
" 6, 8 " " " . . . .
" 7, 10 " " " . . . .

Fig.9

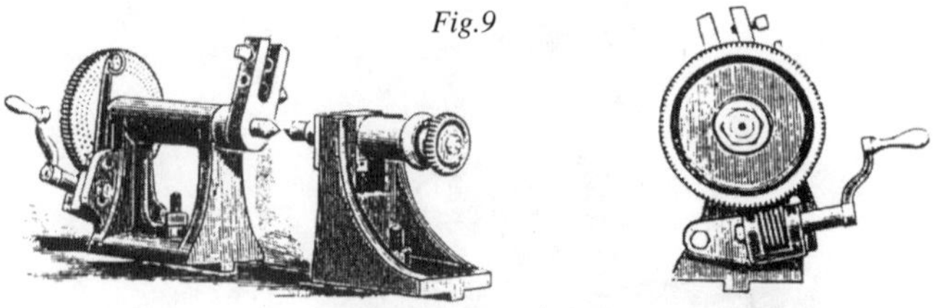

IMPROVED PLANER CENTRES.

PRICES.

10 Inch Swing, ... $
12 " " . . . .

Fig.8

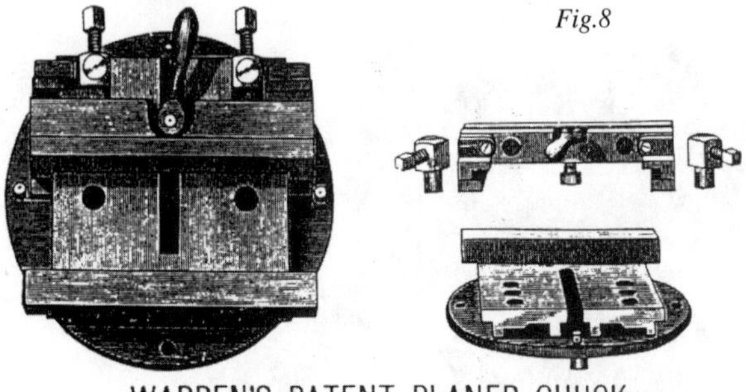

WARREN'S PATENT PLANER CHUCK.

PRICES.

6 Inch Jaws, ... $
10 " " . . . .
12 " " . . . .
15 " " . . . .
18 " " . . . .

W. HENDERSON.
Metal Planing-Machines.
No.147,497. Patented Feb. 17, 1874.

Fig.10

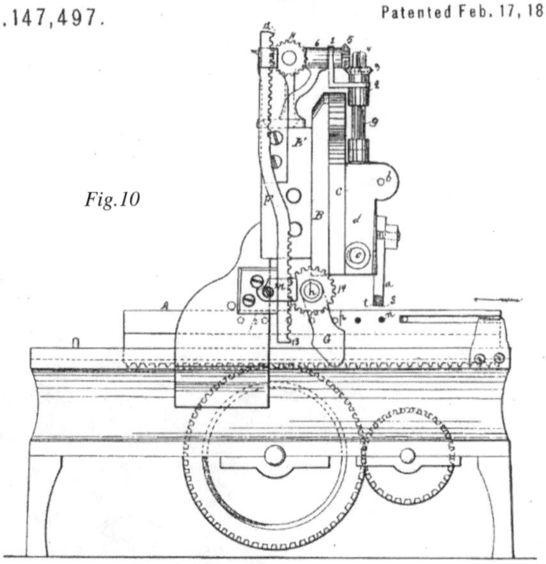

POND MACHINE CO., L.W., Worcester, MA, later

POND MACHINE & FOUNDRY CO., L.W., Worcester, MA

Formed in 1886 by Lucius W. Pond, Henry C. Fish (1825-1906) and Caleb Colvin (1829-1914) to make planers under Pond's patents of February 9, and November 2, 1886, (Figs.1-2). Capital was set at $30,000. Pond, whose original business L.W. Pond had been taken over by his son in 1875 when he was sentenced to a 15 year prison term, had been pardoned in 1882. Fish and Colvin were owners of the new firm; Pond served as superintendent and had no financial interest. Fish left the firm in 1889; Colvin became sole owner in 1891 and merged the company with his foundry to form the L.W. POND MACHINE AND FOUNDRY CO.

The new company advertised itself as "manufacturers and dealers in iron working machinery, improved patent iron planers a specialty." *(continued next two pages)*

DETAILS AND PRICES.

	24 Inch.	28 Inch.	30 Inch.	32 Inch.	38 Inch.	44 Inch.	48 Inch.	52 Inch.	60 Inch.	72 Inch.
Standard length	6 feet.	6 feet	6 feet.	8 feet.	10 feet.	10 feet.	10 feet.	12 feet.	14 feet.	14 feet.
Weight of standard length . .	5500 lbs.	7000 lbs.	7500 lbs.	10,700 lbs	16,500 lbs	21,000 lbs	23,000 lbs	30,500 lbs	37,000 lbs	48,500 lbs
Price of standard length . . .										
Price, per foot, extra										
Price, extra head on rail . . .										
Price, extra head on upright . .										
Size counter pulleys	12 x 4 in.	12 x 4 in.	12 x 4 in.	12 x 7 in.	12 x 7 in	12 x 7 in.	12 x 7 in.	15 x 8	15 x 9 in.	15 x 9 in.
Revolutions counter pulleys . .	325	319	319	418	455	366	366	385	300	300

Fig.3

Fig.1

IRON PLANING MACHINE.

Fig.2

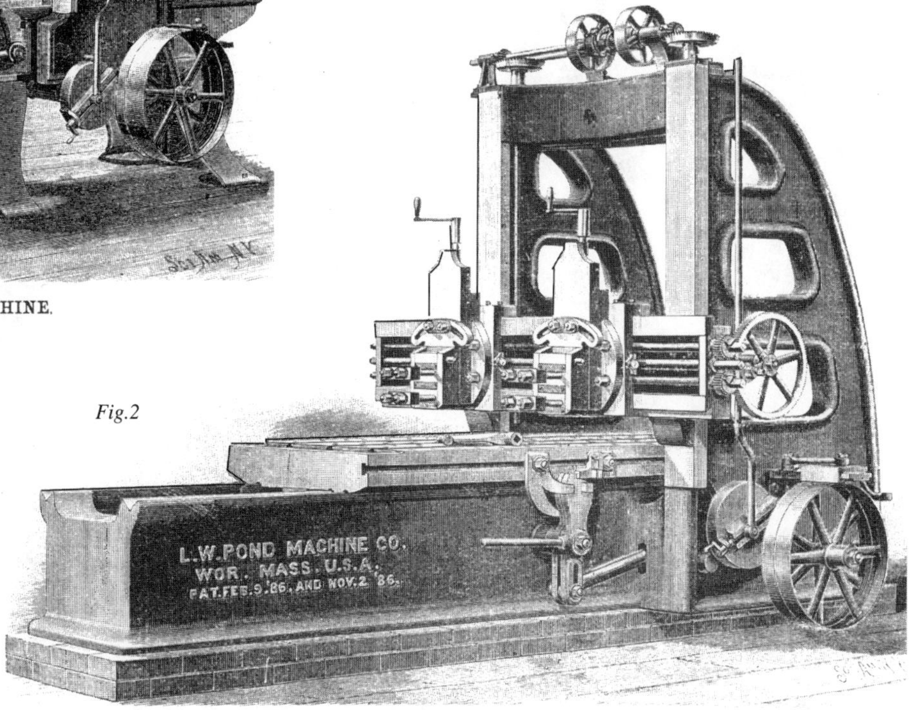

IMPROVED IRON PLANER.

Fig.4

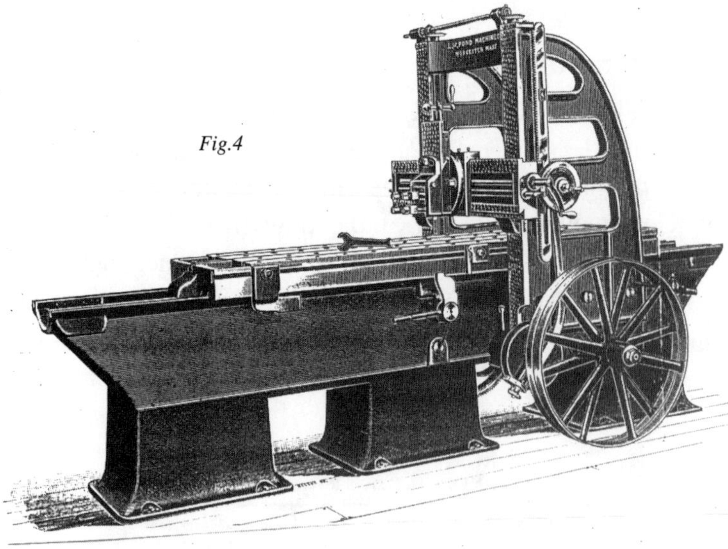

Fig.6

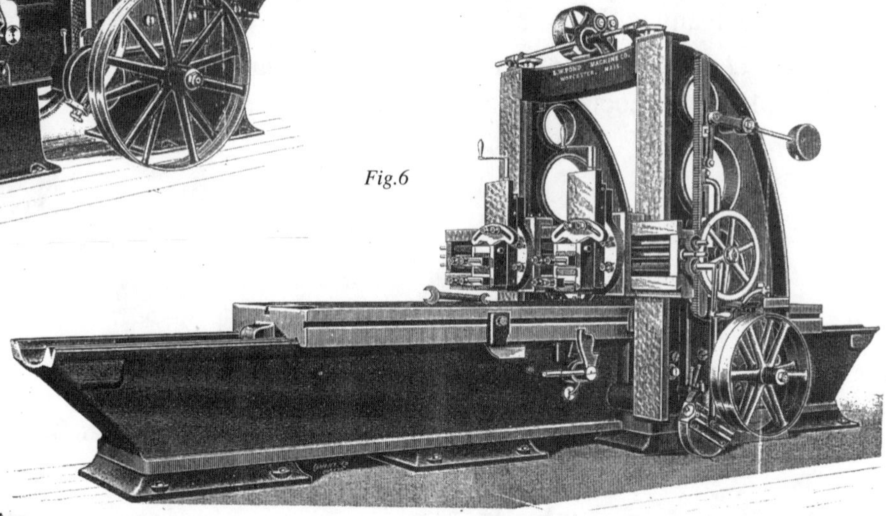

L. W. Pond 60 Inch Planer.

Fiv 5

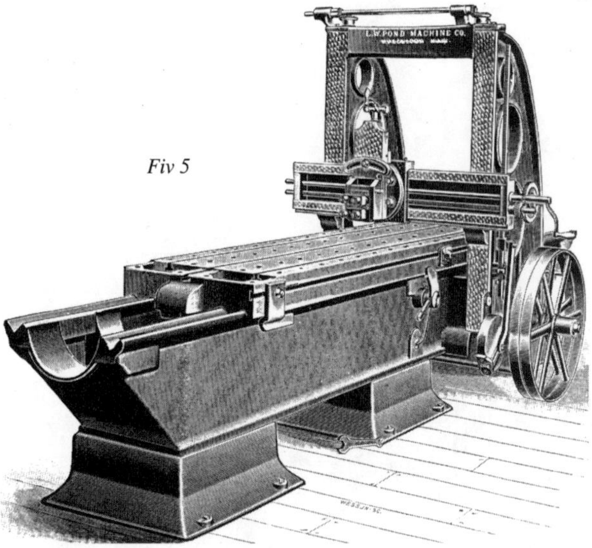

Fig.7

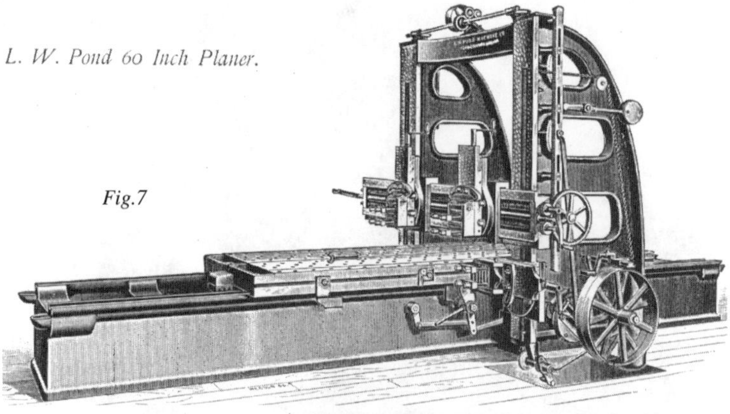

Fig.8

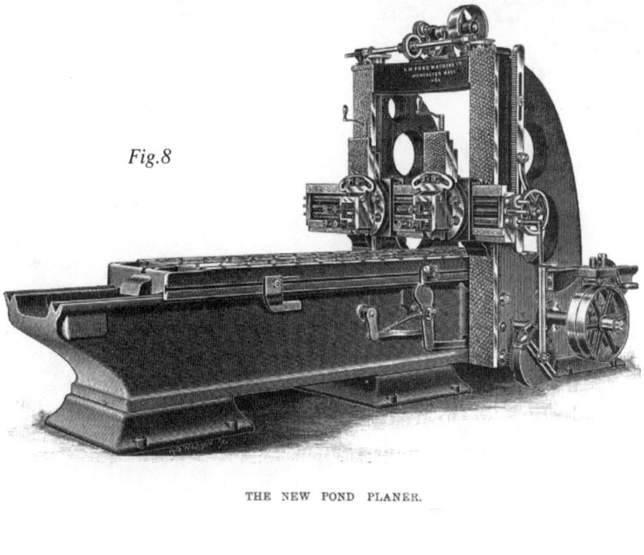

THE NEW POND PLANER.

L.W. Pond Machine & Foundry

Fig.9

"STRAIGHT LINE" PLANER

Fig.10

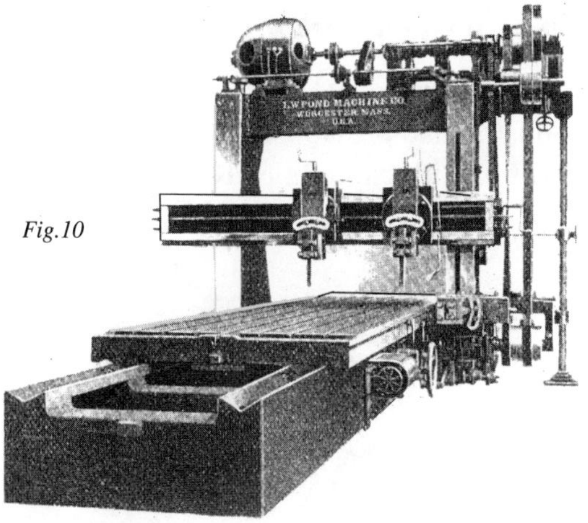

Fig.11

In 1892, a new line of planers in ten sizes (Fig.3), including 24" x 24" (Fig.4), 28" x 28" (Fig.5) 38" x 38" (Fig.6), and 60" x 60" (Fig.7) was offered. Heavier construction planers were introduced in 1896, including a 32" x 32" size (Fig.8).

1900 production included a heavy duty, "straight line" model in 36" x 36" size (Fig.9). A motor driven, 96" x 72"x 24' model (Fig.10) with speed changer giving 15, 20, 26, and 35 FPM forward and 70 FPM reverse speeds was introduced in 1904, and a low price, light duty, 24" x 24" model (Fig.11) in 1905.

PORTER, WALLACE, New Haven, CT

Inventor and maker, in 1885, of the planer chuck shown right. Made in only 9" size, it was finely graduated for machining angles on the shaper.

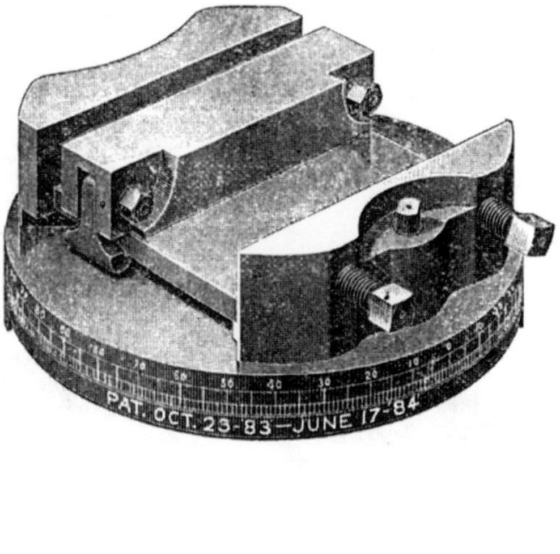

POTTER & JOHNSTON MACHINE CO., Pawtucket, RI

Formed in April, 1893, by James C. Potter (?-1925) and John Johnston to build shapers and manufacturing lathes. Johnston had previously been chief draftsman of the PRATT & WHITNEY CO. The firm incorporated in January, 1899, with capital of $100,000.

In 1898, the firm introduced 15" shapers with swivel table (Fig.1) and 24" shapers with plain table (Fig.2).

Fig.1

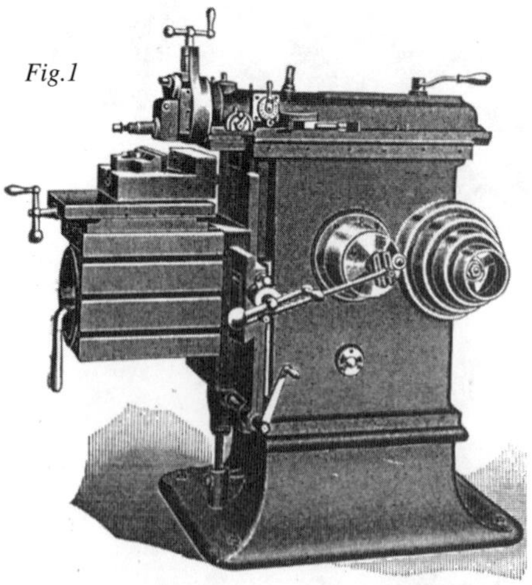

15-inch Shaper with swivel table.

Fig.2

24-inch Shaper with plain table.

POWELL & CO., A.M., Worcester, MA, later
POWELL MACHINE TOOL CO., Worcester, MA

A partnership of Albert M. Powell (1857-1935) and George Carter, formed in 1881 as a reorganization of Wight & Powell. In 1882 the firm employed 50 men building lathes and planers.

In 1884 A.M. Powell & Co. was purchased by George W. Fifield and others and reorganized as the POWELL MACHINE TOOL CO. which was absorbed by the L.W. POND MACHINE CO. in 1886. Powell organized the POWELL PLANER CO. in 1887.

Fig.1

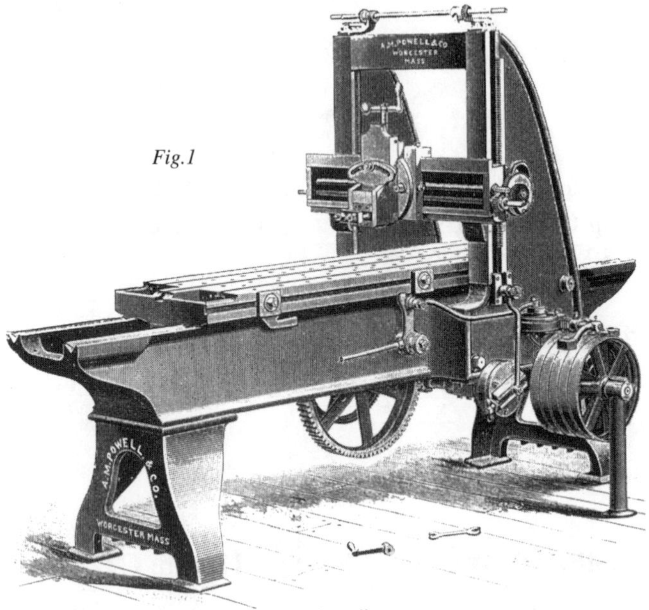

POWELL'S IRON PLANER.

Fig.2

1882 production included 22"x 22"x 5' planers (Fig.1) weighing 4100 pounds. In 1884, an improved, much heavier planer (Fig.2) was introduced.

POWELL PLANER CO., Worcester, MA

Organized in 1887 by Albert M. Powell, Edward M. Woodward and George W. Fifield. The firm reorganized as the WOODWARD & POWELL PLANER CO. in 1899.

Early production included a heavier design planer (Fig.1) in 30" x 30" x "any length" which, by 1894 had been considerably improved (Fig.2) and was available in lengths from 8' to 16'.

Fig.1

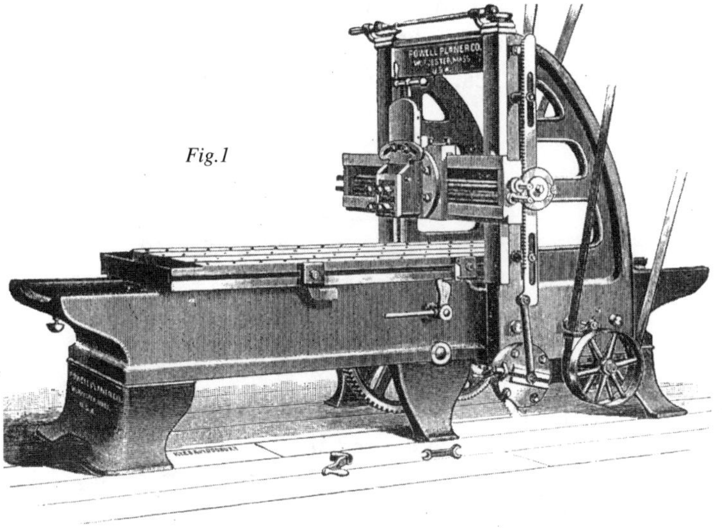

THIRTY-INCH PLANER.

Fig.2

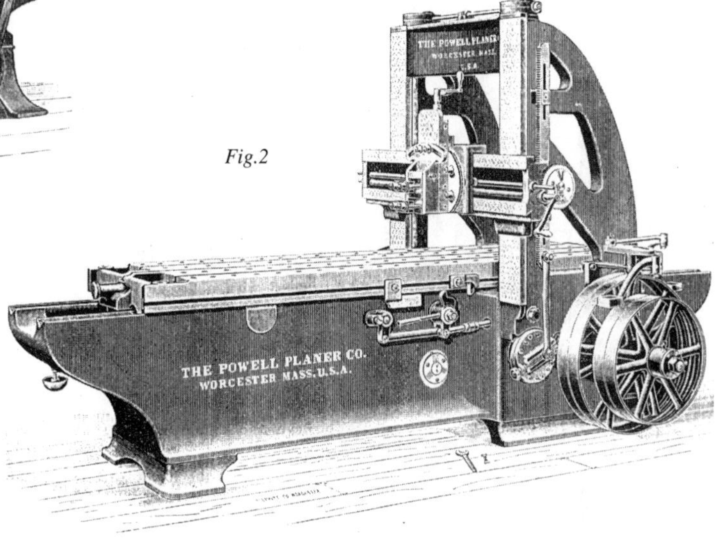

THE POWELL METAL PLANER.

POWELL TOOL CO., Worcester, MA, later

POWELL MACHINE CO., Fitchburg, MA

Formed in 1907 by Albert M. Powell and his sons Arlic M. Powell and Charles S. Powell. In August, 1908, the new firm introduced the Powell HY-SPEED-CUT planer, left, designed to enter a cut at low speed, accelerate through the cut, and finish the cut at low speed.

In 1909, the firm moved to Fitchburg, MA, and reorganized in 1910 as the Powell Machine Co. Business continued until 1915 when the firm was absorbed by the WOODWARD & POWELL PLANER CO.

PRATT, WHITNEY & CO., Hartford, CT, later
PRATT & WHITNEY CO., Hartford, CT

A partnership of Francis A. Pratt (1827-1902) and Amos Whitney (1832-1920), formed in 1860 to make silk machinery, lathes, and planers. Both had previously worked at the Phoenix Iron Works where Pratt was superintendent and Whitney a contractor. Monroe Stannard became a partner in 1862 when he, Pratt, and Whitney, each put $1200 into the firm. This $3,600 capital grew to $75,000 by 1865.

In 1868, the firm offered engine lathes, hand lathes, crank planers with Whitworth quick return (Fig.1), gear planers, planer vises and centers, milling machines, and planers based on Dwight Slate's patent of April 20, 1869, (Fig.2), in 16" x 16" (Fig.3), 24" x 24" (Fig.4), and 30" x 30" (Fig.5) sizes. *(continued next two pages)*

Fig.1

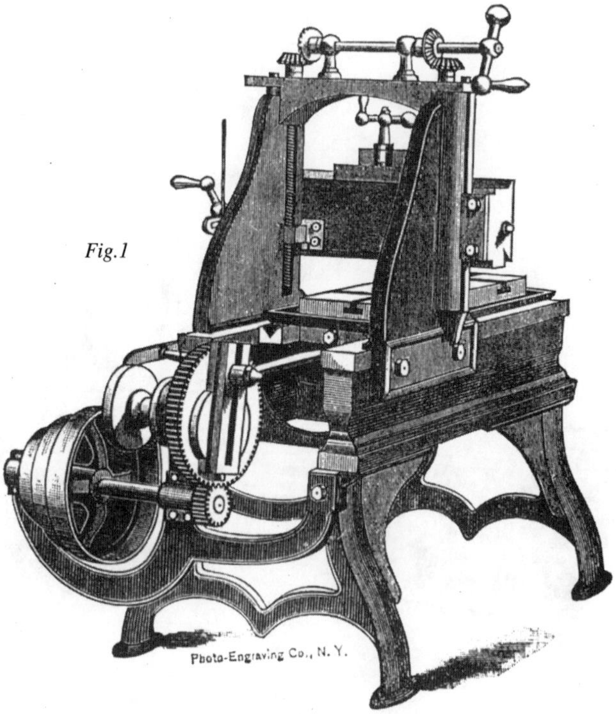

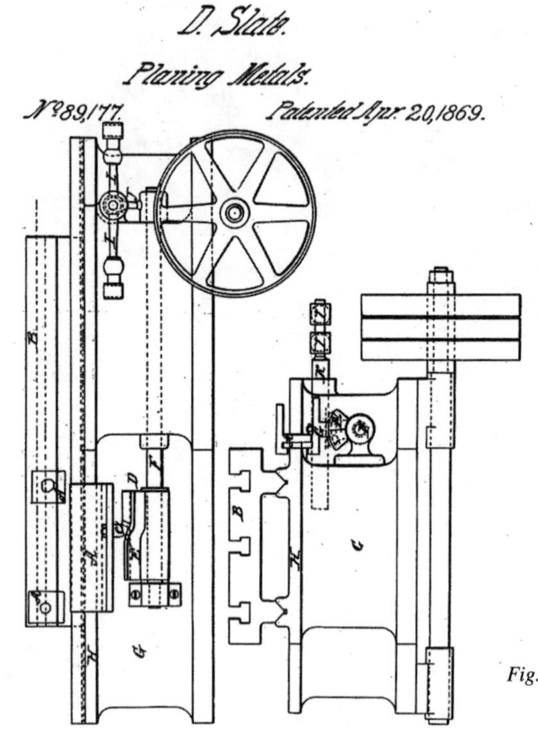

Fig.2

Fig.3

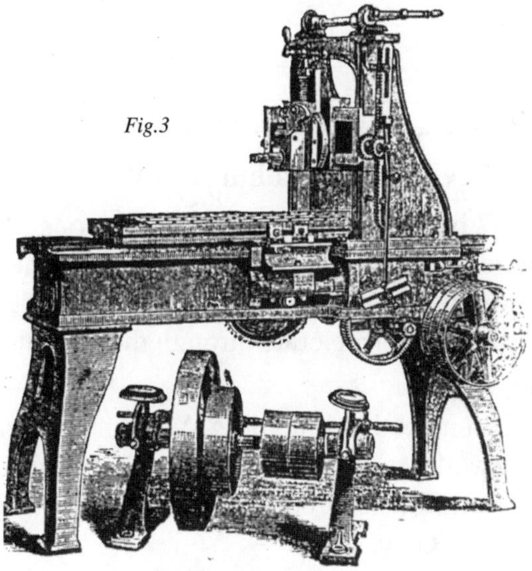

SIXTEEN-INCH PLANE

Fig.4

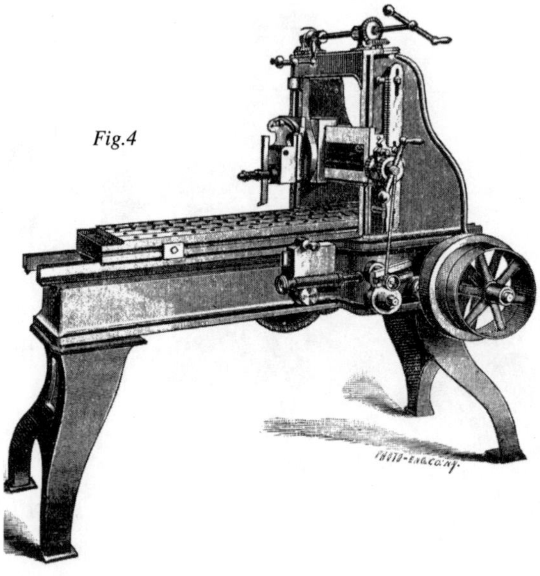

Fig.5

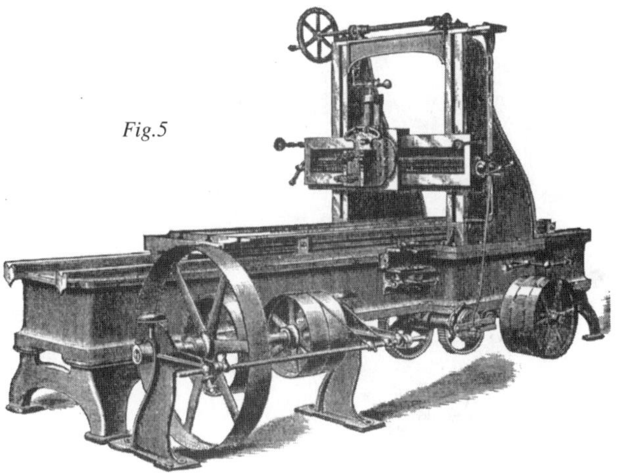

Fig.6

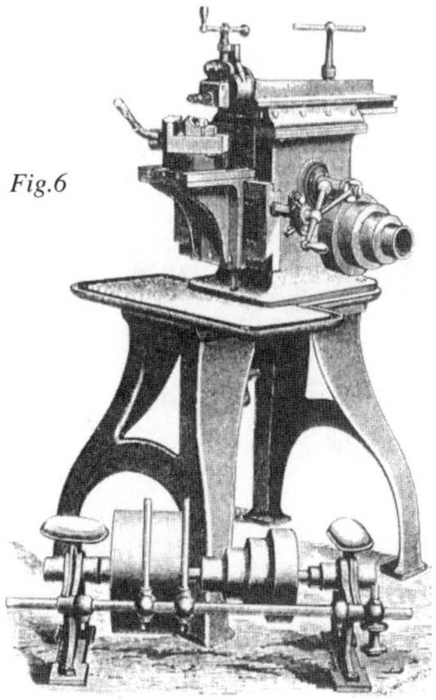

6 INCH PILLAR SHAPER.

Fig.7

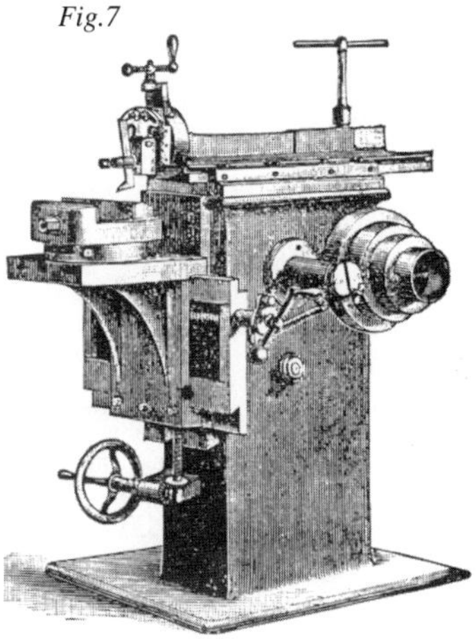

The firm incorporated in 1869 as the Pratt & Whitney Co. with capital of $350,000. Pratt served as president until his retirement in 1898; Whitney was superintendent, becoming president in 1898. Employment reached 675 hands by 1883, growing to 1160 in 1896.

Shaper production began about 1875 with the introduction of 6" (Fig.6) and 12" (Fig.7) stroke pillar shapers. 15" traverse shapers (Fig.8), weighing 2400 pounds, were available by 1883.

In 1883, the firm introduced a roll groving machine (Fig.9), which was a planer with an automatically rotating fixture used to groove textile machine rolls. An improved version (Fig.10) was brought out in 1893.

Fig.8

Fig.9

NEW ROLL GROOVING MACHINE.

Fig.10

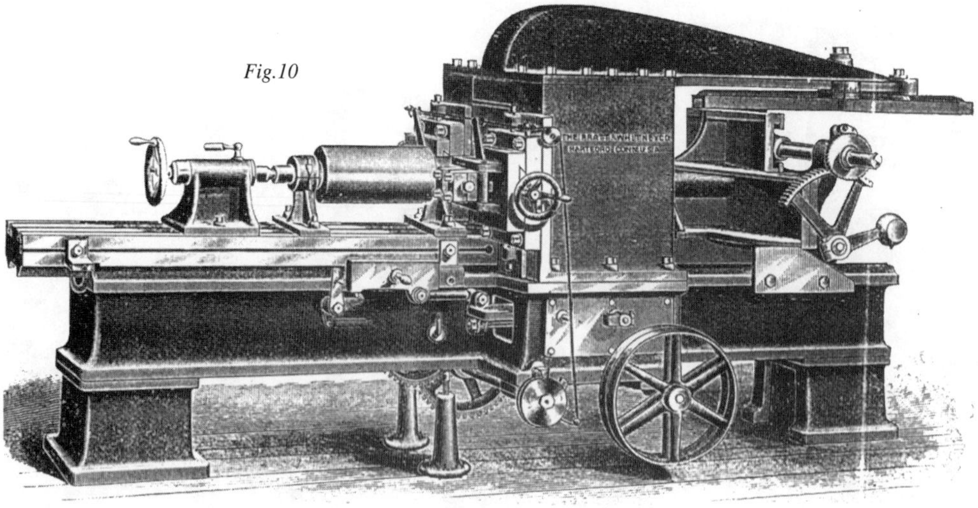

Fig. 77.—Roll Grooving Machine.

1894 production included planers from 16" x 16" (Fig.11) to 40" x 40" size, pillar shapers in 9" and 14" stroke (Fig.12), and traverse shapers in 12" and 14" stroke.

In January, 1901, Whitney sold out to the Niles-Bement-Pond Co., which continued operation of the Pratt & Whitney Co. as a division. Improved, 15" pillar shapers (Fig.13) were offered in 1903, but planer production appears to have ceased about 1902 as the firm concentrated on lathes and milling machines.

Fig.13

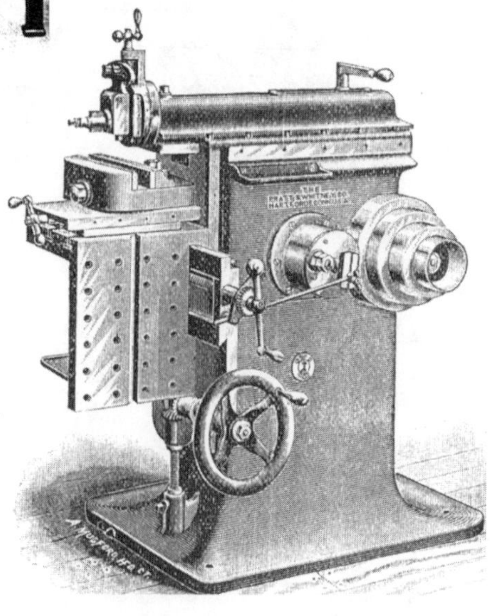

Fig.12

PRENTISS TOOL & SUPPLY CO., New York, NY

A large machinery dealer, the firm sold private label machine tools made for them by H.C. Fish Machine Works, Geo. Juengst & Sons, and Pease Machine Tool Co. in the late 1880s and 1890s.

The friction shaper offered in 1889 and shown right is captioned as "built by the Prentiss Tool & Supply Co.", but was built by Geo. Juengst & Sons.

:TION SHAPER, BUILT BY THE PRENTISS TOOL AND SUPPLY NEW YORK.

PUTNAM, J. & S.W., Fitchburg, MA, later
PUTNAM & CO., J. & S.W., Fitchburg, MA, later
PUTNAM MACHINE CO., Fitchburg, MA

A partnership of John Putnam (1810-1888) and his brother Salmon W. Putnam (1815-1872) formed in 1836 in Ashburnham, MA, moving to Fitchburg, MA, in 1838. Lathes and gear cutting machines were offered as early as 1838.

The brothers reorganized as J. & S.W. PUTNAM & CO. in 1850 when Charles H. Brown and Benjamin Snow were admitted as partners and again as the PUTNAM MACHINE CO. when John Q. Wright, Sylvester Wright and Charles Burleigh were admitted in August, 1854.

Salmon W. Putnam served as president from 1858, when the firm became a stock company, until his death in 1872. John Putnam was not active in company management after 1858. Salmon W. Putnam, Jr. (1844-1923) managed the firm from 1872 until 1882 when, with his brother George E. Putnam (1854-1892), he left to form a competing firm, the PUTNAM TOOL CO. (S.W. Putnam's Sons).

The PUTNAM TOOL CO. was merged into the PUTNAM MACHINE CO. on March 18, 1886, a few months after Salmon W. Putnam, Jr. and his brother rejoined and gained control of the Putnam Machine Co. Salmon W. Putnam, Jr. served as vice president until selling the firm to Manning, Maxwell & Moore in 1913. George E. Putnam served as superintendent until his death in 1892.

The firm built steam engines, cranes and a wide variety of machine tools including planers, shapers, and slotters.

Planer production began not later than 1865 when Putnam offered an 18" x 18" (Fig.1) size. Note the light construction, especially the very light bed castings.

Its 1877 catalog offered "extra heavy iron planers from new and lately improved patterns" in sizes from 18" x 16" to 80" x 76", (Figs.2-4) including a 30" x 30" model (Fig.5). The same catalog also offered the Putnam patent planer chuck (Fig.6) in 12", 15" and 18" sizes; slotting and paring machines, patented March 14, 1871, by S.W. Putnam, Jr., in 10" and 13" (Fig.7) strokes; No. 2 shapers with 10" stroke and 5 1/2' bed and No. 3 shapers with 14" and 6' bed. Both styles of shapers were available with single or double tables.

A 100" x 100" planer (Fig.8) and an improved slotting machine (Fig.9) were introduced in 1892.1901 production included 22", 24" and 28" (Fig.10); 30" x 30" x 8' (Fig.11); 36", 42" and 48" (Fig.12); 54", 60" and

67" (Fig.13); 72" and 84" (Fig.14); and 100" and 120" (Fig.15) planers. Slotters were offered in 11" and 14" strokes (Fig.16).

Small shapers (Fig.17) were offered about 1860. Note the mandrel for keyseating and the lack of a table. The vise, which mounted in the slots below the cutting tool, served as a table. Shapers orginally designed by the PUTMAN TOOL CO. were offered after 1886 when the two firms merged. In 1901, a new eccentric pitman shaper (Fig.18) was offered in 12", 15", 20", and 25" strokes. *(continued next three pages)*

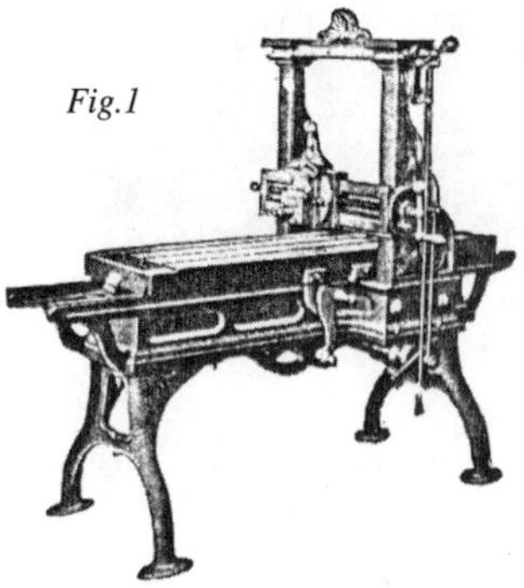

Fig.1

28 PUTNAM MACHINE COMPANY.

Iron Planers.

FROM ENTIRELY NEW AND LATELY IMPROVED PATTERNS.
EXTRA HEAVY.

	PLANING WIDTH.	PLANING HEIGHT.	LENGTH OF PLATEN.	LENGTH OF BED.	WEIGHT.	PRICE.
A.	24 inches.	24 inches.	5 feet.	7 feet.	lbs.	$
	24 "	24 "	6 "	8½ "		
	24 "	24 "	7 "	10 "		
	24 "	24 "	8 "	11½ "		
B.	26 "	26 "	6 "	9 "		
	26 "	26 "	8 "	12 "		
	26 "	26 "	10 "	15 "		
	26 "	26 "	12 "	18 "		
C.	30 "	30 "	6 "	9 "		
	30 "	30 "	8 "	12 "		
	30 "	30 "	10 "	15 "		
	30 "	30 "	12 "	18 "		
	30 "	30 "	14 "	21 "		
D.	36 "	36 "	6 "	9 "		
	36 "	36 "	8 "	12 "		
	36 "	36 "	10 "	15 "		
	36 "	36 "	12 "	18 "		
	36 "	36 "	14 "	21 "		
	36 "	36 "	16 "	24 "		
	36 "	36 "	18 "	27 "		
	36 "	36 "	20 "	30 "		
E.	42 "	42 "	6 "	9 "		
	42 "	42 "	8 "	12 "		
	42 "	42 "	10 "	14 ft. 6 in.		
	42 "	42 "	12 "	16 " 8 "		
	42 "	42 "	14 "	19 " 6 "		
	42 "	42 "	16 "	21 " 8 "		
	42 "	42 "	18 "	24 feet.		
	42 "	42 "	20 "	27 "		
F.	48 "	48 "	6 "	9 "		
	48 "	48 "	8 "	12 "		
	48 "	48 "	10 "	14 ft. 6 in.		
	48 "	48 "	12 "	16 " 8 "		
	48 "	48 "	14 "	19 " 6 "		
	48 "	48 "	16 "	21 " 8 "		
	48 "	48 "	18 "	24 feet.		
	48 "	48 "	20 "	27 "		

Fig.2

Iron Planers.—CONTINUED.

	PLANING WITDH.	PLANING HEIGHT.	LENGTH OF PLATEN.	LENGTH OF BED.	WEIGHT.	PRICE.
G.	54 inches.	54 inches.	8 feet.	12 feet.	lbs.	$
	54 "	54 "	10 "	15 "		
	54 "	54 "	12 "	18 "		
	54 "	54 "	14 "	21 "		
	54 "	54 "	16 "	24 "		
	54 "	54 "	18 "	27 "		
	54 "	54 "	20 "	30 "		
	54 "	54 "	22 "	33 "		
	54 "	54 "	24 "	36 "		
H.	60 "	54 "	8 "	12 "		
	60 "	54 "	10 "	15 "		
	60 "	54 "	12 "	18 "		
	60 "	54 "	14 "	21 "		
	60 "	54 "	16 "	24 "		
	60 "	54 "	18 "	27 "		
	60 "	54 "	20 "	30 "		
	60 "	54 "	22 "	33 "		
	60 "	54 "	24 "	36 "		
	80 "	76 "	24 "	"		

Fig.3

Iron Planers.

PLANING WIDTH.	PLANING HEIGHT.	PLANING LENGTH.	WEIGHT.	PRICE.
18 inches.	16 inches.	3 feet.	lbs.	$
22 "	20 "	5 "		
30 "	28 "	7 "		
30 "	28 "	10 "		

The above Planers are made with power down, angular and cross feeds; the 22 and 30 inch with universal power feed in the head; the side screws have adjustable steel steps, and the cross beams are attached to posts with gibs. All gears are cut including the rack and inside gears. Overhead pulleys and hangers complete, furnished with each machine.

Fig.4

Fig.5

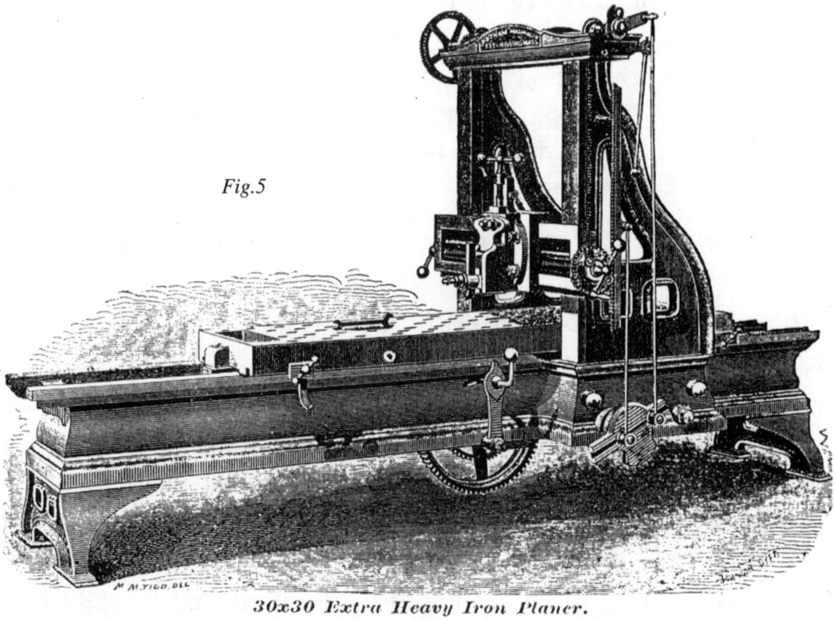

30x30 Extra Heavy Iron Planer.

Putnam Patent Planer Chuck.

The above cut represents the Putnam Patent Planer Chuck. The centre view is the Chuck complete, the outside views are sectional representations showing its internal constructions. The adjustment of these Chucks to position requires the operation of only one screw. They are graduated and are first-class in workmanship and materials throughout, and are the most convenient and efficient Chucks made.

Prices:—12 inch, $50; 15 inch, $60; 18 inch, $75.

Fig.6

Fig.7

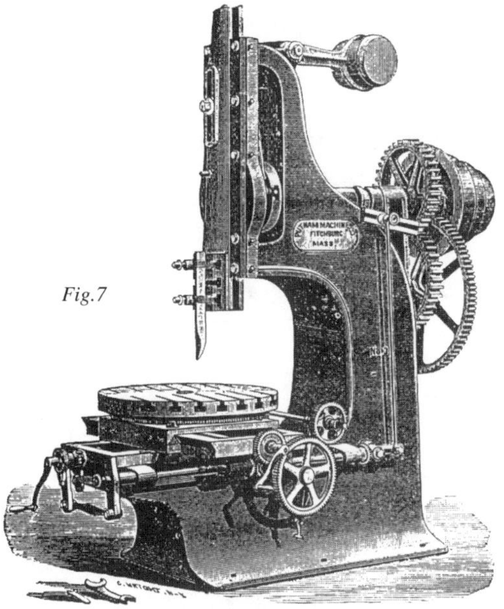

13 Inch Slotting and Paring Machine, with Patent Relief Motion.

Fig.8

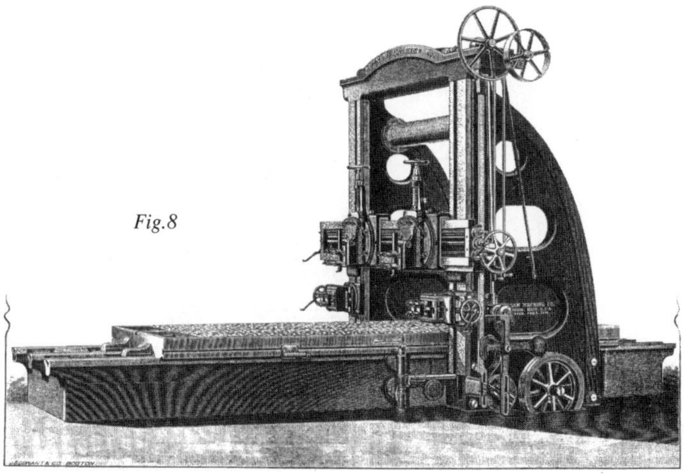

THE PUTNAM PLANER.—100 BY 100 INCH.

Fig.9

28, 24, AND 22 INCH PLANER.

Fig.10

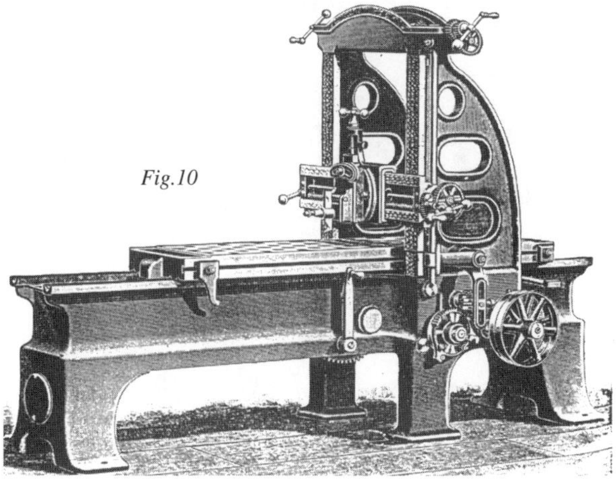

Fig.10

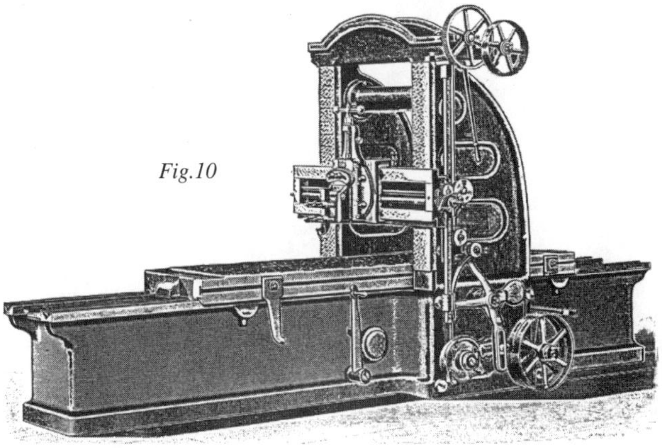

Fig.11

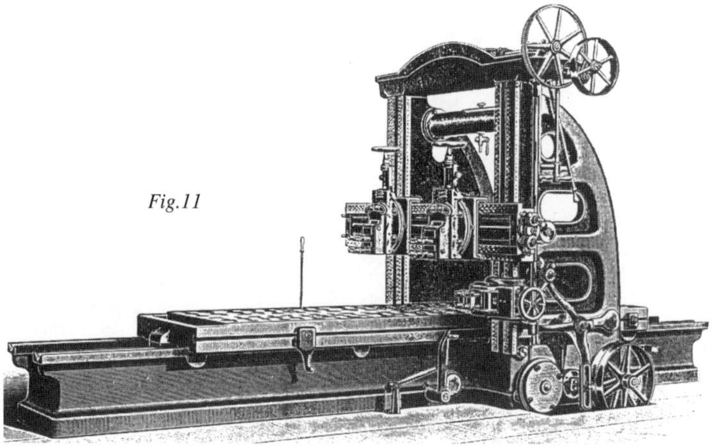

Fig.12

67, 60 AND 54 INCH PLANER.

Fig.13

84 AND 72 INCH PLANER.

Fig.14

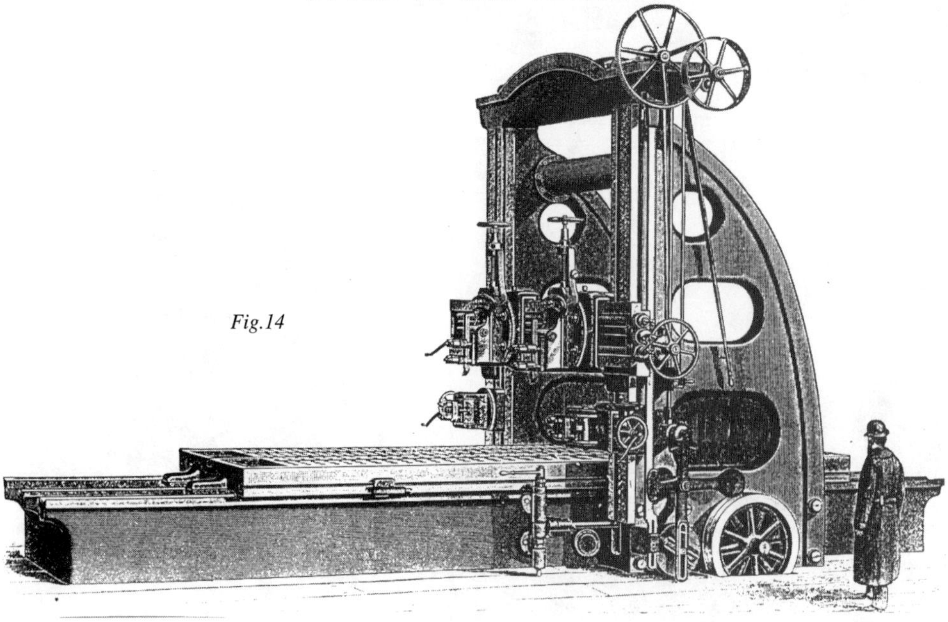

Fig.17

120 AND 100 INCH PLANER.

Fig.15

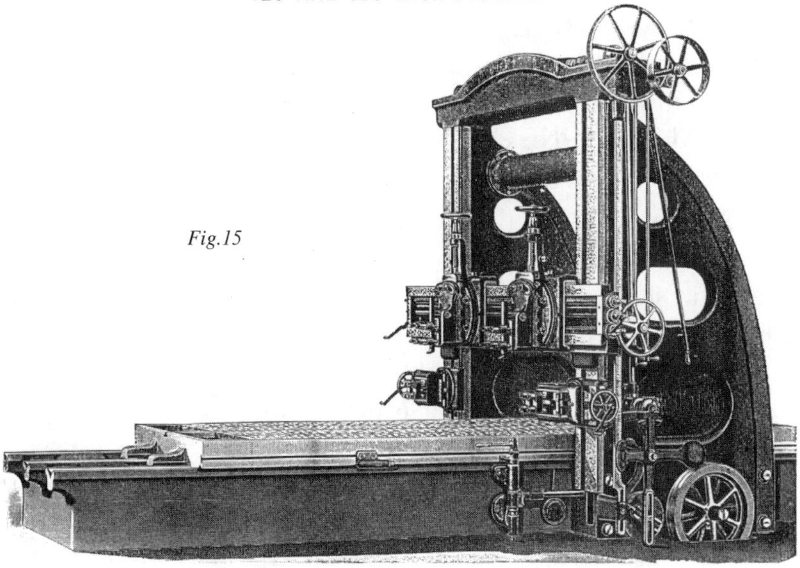

Fig.16

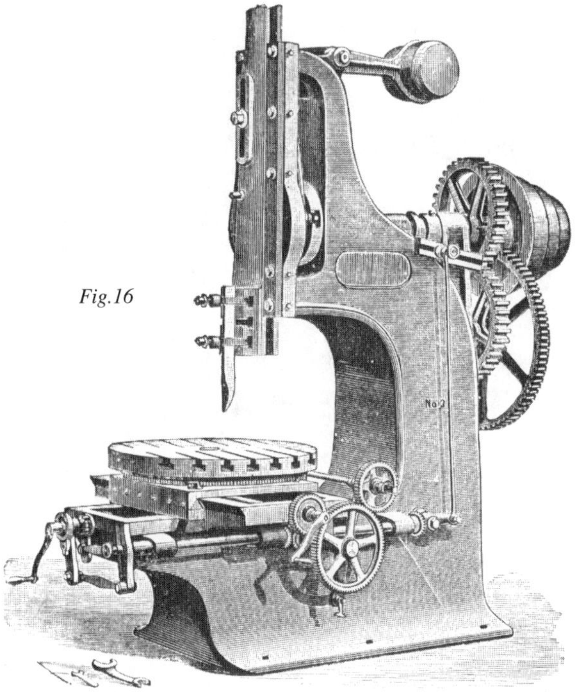

NEW ECCENTRIC PITMAN SHAPING MACHINE.

Fig.18

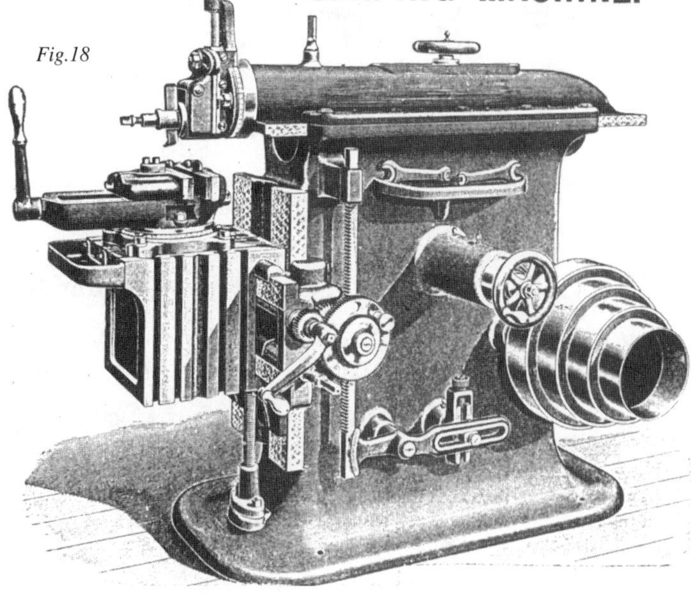

PUTNAM TOOL CO. (S.W. PUTNAM'S SONS), Fitchburg, MA

Formed in 1882 by Salmon W. Putnam, Jr. and his brother George E. Putnam when they left the PUTNAM MACHINE CO., founded by their father and operated by members of the Putnam family. The firm was short-lived and was merged into the PUTNAM MACHINE CO. on March 18, 1886, shortly after the brothers had rejoined and taken control of the family firm.

Shaper production included a two-speed model (Fig.1) for steel and cast iron, a rack cutting attachment (Fig.2), and an improved model (Fig.3) offered in 12", 15", 20" and 25" strokes. Production of these shapers was continued by the Putnam Machine Co. after the merger.

Fig.1

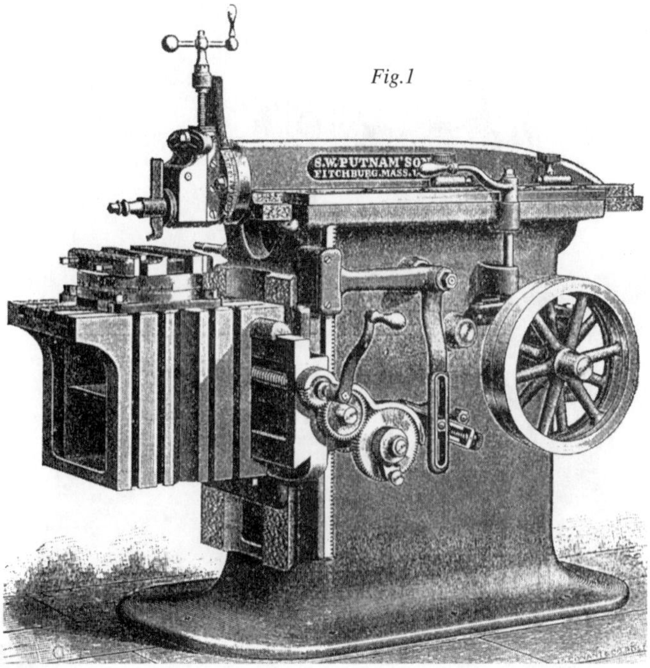

Fig.2

RACK-CUTTING ATTACHMENT FOR PUTNAM SHAPER.

Fig.3

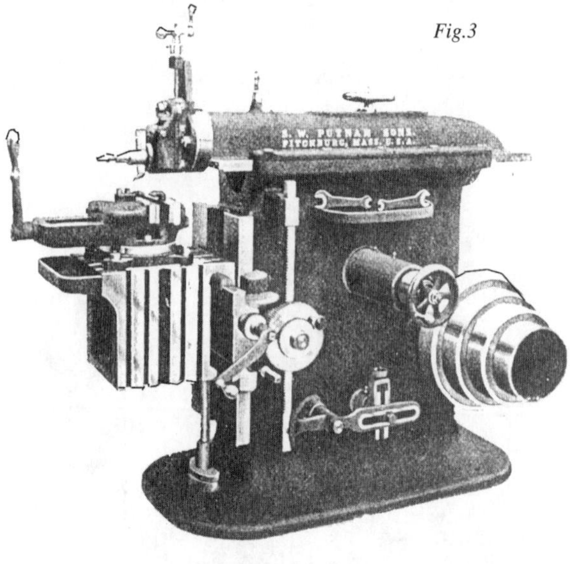

QUEEN CITY MACHINE TOOL CO., Cincinnati, OH

Formed in 1903 with William Rohche as president and A.M. Wachter, secretary and treasurer. Richard K. LeBlond was the finanical backer.

Products included 16" crank shapers introduced in 1903 (Fig.1), a heavy duty 16" model (Fig.2) introduced in 1904, and an extended base, outboard support model available in 1909 (Fig.3).

The company failed in 1927; remaining assets were sold to Manufacturers Gear & Machine Co.

(continued next page)

Fig.1

Fig.2

Fig.3

QUEEN CITY MACHINE WORKS, Cincinnati, OH

Operated by the partnership of Peter W. Reinshagen and John H. Buckman from 1868 to 1883. The firm built a variety of machine tools including lathes and planers.

RHODES & CO., L.E., Hartford, CT

Formed in 1897 as a reorganization of Finney & Rhodes and reorganized again, as the Rhodes Mfg. Co. in 1913.

Products included a 7" stroke shaper as shown below in a 1903 ad (Fig.1). In 1911, the shaper was available with an attachment to rotate the head 90 degrees for use as a slotter (Fig.2).

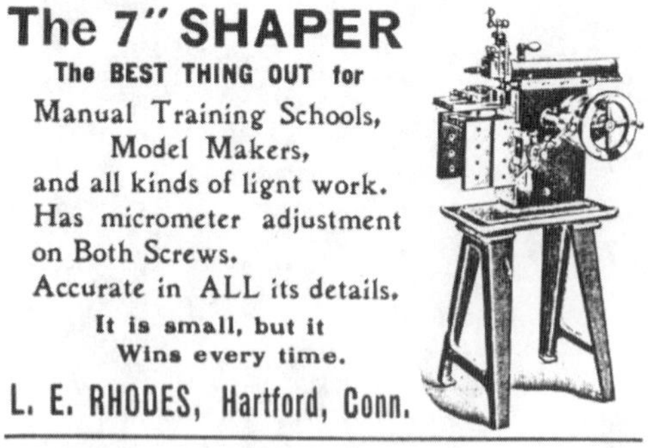

Fig.1

Fig.2

RIDER, JOHN F.C., South Newmarket, NH

Builder of "steam engines, pumps, engine lathes, planers, shaping machines, and machinists' tools of all kinds," operating c1867-1882.

RIDGEWAY MACHINE TOOL CO., Ridgeway, PA

Formed in 1904 by Harry R. Hyde to build large machine tools for heavy industry. Products included driving wheel lathes, large vertical boring machines and heavy planers, such as shown right, weighing 75,000 pounds.

Short lived, the company was absorbed by the Niles-Bement- Pond Co. in 1906.

ROBBINS & LAWRENCE CO., Windsor, VT

Formed in 1850 by Samuel E. Robbins (1810-1874) and Richard S. Lawrence (1817-1892) as a reorganization of Robbins, Kendall & Lawrence. Primary products were a variety of firearms, most made on contract for the U.S. and British governments. Machine tools soon became a secondary product when the company began selling machines that had been designed for its own firearms production. In 1853, the firm received an order for about 150 machine tools from the British government, nearly all those required to tool the new Small Arms Manufactory at Enfield Lock.

Robbins, who was a Bangor, ME, businessman, served as president and Lawrence as superintendent until the firm failed in 1856 due to failure to fulfill a British contract for 25,000 Enfield rifle-muskets. The plant and equipment were bought by Ebenezer G. Lamson in 1859 who then organized Lamson, Goodnow & Yale. Lawrence moved to Hartford, CT, where he became superintendent of the Sharps Rifle Mfg. Co.

Planers were made in six sizes and included a small planer (Fig.1) photographed in 1924 still being used by the Lamson & Goodnow Mfg. Co., and larger, more rigid planers, seven of which were still in operation at Jones & Lamson Machine Co. in 1897 (Fig.2).

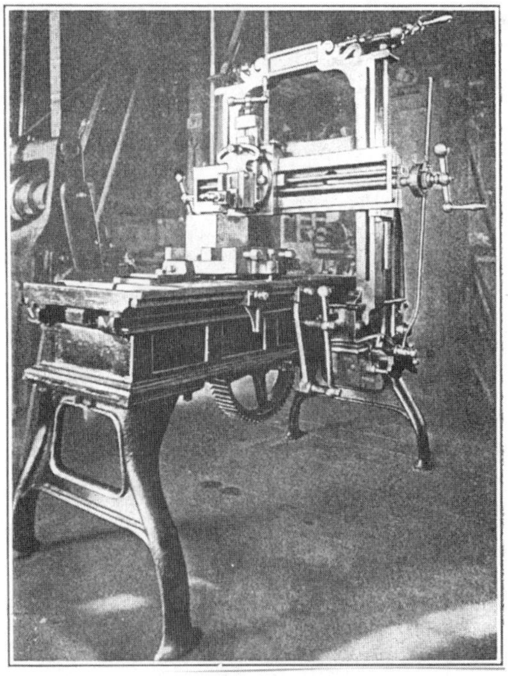

Fig.1

Fig.2

ROCHESTER DIE SHAPER CO., Rochester, NY

Maker, in 1902-1903, of an attachment that converts a horizontal milling machine to a die shaper. As shown next page in a 1902 ad, the attachment mounted on the overarm and was driven by an adaptor from the milling machine spindle.

ROCHESTER MACHINE TOOL WORKS, Rochester, NY

Formed in 1883 to take over the planer business of Geo. E. Brettell. George W. Davison, president, had been associated with the Providence Tool Co.

Early production was a continuation of the Brettell planer. In 1885, the firm introduced 15" pillar shapers (Fig.1) weighing 2400 pounds and equipped with a 3 1/2:1 quick return, and improved 30" x 30" planers (Fig.2) equipped with a 3:1 quick return. The firm also offered a planer tool holder, patented April 1, 1884, by E.R. Bryant, which allowed orientation of the cutting tool to plane the underside of lips (Fig.3). By 1889, production appears to have shifted to small marine steam engines and boilers. *(continued next page)*

Fig.1

FIFTEEN-INCH PILLAR SHAPER.

Fig.3

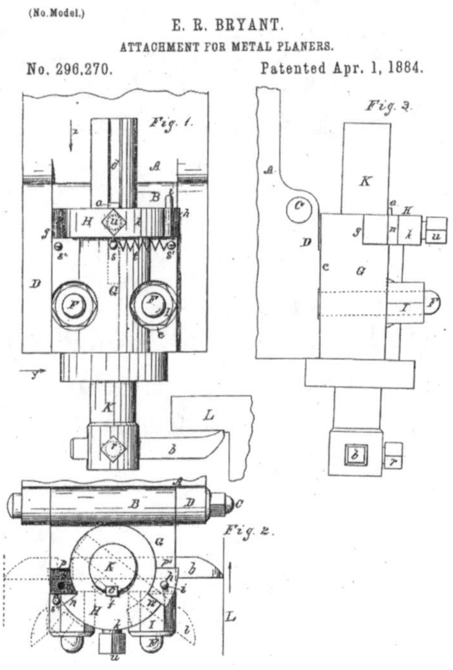

Rochester Machine Tool Works

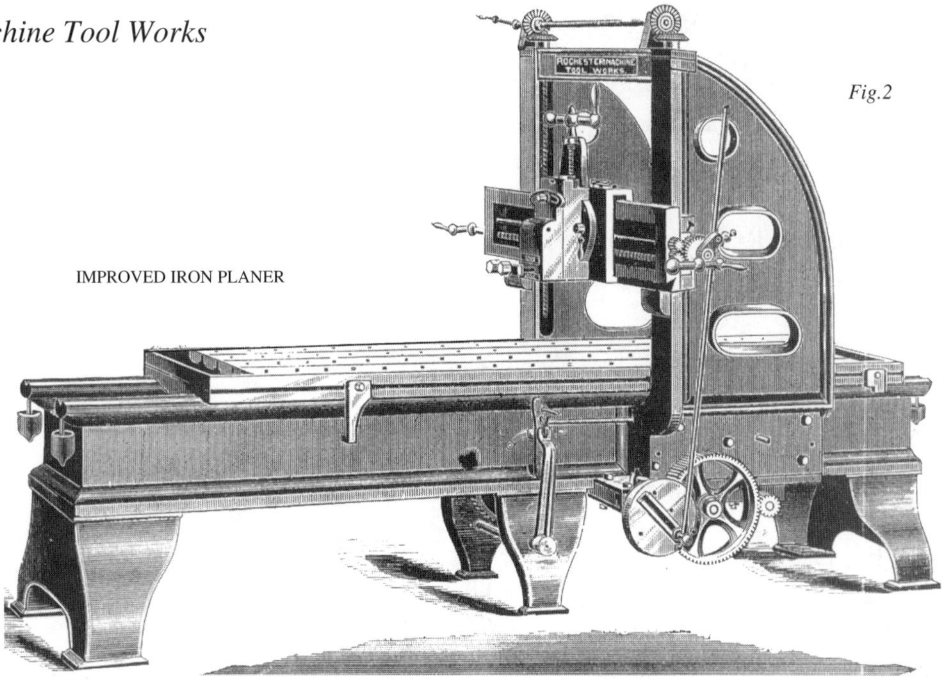

Fig.2

ROCKFORD MACHINE TOOL CO., Rockford, IL

Formed in 1905 by Robert C. Lind (1856-1935) who served as president until his death. The company was a reorganization of the National Engine Co. founded by Lind in 1902.

Products offered in 1908 included ROCKFORD back geared shapers made in 12", 16", 20" and 24" (Fig.1) strokes, and ROCKFORD planers made in 24", 28", 32" and 36" strokes. The 24' x 24" size (Fig.2) weighed 7100 pounds and was equipped with 30 FPM feed and 95 FPM return speed.

Fig.1

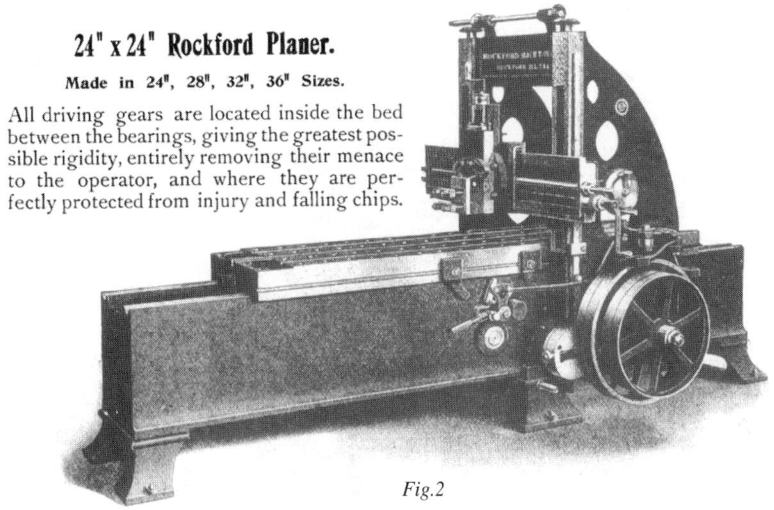

Fig.2

ROWLAND, F.C. & A.E., New Haven, CT, later
ROWLAND MACHINE CO., New Haven, CT

A partnership of Amory E. Rowland (1853-1912) and Frederick C. Rowland (1844-1904), formed in 1877 to build machinists' tools, including planers and engine lathes. They claimed to have sold 19 planers and lathes in 1882.

The firm reorganized as the ROWLAND MACHINE CO. soon after the death of Frederick C. Rowland in 1904.

SAUNDERS, DAVID, Yonkers, NY

Formed in 1857 by David Saunders (1809-1873) to build lathes and drilling machines. A combination shaper and slotter, with a ram that tilted from vertical to horizontal (right), was patented October 28, 1862, and offered until his factory burned in 1868. Saunders rebuilt, but production from that point appears to have been limited to threading machines.

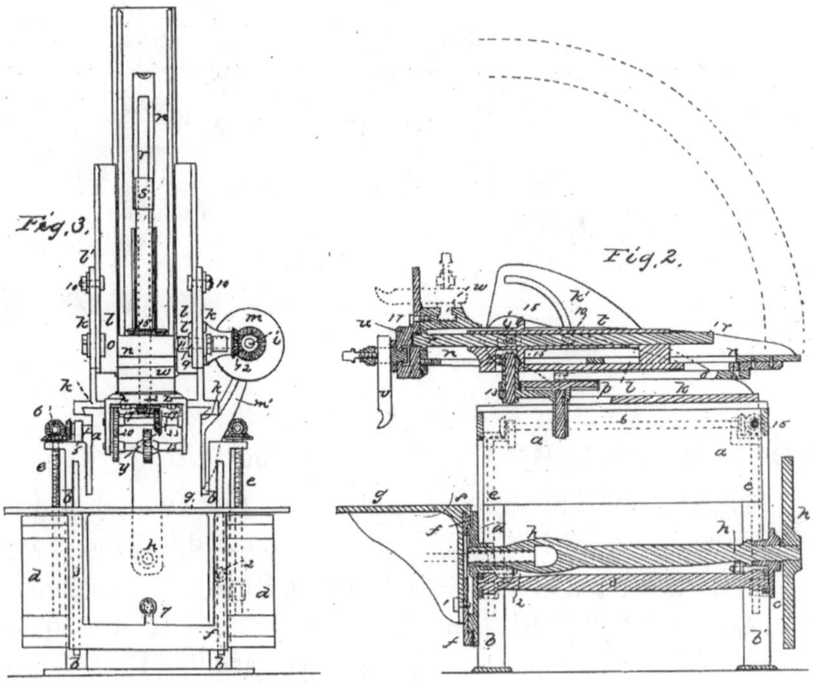

Joseph A. Sawyer & Son's Combined Hand and Power Planer.

SAWYER & SON, JOSEPH A., Worcester, MA

A partnership of Joseph A. Sawyer (?-1888) and his son Thomas J. Sawyer, formed in 1871. Builder of "Sawyer's combined hand and power planer" introduced in 1874. The son continued the firm after his father's death in 1888.

The only known model, shown left as offered in 1879, would cut 46" long, 15" wide and 13" high. It was priced at $240 with power drive only ($375 for combination hand and power drive) and is probably the largest planer made for hand operation.

SCHNEIDER MACHINE TOOL CO., Cincinnati, OH, later
SCHNEIDER & GOOSMANN MACHINE CO., Cincinnati, OH

Formed in 1909 to build a hand-operated, 10" x 8 ½" x 24" planer (Fig.1), with rack and gear drive.

The firm reorganized as the SCHNEIDER & GOOSMANN MACHINE CO. in 1910 and introduced a larger, 16" x 16" x 36" power planer (Fig.2) the same year. Also rack and gear driven, it weighed 1150 pounds.

Fig.1

Fig.2

SCHUYLKILL FOUNDRY & MACHINE WORKS, Conshohocken, PA

Builder, in 1894, of the plate planer shown below. The machine was designed for planing the edges of boiler plates that were already punched with the rivet holes. The plates were bolted, through the rivet holes, to the machine's rail. The machine could plane plates 1/8" to 3/4" thick and up to 16' long.

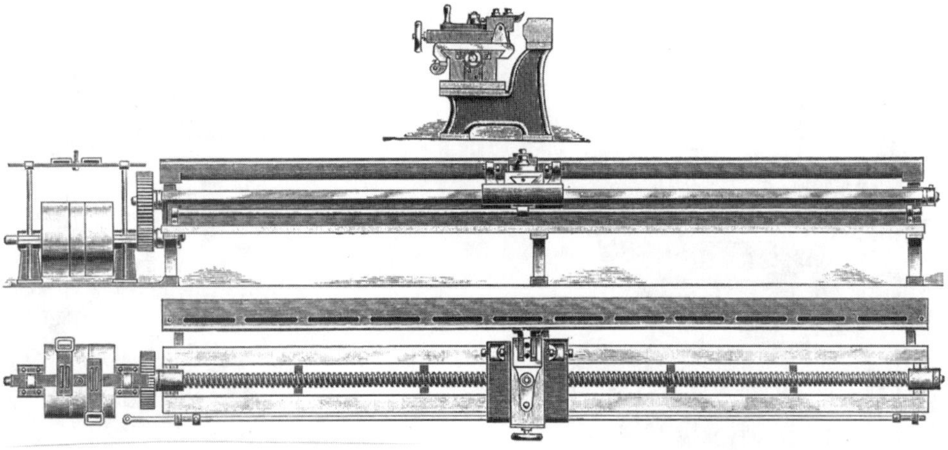

SCRANTON & PARSHLEY, New Haven, CT

In 1851 the firm announced that they "have finished 2 power planers ready to ship, that will plane 9 feet long, 31 inches wide, and 24 inches high, with angle feed, splining and centre heads, with index plate and weigh over 5,000 pounds; also 2 power planers that will plane 5 feet long, 22 inches wide and 20 inches high and weigh 2,400 pounds."

SEBASTIAN LATHE CO., Cincinnati, OH

Formed in 1891 by Benjamin Sebastian, Jr. (1853-1919) and his wife Clara Sebastian. Sebastian was previously a partner in the Sebastian-May Co. but sold out in 1891, returned to Cincinnati and began building foot lathes and engine lathes similar to those made by the Sebastian-May Co. By 1895, Sebastian advertised "shapers, planers, drills and foot & power lathes." In March, 1896, the company moved to a new factory across the river in Covington, KY, where Sebastian headed the firm until retiring in 1917.

In 1898, the firm offered adjustable crank shapers (Fig.1) in 16", 20" and 25" strokes. The stroke could be "quickly changed and adjusted while the machine is in motion or at rest." By 1905, the 16" (Fig.2) and 20" (Fig.3) models had been improved and the line expanded to include a 14" model (Fig.4) weighing 1400 lbs.

Fi.1

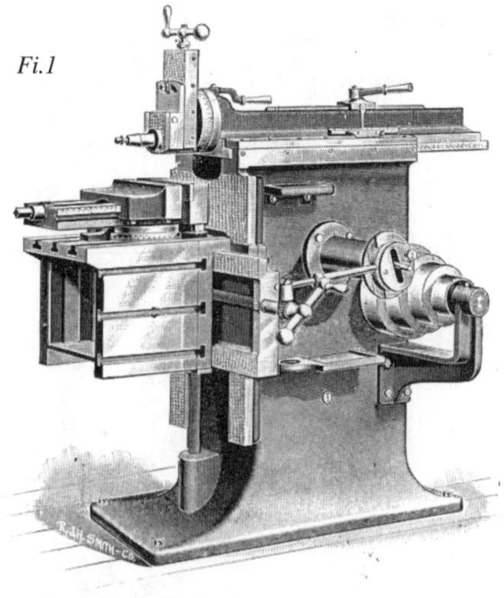

Improved Adjustable Crank Shaper.

	16-Inch SHAPER.	20-Inch SHAPER.	25-Inch SHAPER.
Length of Stroke	16 in.	20 in.	25 in.
Automatic Cross Traverse	20 "	24 in.	28 in.
Vertical Adjustment	16 "	16 in.	16 in.
Feed of Tool Block	6 "	8 in.	9 in.
Top of Table	10x16 in.	13x18 in.	14x21 in.
Largest Speed of Cone Pulley	11 in.	12 in.	15 in.
Size of Belt	2½ "	3 in.	3½ in.
Bearing in Column Slides when Ram is at Full Stroke	22 "	26 in.	31 in.
T. & L. Pulleys on C. S	12x3 in.	14x3 in	16x4
Revolutions per minute	125	125	175
Weight	2,000 lbs.	2,300 lbs.	3,000 lbs.

Fig.3

20-INCH IMPROVED CRANK SHAPER STYLES

Fig.2

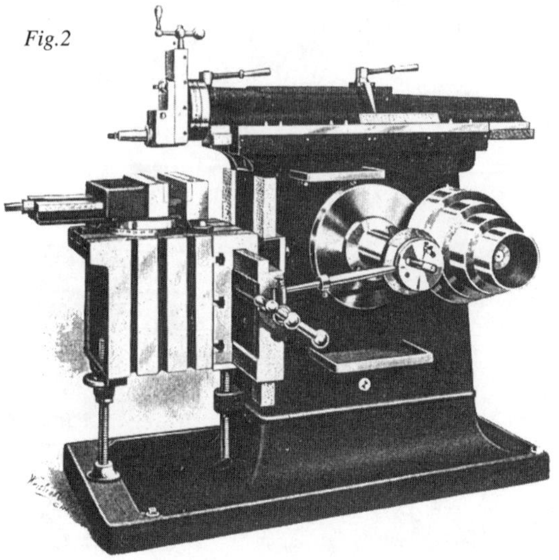

16-INCH IMPROVED CRANK SHAPER STYLE S

Fig.4

14-INCH CRANK SHAPER STYLE S

SELLERS & CO., WILLIAM, Philadelphia, PA

A partnership of William Sellers (1824-1905) and his brother John Sellers, Jr. (1826-1906), formed in 1855 when Edward Bancroft died and the partnership of Bancroft & Sellers was reorganized. Their cousin, Coleman Sellers, who had served as superintendent at NILES & CO., joined the firm in 1856 as chief engineer. In 1873, J. Sellers Bancroft (1843-1919), son of Edward Bancroft, and James C. Brooks (1834-1911) became partners.

The firm made a variety of mechanical products, including shafting, presses, etc. Metal working machinery was the primary product from the beginning and centered around heavy machine tools for the railroad and shipbuilding industries located in Philadelphia. 1860 production included planers and slotters.

William Sellers is credited with a major advance in planer performance when he developed the Sellers Spiral Planer Drive, patented August 15, 1862, (Fig.1) with improvements patented May 17, 1864 (Fig.2). Offered first on 25" x 25" planers (Fig.3), the spiral drive gave an unusually smooth feed and was widely copied after expiration of the patent. *(continued on next three pages)*

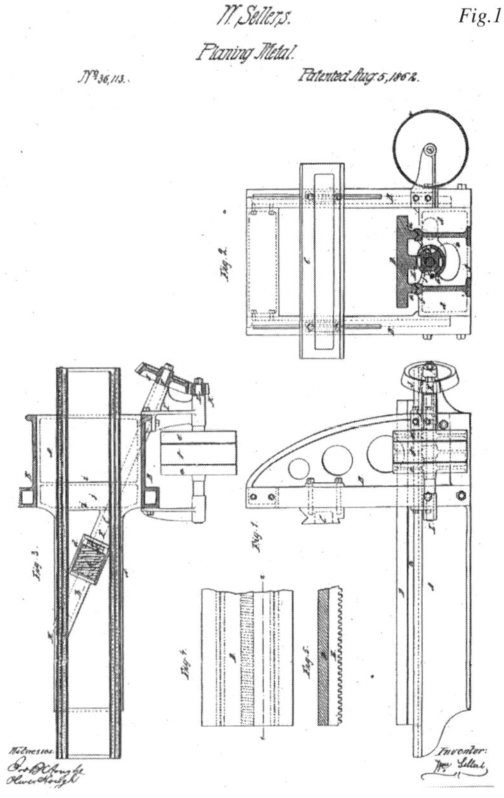

Fig.1

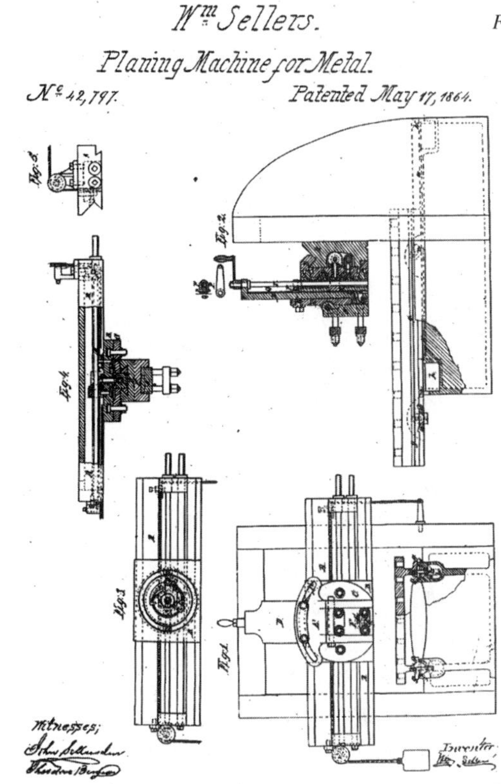

Fig.2

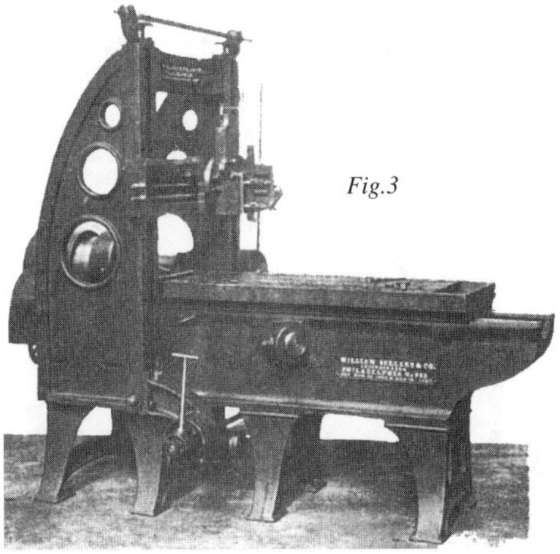

Fig.3

Name of Planer.	Will plane in width.	In height.	Shortest length of table
20 inches.	20 inches.	20 inches.	3 feet.
25 "	25 "	25 "	3 " 7 inches.
30 "	30 "	30 "	4 " 2 "
36 "	36 "	36 "	4 " 8 "
42 "	42 "	42 "	5 " 4 "
48 "	48 "	48 "	6 "
54 "	54 "	54 "	6 " 7 "
60 "	60 "	60 "	7 " 3 "
72 "	72 "	72 "	8 " 6 "
84 "	84 "	84 "	10 "
120 "	120 "	120 "	13 " 6 "

These machines can be of any required length.

Fig.4

Sellers' 1877 catalog offered planers in 11 sizes (Fig.4) including 25" x 25" (Fig.5) and 48" x 48" (Fig.6); plate planers (Fig.7) to plane up to 16'; rod planers (Fig.8) to plane locomotive connnecting rods from 3 1/2' to 10' long; slotters in 7 1/2", 9", 10 1/2", 12" (Fig.9), 15", 18" strokes; traverse shapers in 9" x 36", 12" x 48" (Fig.10), 16" x 66" and 20" x 84" sizes. By 1880 the firm offered a traveling head slotter (Fig.11).

Fig.5

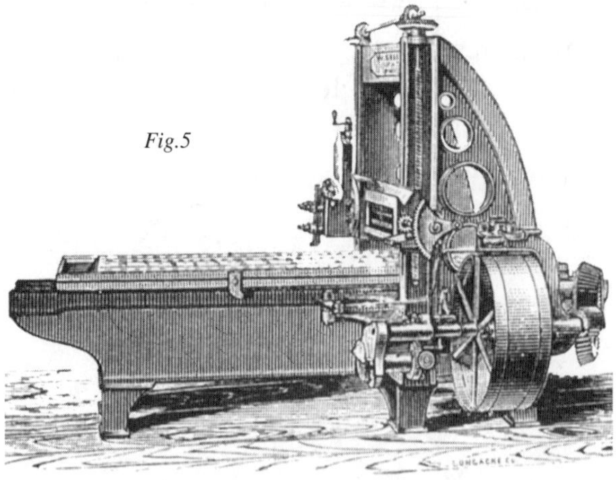

PATENT SELF-ACTING PLANING MACHINE.

Fig.6

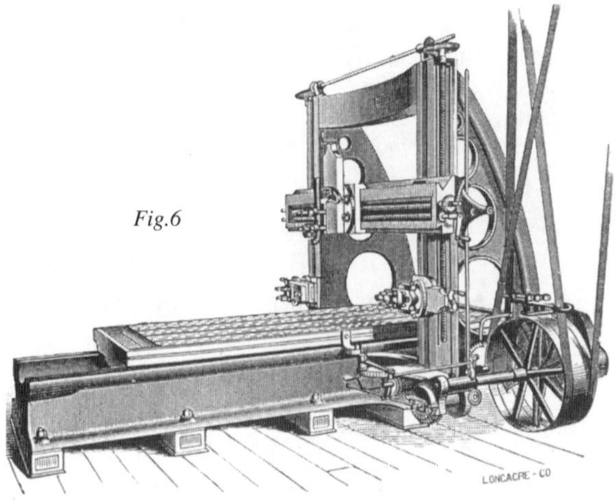

PATENT SELF-ACTING PLANING MACHINE.

Fig.7 PLATE PLANING MACHINE.

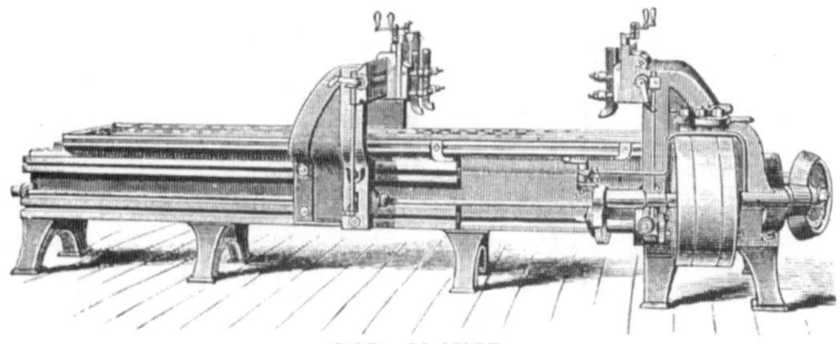

Fig.8 ROD PLANER.

Fig.9

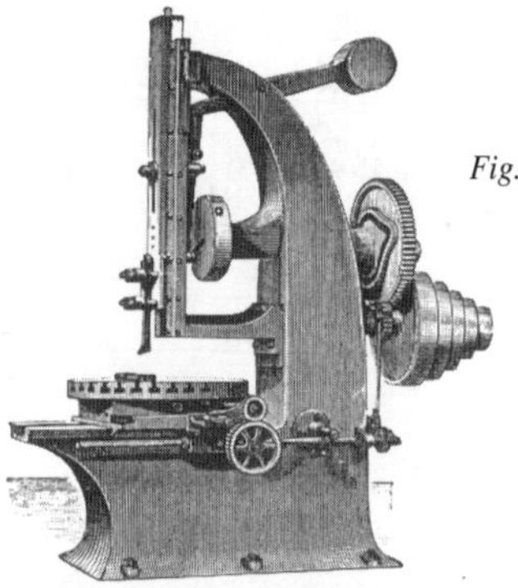

SLOTTING MACHINE.

Fig.10

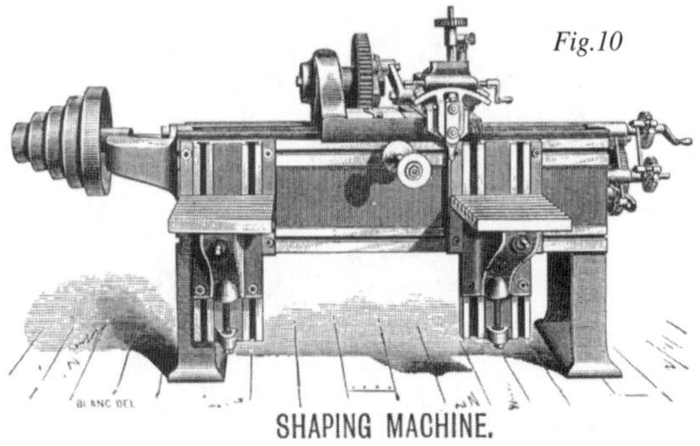

SHAPING MACHINE.

Fig.11

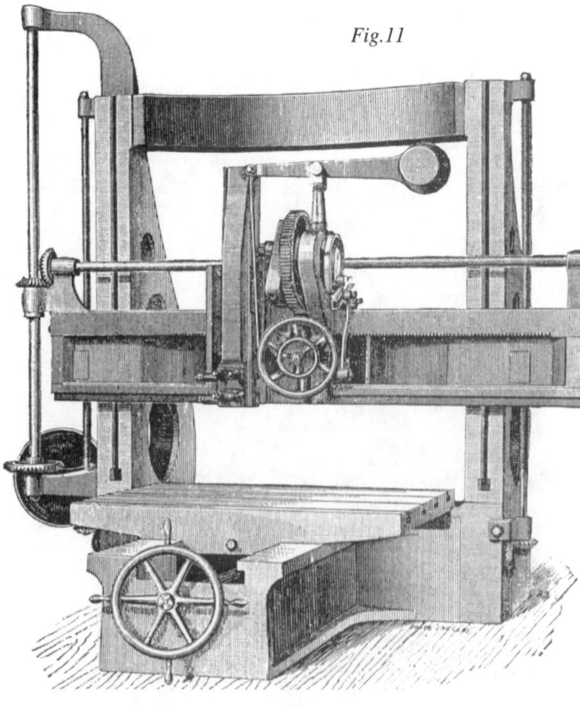

Fig.12

Fig.13

W. SELLERS & J. S. BANCROFT.
PLANING MACHINE FOR METALS.
No. 374,908. Patented Dec. 13, 1887.

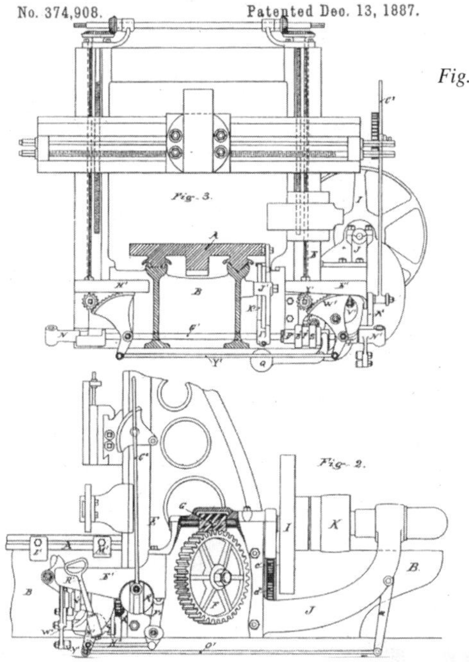

Fig.14

Fig.15

SELLERS SINGLE-BELT-DRIVE PLANER WITH MECHANICALLY-OPERATED CLUTCHES. PATENTED 1893

Fig.16

Wm. Sellers & Co.

The 1884 catalog continued to offer 11 sizes of planers, incuding 36" x 36" (Fig.12) and 60" x 60" (Fig.13) sizes. In 1887 a new, two-belt, improved planer drive, patented December 13, 1887, (Fig.14) was introduced, followed in 1893 by a single belt drive with mechanical clutches (Fig.15).

By 1881, the firm had grown to employ 600 hands and, in 1886, incorporated with capital of $1,500,000. William Sellers was elected president, serving until his death in 1905, John Sellers, Jr., vice president, J. Sellers Bancroft, manager, Coleman Sellers, engineer, and Justus G. Schwacke, secretary.

A very large planer (Fig.16), 12' x 10' x 25' was offered in 1902, following in 1905 by large planers with a choice of pneumatic clutch (Fig.17) or shifting belt (Fig.18) reversing mechanism.

William Sellers & Co., Inc. was aquired by the Consolidated Machine Tool Corp. in 1947 and operated, for a short time, as a division.

SHAW, THOMAS, Philadelphia, PA

Inventor and probably maker of SHAW'S planer bar, patented February 18, 1873. The bar, shown right, was designed to reach through work into areas which could not be planed in a conventional manner. It is attached to the planer head to use the machine's down feed and pivots at the rear.

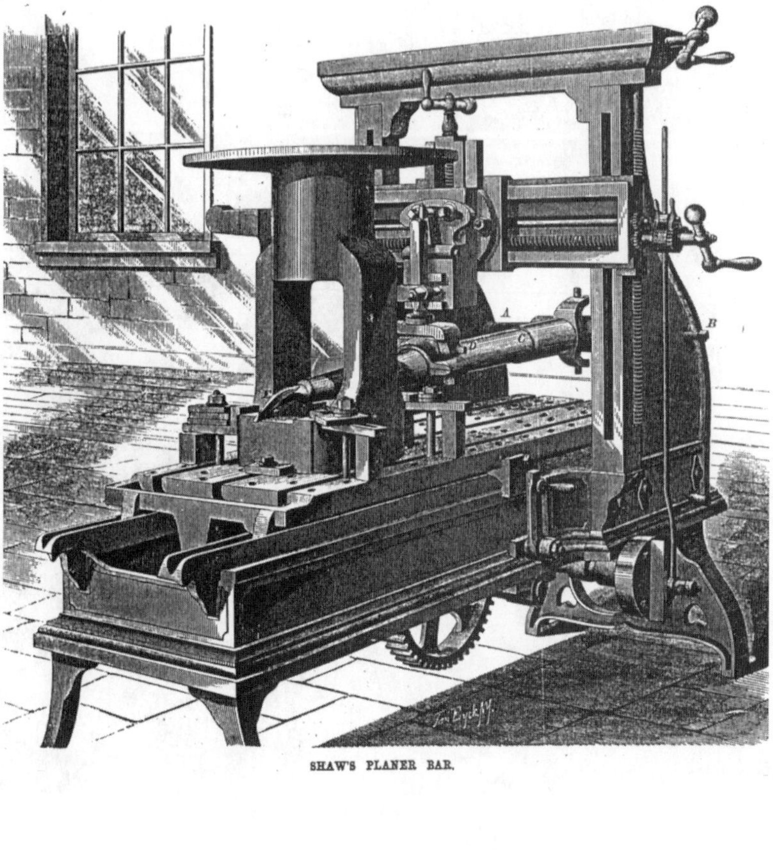

SHAW'S PLANER BAR.

SHEPARD & CO., H.L., Cincinnati, OH, later
SHEPARD LATHE CO., Cincinnati, OH

Founded in 1875 by Herbert L. Shepard to build foot lathes and other light machine tools. In 1892, Shepard introduced a hand planer, shown right, offered in 9" x 8" x 12" and 12" x 12" x 24" sizes.

The firm reorganized as the SHEPARD LATHE CO. when Shepard retired in 1898 and his son took over the business. Products offered in 1905 included lathes in several types and sizes, planers, shapers and drill presses. Production continued as late as 1921.

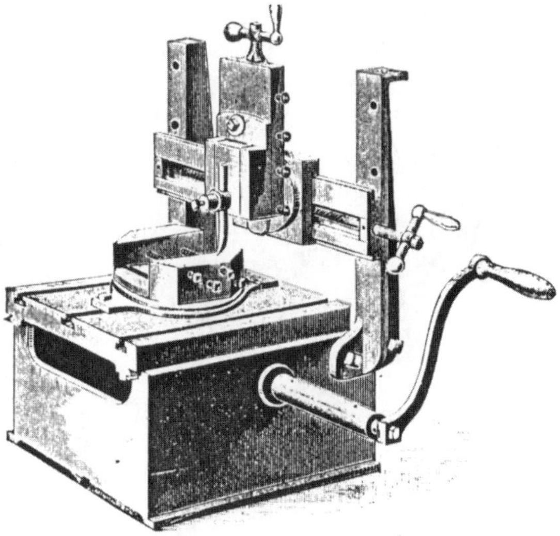

SHEPHARD'S NEW HAND PLANER.

SHEPARD, LATHE & CO., Worcester, MA

A partnership of Russell R. Shepard, Martin Lathe, and Edwin Morse, formed in 1853 as successor to S.C. COOMBS & CO. Builder of a variety of machine tools including 14"x 14" x 30" hand planers, and power planers as shown in the chart below.

Planes Width	Height	Weight	Price
4 ft. long	20 in.	2000	$335
5 ft. long	24 in.	3000	$405
6 ft. long	24 in.	3500	$435
6 ft. long	32 in.	4500	$550
8 ft. long	32 in.	5200	$600
10 ft. long	36 in.	8000	$850
12 ft. long	36 in.	10800	$1000
16 ft. long	42 in.	14000	$1300

The firm reorganized as Lathe & Morse when Shepard left in 1864.

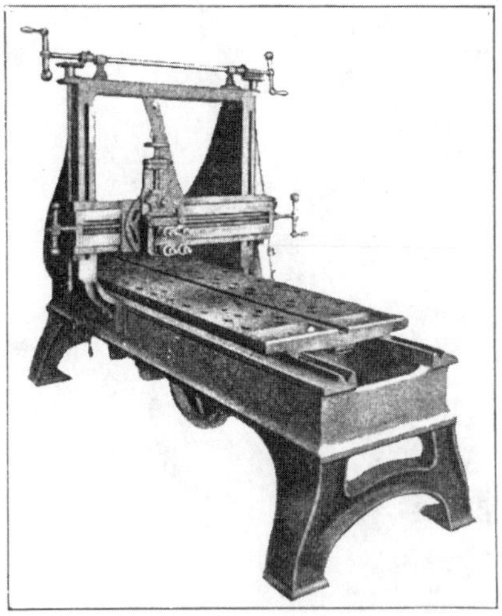

SHRIVER & BRO., Cumberland, MD

Builder, c1850, of the planer shown left. The machine was photographed, still in use, in 1910.

SILBEY, W.L., Waltham, MA

Planer builder operating c1860. One of its planers was examined in 1908 as part of a study of old machine tools. It was described as "highly ornamented with uprights having cast-in ladies with flowing robes holding lyres. Another lyre was located below each lady." The 1908 writer couldn't resist the pun "how could we swear to the truth of work done by a planer with four lyres." Truth of work, at that time, expressed the accuracy with which a machine cut metal.

SILVER & GAY, North Chelmsford, MA, later
SILVER & GAY CO., North Chelmsford, MA

A partnership of Harvey Silver (?-1884) and Ziba Gay, Jr. (1823-1902) formed in 1857 as a reorganization of Gay, Silver & Co. In 1884, the firm reorganized as the SILVER & GAY CO.

Products incuded textile machinery, lathes, planers and other machine tools. Machine tool production, however, ceased prior to 1901.

SLATE & BROWN, Windsor Locks, CT

A partnership of Dwight Slate (1816-1906) and F.M. Brown, formed in 1844 to make planers driven by a large spur gear (bull wheel) meshed with a rack attached to the table. The partnership ended in 1850 when Slate moved to Augusta, GA, to become superintendent of the Augusta Machine Works.

The firm was one of the first to make planers as a production item.

SMITH & MILLS, Cincinnati, OH, later
SMITH & MILLS CO., Cincinnati, OH

Formed in 1888 as a partnership of Albert S. Smith (1858-1917) and James Mills (1839-1913). Both Smith and Mills had previously worked at the JOHN STEPTOE SHAPER CO. The firm incorporated as the Smith & Mills Co., January 5, 1907, with capital of $160,000; Smith was president and Mills, vice president.

The firm built shapers only and, by 1899, production reached 30 to 35 monthly. 1891 production included 15" adjustable stroke crank shapers (Fig.1). By 1900, the firm offered triple geared shapers from 12" to 32" stroke and adjustable stroke crank shapers in the same sizes (Fig.2). 1910 production included crank shapers in 12" to 25" stroke and geared shapers in 16" to 32" stroke (Fig.3).

Fig.1

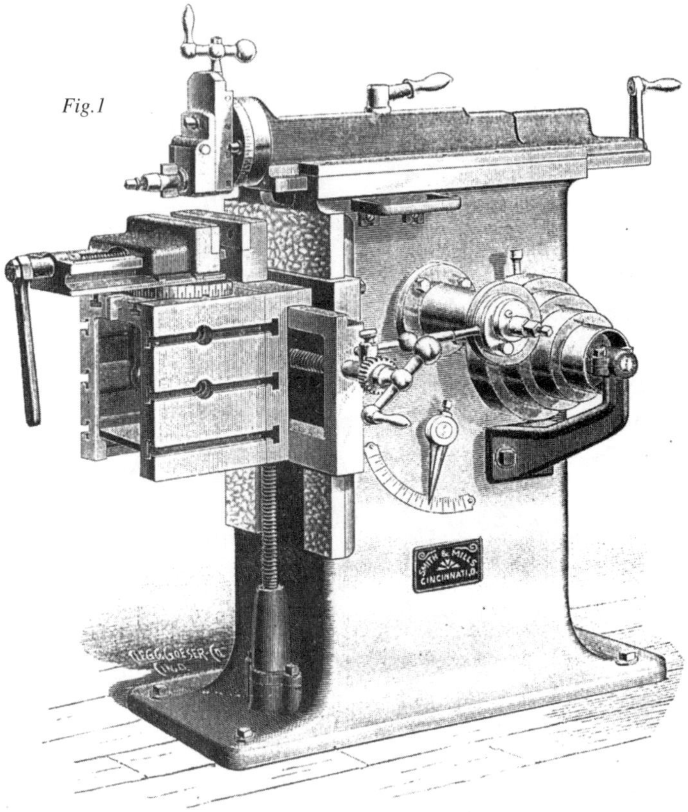

Improved Crank Shaper.

Fig.3

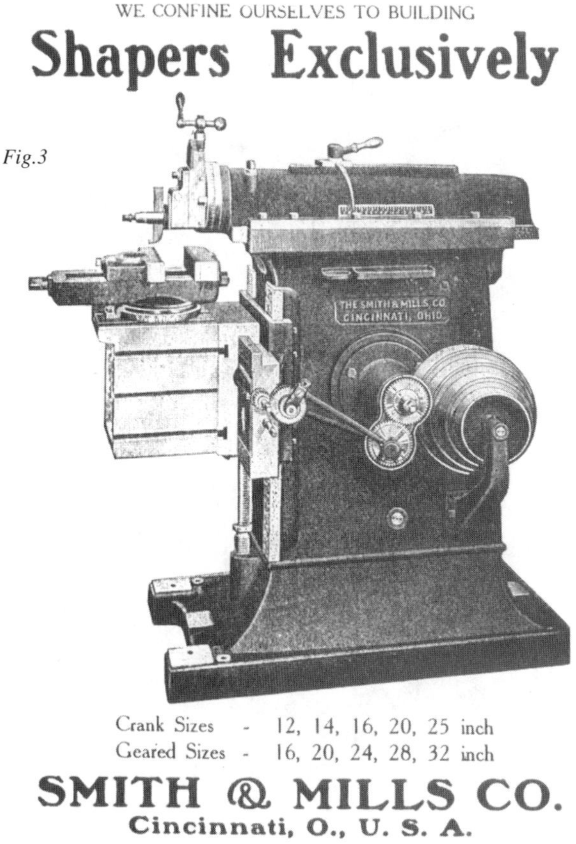

Fig.2

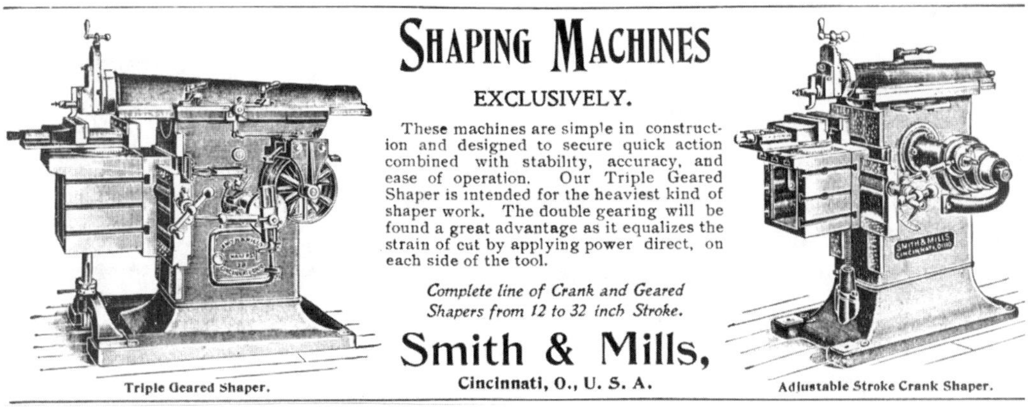

SMITH & SILK, Cincinnati, OH, later

SMITH & SILK MACHINE TOOL CO., Kenton, OH

A partnership of William D. Smith (1860-1939) and P.P. Silk, formed in 1887 to build planers and shapers (Fig.1, right). The firm moved to Kenton, OH, and reorganized as the SMITH & SILK MACHINE TOOL CO. in 1891. Silk sold out in 1897 and returned to Cincinnati. Smith then reorganized the firm as the OHIO MACHINE TOOL CO. *(continued on next page)*

Products included a 20" shaper (Fig.2), weighing 2600 pounds introduced in 1891; and 18" and 22" crank shapers (Fig.3) offered in 1897.

Fig.2

Twenty-six-inch Shaper.

18-inch and 22-inch Stroke.

Fig.3

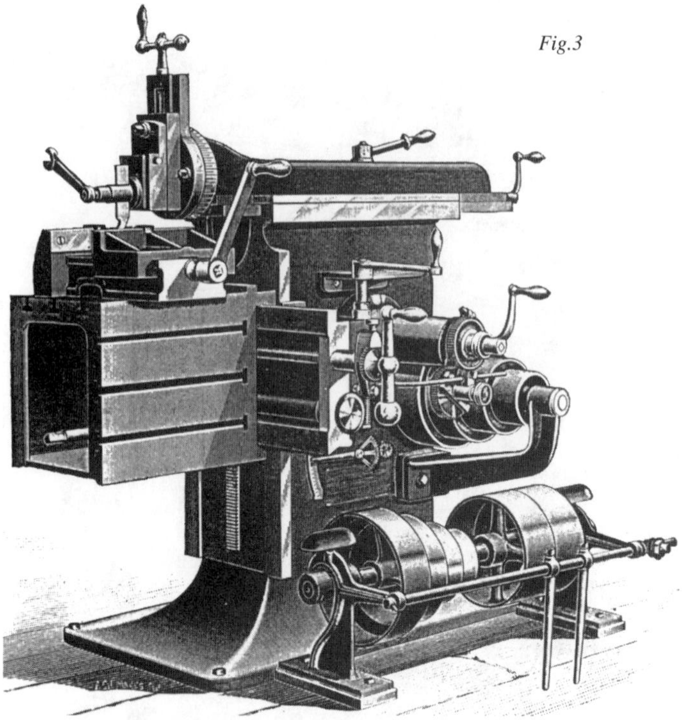

SMITH MACHINE CO., H.B., Smithville, NJ

A major builder of wood-working machinery, the firm entered the metal-cutting machine tool market in 1882 with the introduction of the planer shown right. The machine could plane 30" wide by 20" high and 6' long and "working parts were made 1/3 heavier than usual." The venture into metal-cutting appears to have been short lived; no other machine tools have been noted.

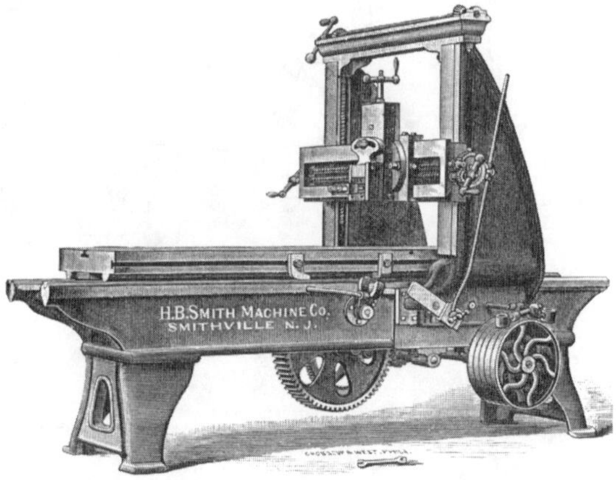

New Iron Planer.

SPRINGFIELD MACHINE TOOL CO., Springfield, OH

Founded in 1887 by Phillip E. Montanus (1854-1932), William H. Owen (?-1906) and Frank Kempsmith (1848-1904) to build lathes under contract for Lodge, Davis & Co. Montanus served as president until his death in 1932. Owen left in 1893 to found the Owen Machine Tool Co. Kempsmith left in 1888 to found the Kempsmith Machine Tool Co. *(continued next two pages)*

In 1891, the firm incorporated with a capital of $50,000 and began offering hand and power presses under its own name. Edward A. Muller, who had been superintendent of Lodge & Davis Machine Tool Co., joined the firm as superintendent in 1894.

In 1894, a line of crank shapers in 12" (Fig.1), 15" (Fig.2) and 20" (Fig.3) stroke was introduced and, by 1895, the firm claimed to have shipped 600 shapers and to be the second largest builder of 15" and 20" crank shapers in the U.S. By 1903, the line had expanded to include 18" (Fig.4) and 24" triple geared crank shapers weighing 1800 pounds and 2400 pounds respectively. A 16" crank shaper (Fig.5) with a newly designed drive was introduced in 1904.

Fig.1

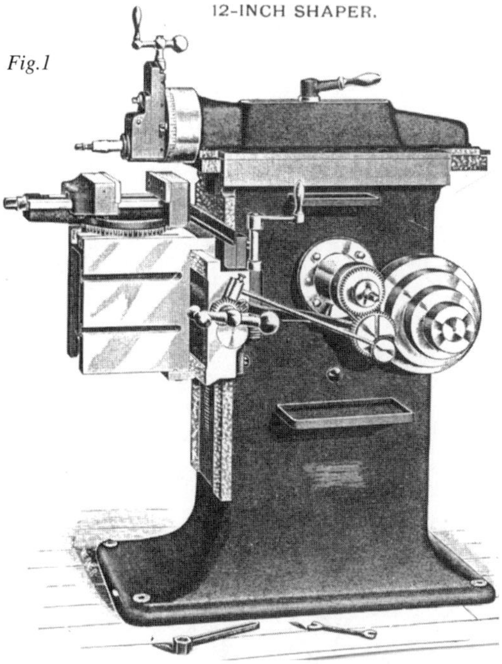

Fig.2

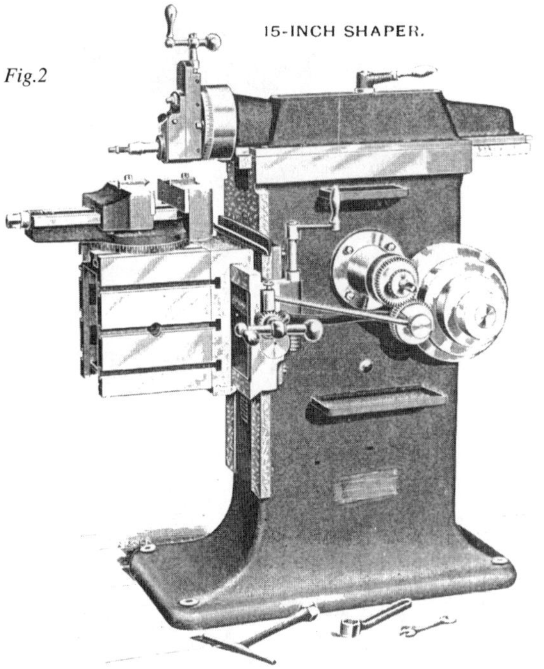

Fig.3

Fig.4

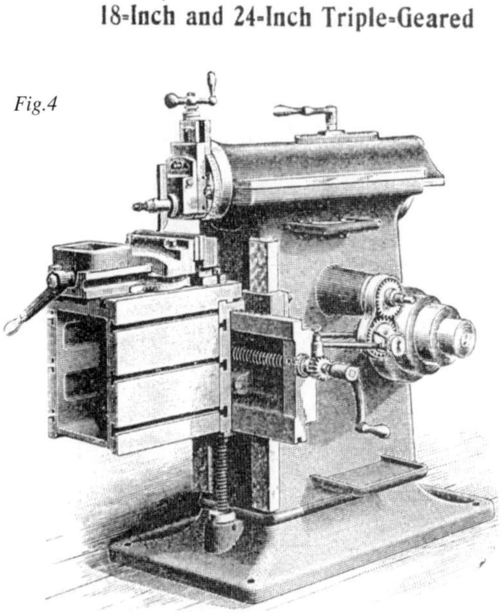

Fig.5

A NEW 16-INCH SHAPER.

Springfield Machine Tool Co.

SPRINGFIELD TOOL CO., Springfield, MA

Operated by Chester Van Horn. Maker, c1855-1860, of 14" engine lathes equipped with Van Horn's tool elevator, patented April 17, 1855.

In 1856, Van Horn introduced a planer patented August 12, 1856. An example, shown right, was photographed, still in use, in 1911. Note the unique design with a large "overarm" supporting one end of the crossrail and connecting to an upright offset from the upright supporting the other end of the crossrail. The other end of the overarm connnects to a third upright mounted at the other end of the bed. The overarm was designed to move vertically as the tool was raised or lowered.

This feature resulted in a form of open-side planer which could handle workpieces much wider than the platen.

STEPTOE, McFARLAN & CO., Cincinnati, OH, later
STEPTOE & CO., JOHN, Cincinnati, OH, later
STEPTOE SHAPER CO., JOHN, Cincinnati, OH

A partnership of John Steptoe (1804-1888) and Thomas McFarlan, formed in 1860. The firm failed in 1878 and was reorganized as JOHN STEPTOE & CO. Steptoe is credited with being one of the first machine tool builders in Cincinnati.

Woodworking machinery was the bulk of its business at first, although the firm reportedly offered a copy of the Putnam engine lathe in the 1860s. By 1870 Steptoe employed 300 hands and production included metalworking lathes, planers, radial drills, shapers and slotters. Advertisements claimed "we employ none but the best workmen." An 1874 ad offered "machinists tools (of our own make) such as engine lathes, drills, planers, shapers, etc."

In 1887, Steptoe offered 10" and 15" crank shapers, 18" and 26" geared shapers, and 22" to 60" iron planers. A double geared 26" shaper, weighing 2600 pounds (Fig.1) was introduced in 1887, with an improved model available in 1891 (Fig.2). An improved 16" crank shaper (Fig.3) with Whitworth quick return was introduced in 1901.

The firm incorporated in 1903 as the JOHN STEPTOE SHAPER CO. with capital of $125,000; George Otting was president and Adam Lauther secretary and treasurer. Motor driven shapers were introduced in 1907 in 16", 20" and 25" strokes, either plain or back geared. The 25" shaper (Fig.4) weighed 4500 pounds. A 26" triple geared model (Fig.5) was introduced in 1910. *(continued on next page)*

Fig.1

Fig.2

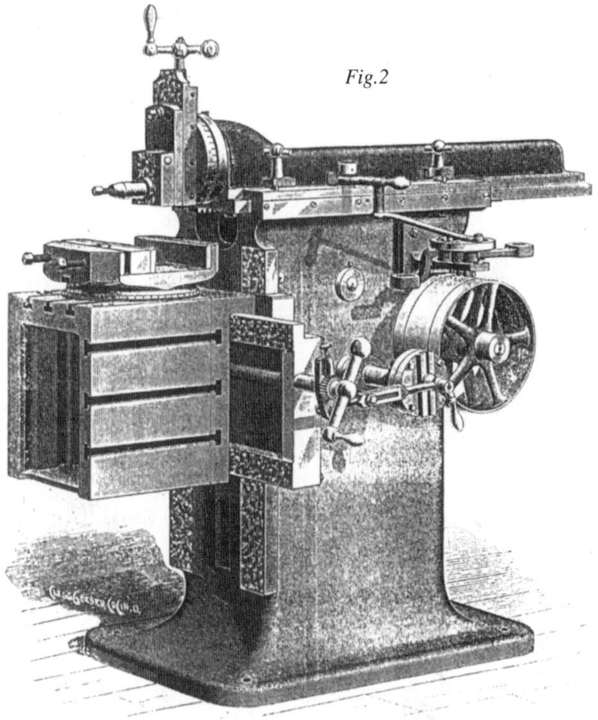

TWENTY-SIX-INCH DOUBLE-GEARED SHAPER.

Fig.3

Fig.4

Steptoe Shaper Co.

Fig.5

STOCKBRIDGE MACHINE CO., Worcester, MA

Founded in 1899 by Radford Stockbridge (1852-1925) who served as president until his death. The company specialized in shapers equipped with a two piece crank developed by Stockbridge. The crank, Stockbridge claimed, “delivers all the power developed by the driving shaft to the tool point and secures an even cutting speed throughout the length of the cut.”

First production was a 16" stroke crank shaper (Fig.1) sold through the Niles Tool Works in 1900. Motor driven shapers were introduced in 1903 with a well packaged drive (Fig.2), and expanded in 1904 with a complex speed changer consisting of a five speed motor and four gear changes (Fig.3) giving 20 speed changes. 1905 production included new 16" (Fig.4) and 20" crank shapers with 3:1 quick return. A new 18" all geared shaper (Fig.5) was introduced in 1909 and a new 16" heavy duty, back geared shaper (Fig.6), weighing 2850 pounds, in 1910. *(continued on next page)*

Fig.1

Fig.2

Fig.3

Fig.4

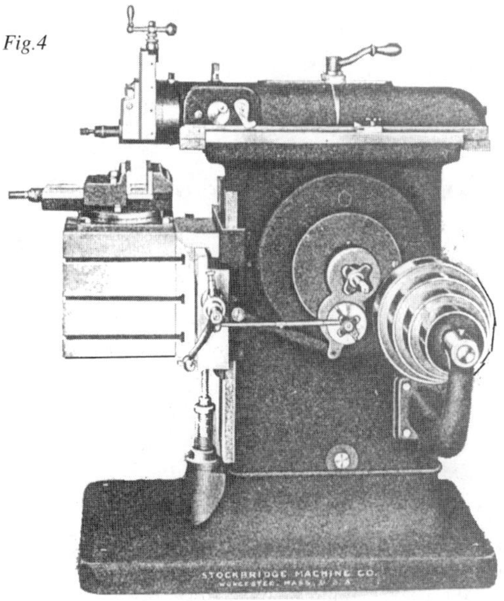

Fig.5

Fig.6

STOCKMAR & DUVINAGE, New York, NY

A partnership of Alexander Stockmar and Lewis Duvinage, formed about 1862 to build "shapers, slide and hand lathes, and other machinists' tools." The firm was dissolved in 1868.

THAYER, A. & S., Worcester, MA, later

THAYER, HOUGHTON & CO., Worcester, MA

A partnership of Alexander Thayer (1812-1895) and Sewell Thayer formed in 1845 to build lathes, planers, and other machine tools. The firm reorganized as Thayer, Houghton & Co. in 1853 when Sewell Thayer died and was replaced by Hannibal H. Houghton (1827-1898) and E.C. Cleveland. *(continued next page)*

In 1854, the firm was burned out in the Merrifield Building fire. Within a year the partners built the Washington St. Machine Shop and continued production of a variety of machine tools as shown in Fig.1. Planers, patented July 29, 1856, by E.C. Cleveland (Fig.2), were made with elaborately ornamented castings as shown on a c1856 planer photographed in 1903 (Fig.3), still in use.

In 1862, the partners sold out to the New York Steam Engine Works which continued production at the Worcester factory. Alexander Thayer stayed on as superintendent until 1864, when he left to join the New Haven Mfg. Co.

Fig.1

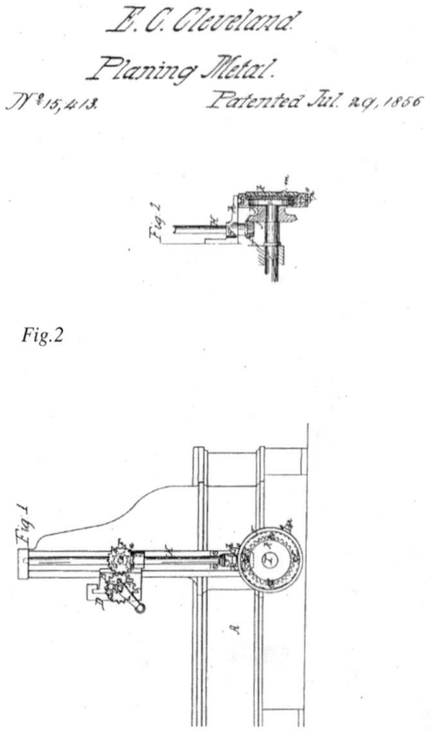

Fig.2

Fig.3

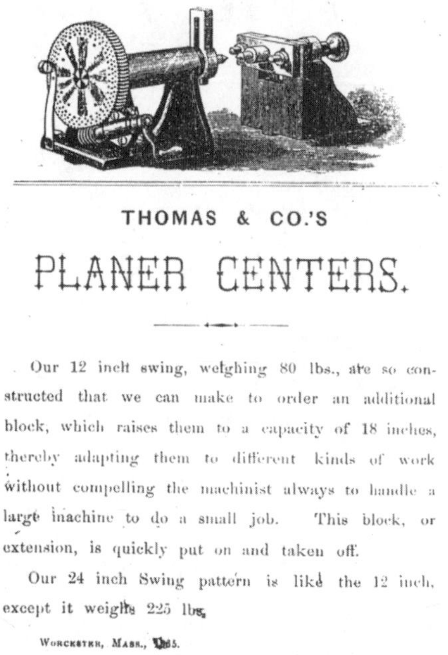

THOMAS IRON WORKS, Worcester, MA

Founded by Alfred Thomas in 1864 to build 17", 20" and 22", heavy engine lathes and planer centers shown in the 1865 ad at right. The business failed in 1870.

THOMPSON, SKINNER & CO., Worcester, MA

A partnership of Elijah Thompson and Franklin Skinner, formed in 1845 to build machinery and machine tools, including lathes and planers. The firm was absorbed by the New Haven Mfg. Co. in 1853.

TODD & CO., JAMES, Cincinnati, OH

Listed in an 1851 directory as employing 50 hands building steam engines, planers and lathes.

TOLMAN & CO., C.S., Fitchburg, MA, later
TOLMAN, C.S., Fitchburg, MA

A partnership of Cyrus S. Tolman and Asher Green, listed in the 1855 city directory as a builder of iron planers, engine lathes and hand lathes. In 1868, Tolman offered "new and improved shaping machines with chuck, centers, and countershaft" in the ad shown left.

NEW AND IMPROVED SHAPING MACHINE, from new and improved patterns, quick return motion, circular planes attached. Also CHUCK, CENTRES, and COUNTER SHAFT.

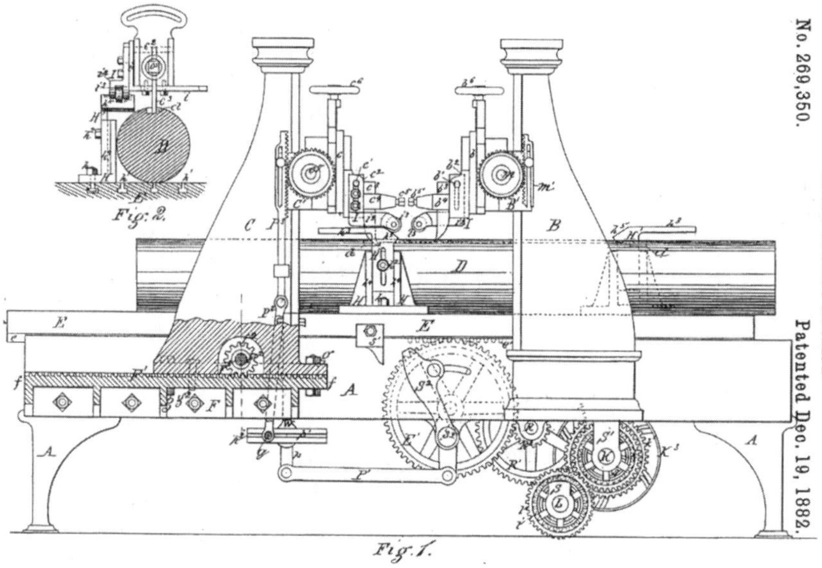

TOTTEN & HOGG IRON & STEEL FOUNDRY CO., Pittsburgh, PA

An important maker of rolling mill machinery, the firm also built heavy machine tools for making and repairing the large rolls used in the machinery. Products included large lathes for turning the rolls and a two column planer for machining keyways and flutes in the rolls. Patented December 19, 1882, the machine was designed to machine in both directions of travel and thus eliminate the lost time of return travel.

TWISS, PRATT & HAYES, New Haven, CT, later
TWISS, HAYES & CO., New Haven, CT

Formed about 1867 to build iron planers, shapers, lathes, screw machines, etc. The firm reorganized as TWISS, HAYES & CO. in 1869.

UNION IRON WORKS,
San Francisco, CA

Founded in 1849 by Peter Donahue and his brothers. By 1863, the firm was a major west coast builder of steam engines and mining machinery. A shipyard was added in 1883 and in the late 1880s the firm began building large warships for the U.S. Navy, including the battleship Oregon.

To machine the large workpieces required, the firm built a number of large machine tools, including the open side planer shown below. Note the very heavy V shaped brace behind the bridge. The workpiece, shown below as supported on an outrigger, is the ram for the battleship OHIO building in 1899.

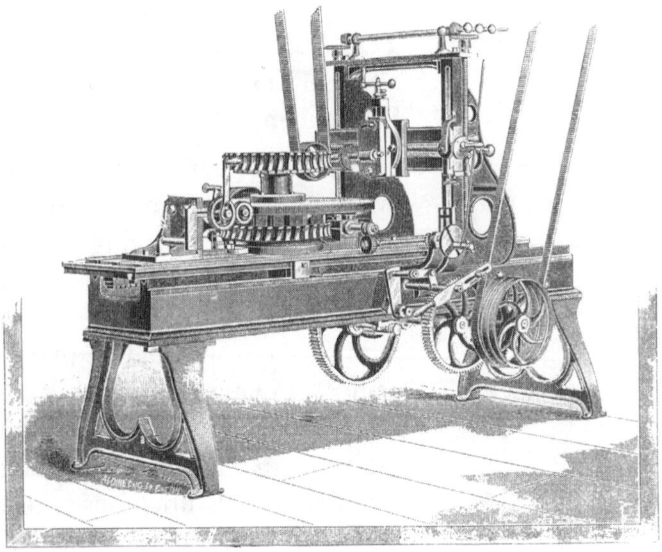

UNION MACHINE CO.,
Providence, RI

Maker, in 1889, of a planer attachment, shown left, for cutting spur and worm gears on a planer.

UNION WORKS, South Boston, MA

Founded about 1848 by Seth Wilmarth (1810-1886) who remained the proprietor until his death. The firm designed and made very large lathes (up to 15' swing x 50' bed) and planers (up to 10' x 60').

The planer shown next page (Figs.1-2) was built for the Charlestown Navy Yard in 1863 and could plane 18' wide, 14' high and 20' long. A planer with a unique side head (Fig.3) was patented by Wilmarth on January 1, 1869.

Fig.1

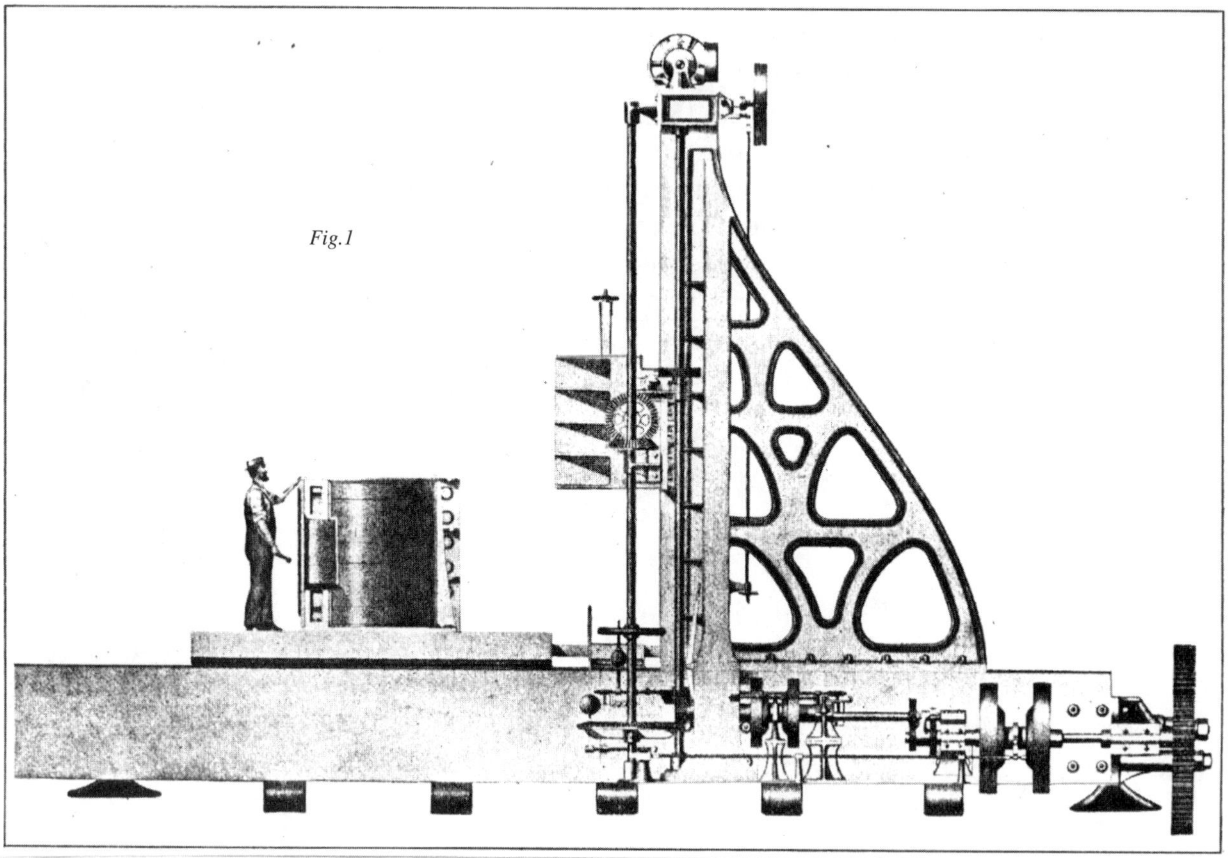

Fig.2

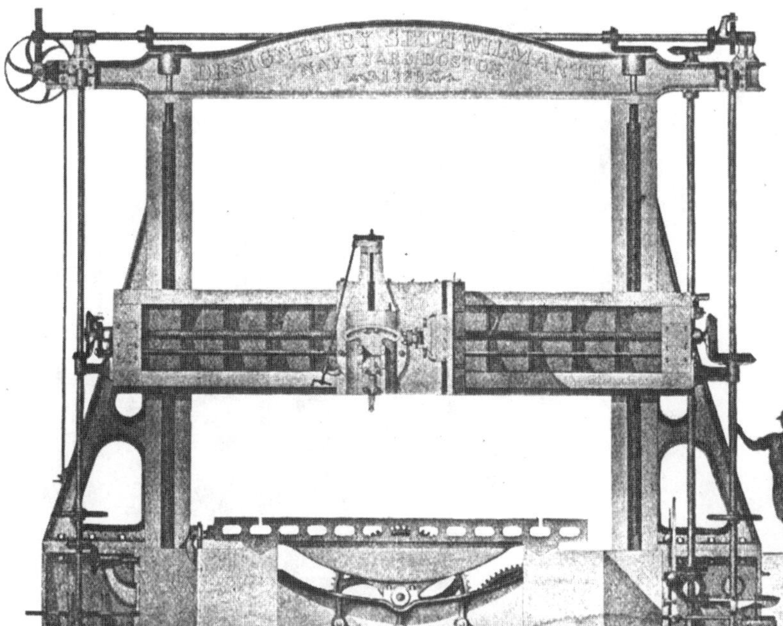

Fig.3

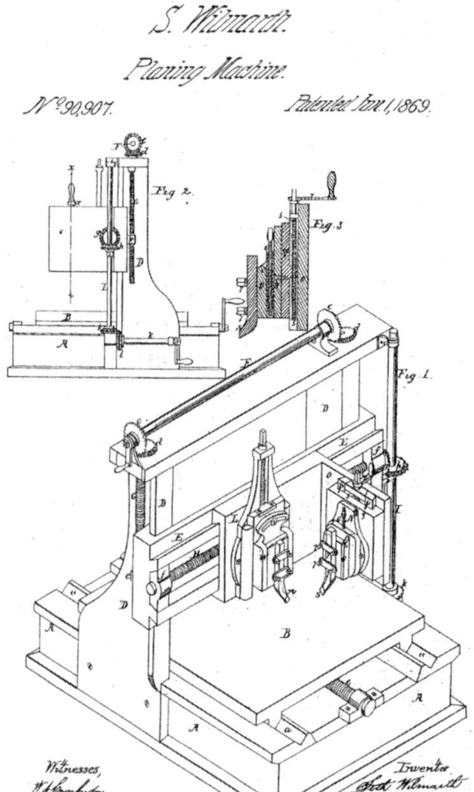

VAN HAAGEN & CO., C., Philadelphia, PA

A partnership of Claus Van Haagen and his brother Anthony Van Haagen formed about 1870. In 1875 the brothers advertised themselves as "makers of improved machine tools" and offered twist drill grinding machines, rotary shapers, planers, and drilling machines. The rotary shaper (Fig.1), a combination planing, turning and slotting machine, was patented October 11, 1870, by Claus Van Haagen; the planers were patented June 18, 1872, (Fig.2) and May 30, 1876, (Fig.3).

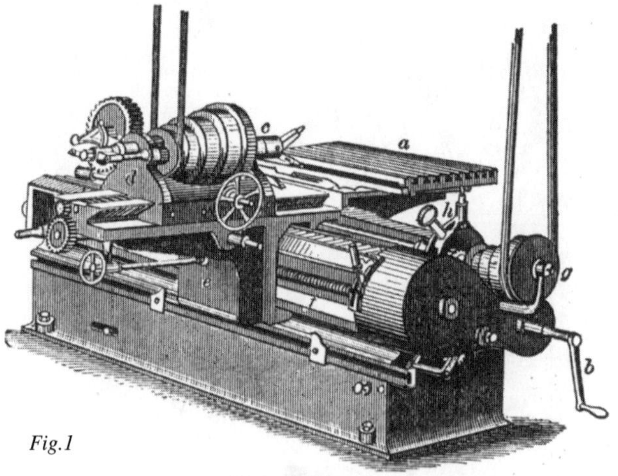

Fig.1

Rotary Shaper.

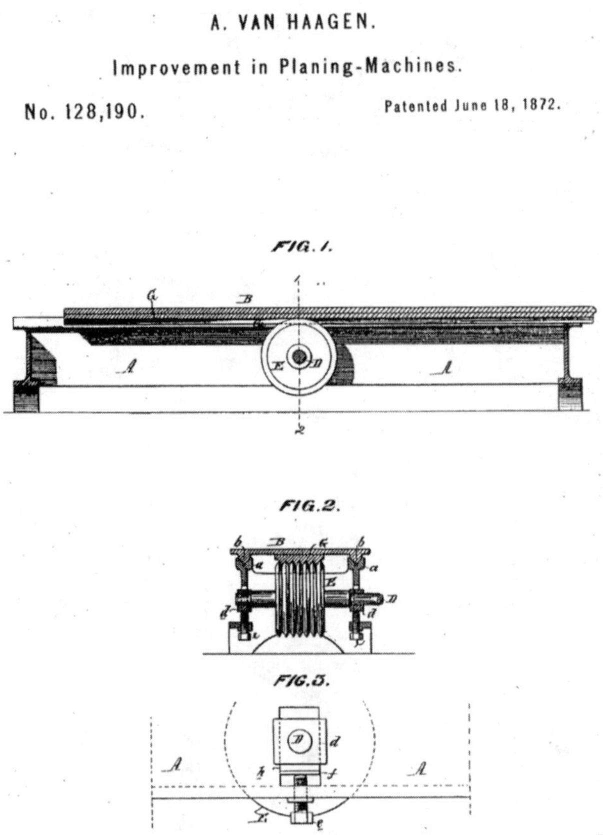

Fig.2

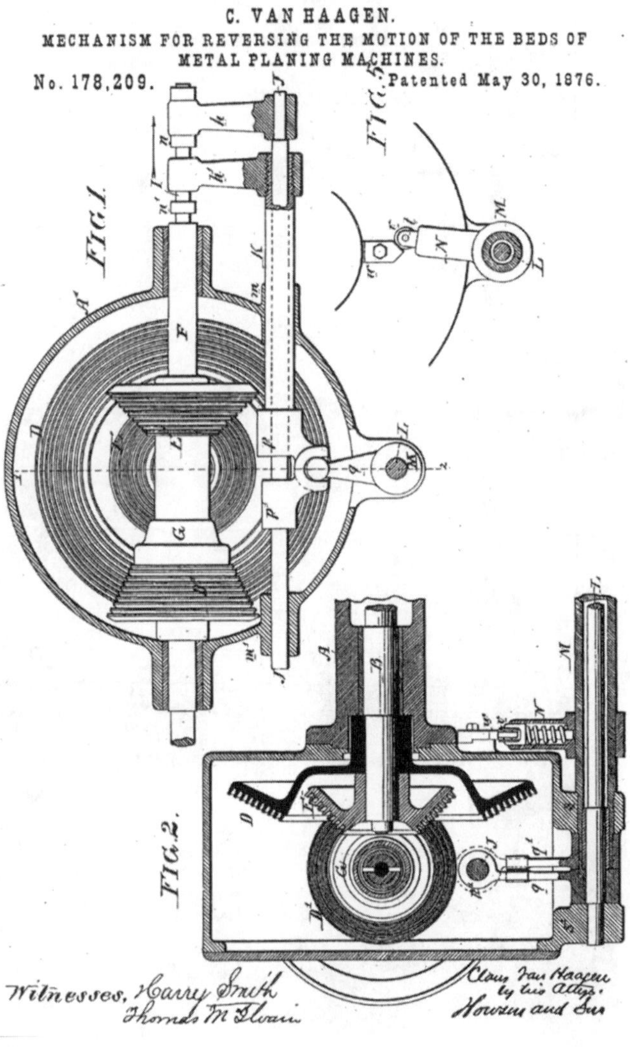

Fig.3

WALCOTT & SON, GEORGE D., Jackson, MI, later

WALCOTT & WOOD MACHINE TOOL CO., Jackson, MI

A partnership of George D. Walcott and his son Edward A Walcott (1860-1904) formed in 1881. George Walcott's daughters, Martha C. Walcott and Caroline L. Walcott, with Erwin E. Wood, reorganized the firm as the WALCOTT & WOOD MACHINE TOOL CO. in 1907.

The firm is best known for shapers, with production of 22" and 24" models beginning in 1881. In 1888 Walcott offered shapers in 15" (Fig.1), 24" and 32" strokes. Improved 22" (Fig.2) and 48" (Fig.3) sizes were introduced in 1890. By 1900 geared shapers were offered in 15", 22", 26", 30", 34" and 48" strokes, and elliptical gear crank shapers in 14" (Fig.4), 16" and 18" (Fig.5) strokes. 1909 production included a new 20" crank shaper (Fig.6) with extension bed and outboard support. *(continued next page)*

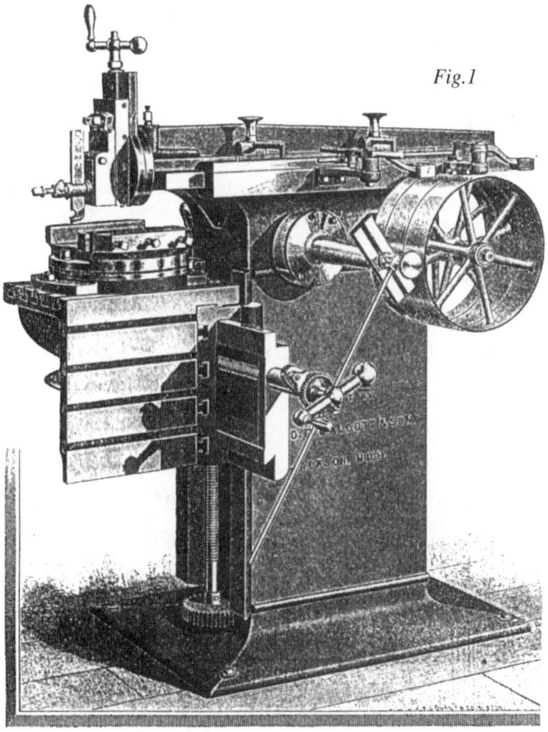

Fig.1

Fig.2

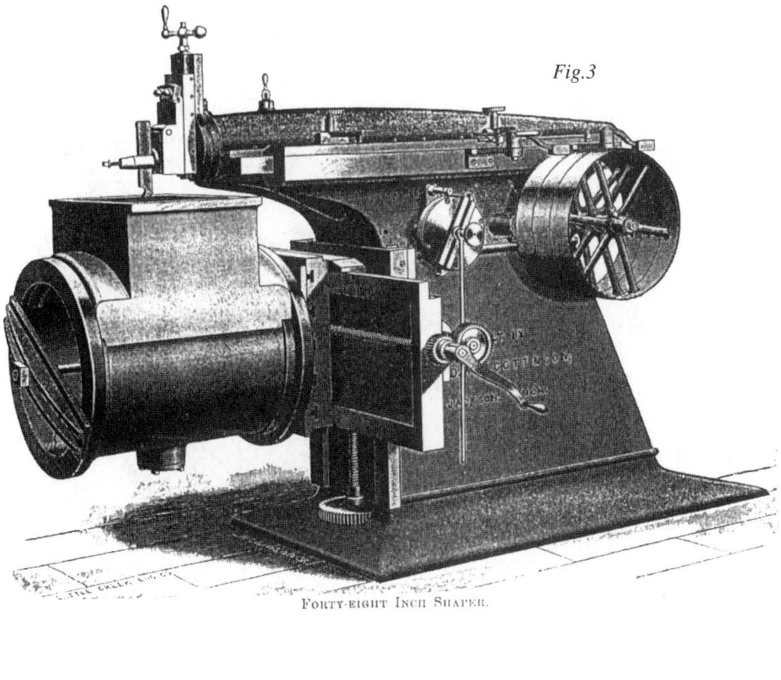

Fig.3

Forty-eight Inch Shaper.

Fig.4

14 in. Elliptical Gear Crank Shaper.

Fig.5

18-INCH ELLIPTICAL GEAR CRANK SHAPER.

Fig.6

WALKER, E.A., Philadelphia, PA

Builder, beginning in 1882, of Richard's patent combination planer and shaper (Fig.1). The machine was designed by John Richards, superintendent of the San Francisco Tool Co. The patent was owned by Geo. Richards & Co., Manchester, England, which appears to have made the machine in England while Walker made it in the U.S. Technically, the machine is a shaper but the longer than normal tool travel gives it a characteristic of a planer. A slightly different model (Fig.2) was offered in 1886, with an improved version available in 1900 (Fig.3). *(continued next page)*

Fig.1

Fig.3

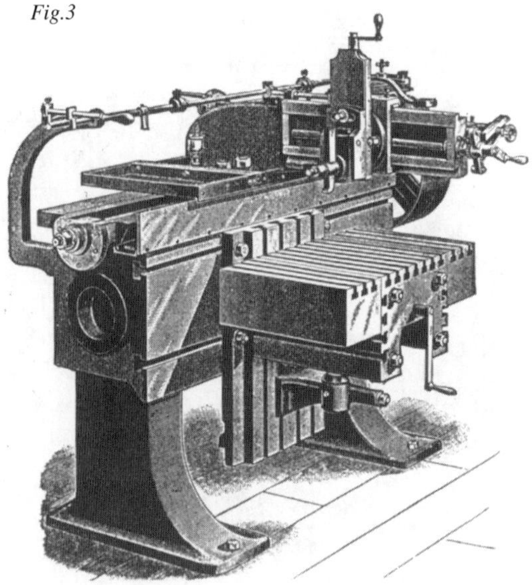

Fig.2

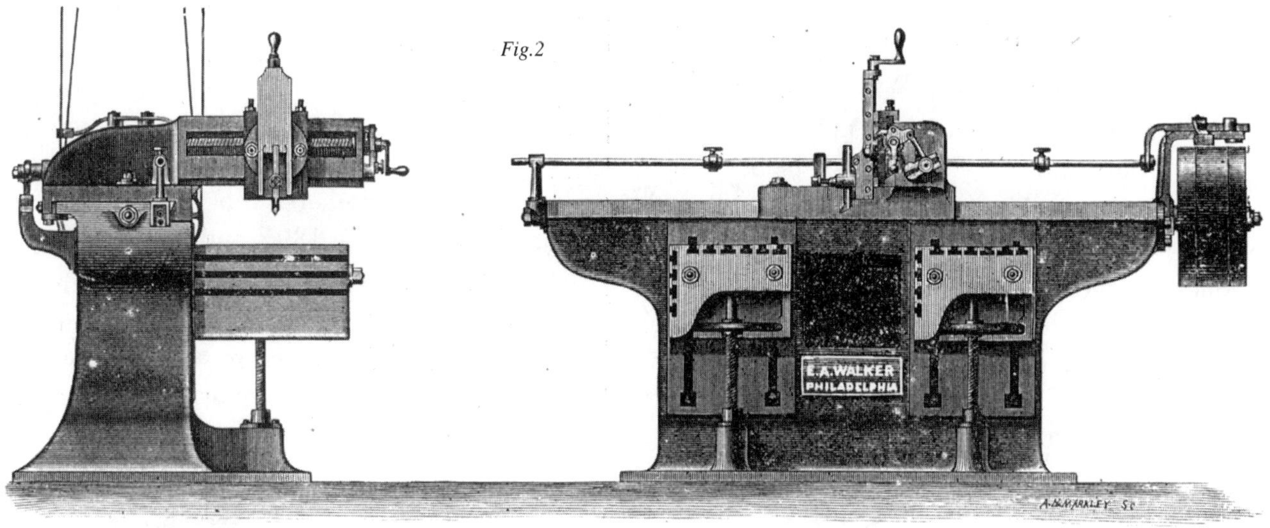

Combinel Planer and Shaper.

WALTER BROTHERS, Bridgeport, CT, later
WALTER, E.P., Bridgeport, CT

Founded about 1882 by Edward P. Walter and his brother Henry C. Walter to build planers, including a 16" x 42" model (Fig.1). The partnership was dissolved in 1887 and was reorganized as E.P. Walter. By 1901, Walter also offered 24" shapers (Fig.2).

Fig.1

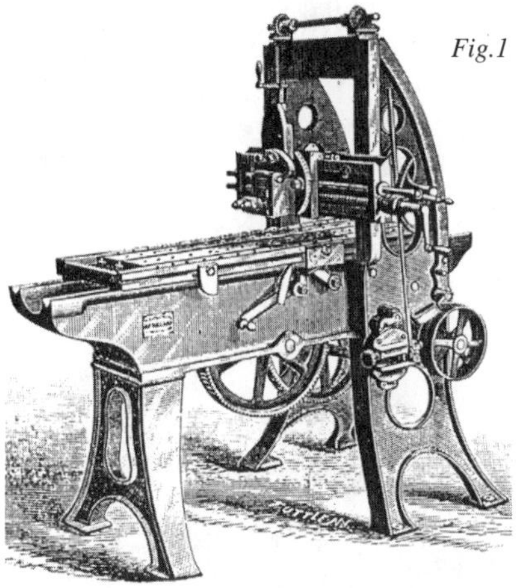

The "Walter" 16x42-Inch Planer.

FOR SALE.
PROMPT DELIVERY.
This new 24-inch stroke
SHAPER.

BARGAIN.

E. P. WALTER,
P. O. Box 151,
Bridgeport, Conn.

Special machines built to order.

Fig.2

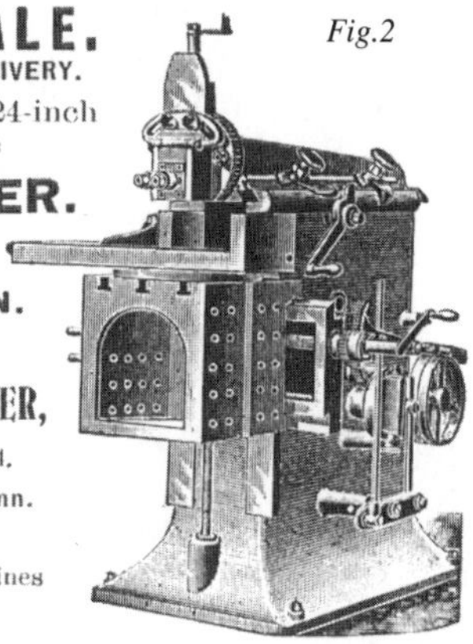

WARNER, WHITNEY & CO., Nashua, NH

A partnership of David A.G. Warner and George Whitney, formed as a reorganization of Gage, Warner & Whitney when John H. Gage died in 1862. One of their fluted column slotters, right, made during the Civil War, was photographed still in use in 1937. The Perkins Machine Co., a machine tool builder, was using the machine but, it was careful to note, the slotter "is not typical of their other machine equipment."

WARREN, W.H., Worcester, MA, later

WARREN MACHINE TOOL WORKS, W.H., Worcester, MA

Working at WOOD, LIGHT & CO., William H. Warren (1839-1899) was granted several patents for planers and shapers from 1868 to 1872, and for a planer chuck, March 10, 1868, which was made by several firms. By 1880, Warren was building shapers, die slotters and radial drills on his own. He reorganized as the W.H. WARREN MACHINE TOOL WORKS in 1888, sold out to James A. Colvin in 1896, and died in 1899.

Products included Warren's improved, 14" stroke x 42" traverse, shaper (Fig.1) introduced in 1883; a combination slotting, drilling and milling machine (Fig.2) designed for gear work up to 20" diameter and with a 4" stroke, introduced in 1888; 26" stroke, 70" traverse head shapers (Fig.3) designed for ordnance work were built in 1889; and a 17" stroke, 34" traverse head shaper (Fig.4) with Whitworth quick-return and weighing 8800 lbs. was introduced in 1895.

Warren's Improved Shaper.

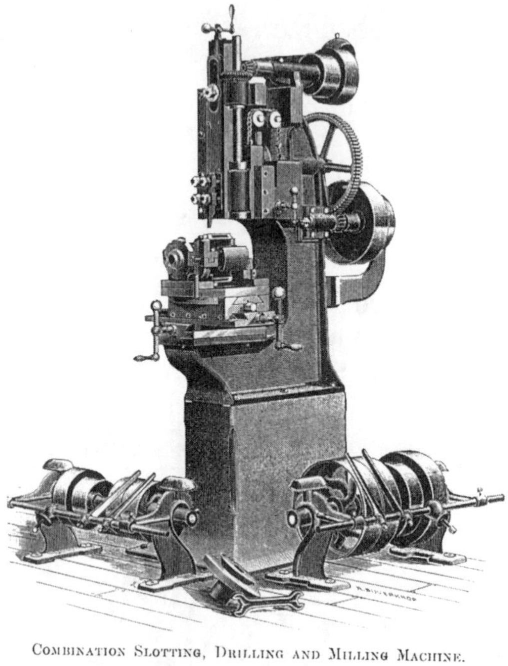

COMBINATION SLOTTING, DRILLING AND MILLING MACHINE.

Fig.3

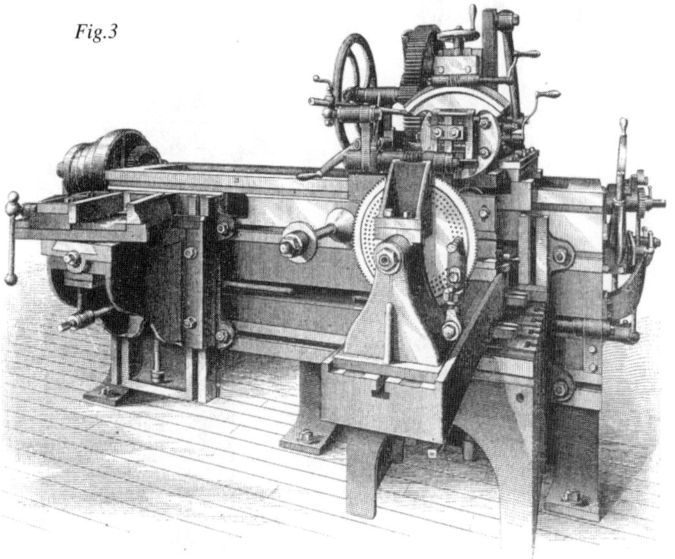

SHAPING-MACHINE FOR GUN-WORK, BUILT BY W. H. WARREN.

Fig.4

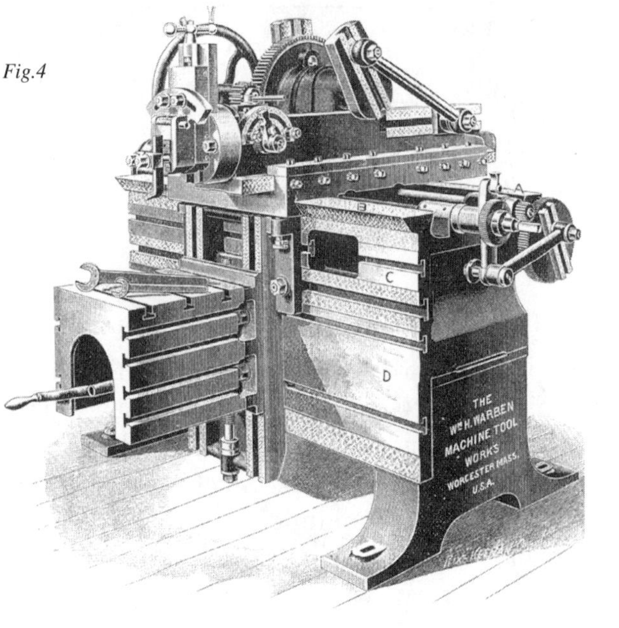

THE WARREN TRAVERSE HEAD SHAPER.

WATTS & BELCHER, Newark, NJ, later
WATTS, CAMPBELL & CO., Newark, NJ, later
WATTS, CAMPBELL CO., Newark, NJ

Founded in 1850 by George Watts, the firm operated until Belcher's death in 1856. Watts was then joined by his brother William Watts (1825-1883). The brothers reorganized as Watts, Campbell & Co. when Daniel T. Campbell joined in 1865 and incorporated as the Watts, Campbell Co. November 1, 1883.

The firm built steam engines and other machinery as well as planers, shapers, drills, and lathes. In 1882, a 54" x 20' planer was built for the Fort Pitt Foundry.

WHEELER & CO., J.S., Worcester, MA

A partnership of Johsua S. Wheeler, Asa N. Wheeler and Orange Wheeler, formed in 1867 to build lathes, planers, upright drills, milling machines, gear cutters and other items as shown in their 1872 ad (Fig.1).

Planers (Fig.2) were offered in 18 sizes (Fig.3) in 1874. Comparing the Wheeler planer with those made by Wood & Light c1865, it is clear that Wheeler used the Wood & Light design feed mechanism, or that Wood & Light actually made the planers offered by Wheeler. The firm operated until 1905.

J. S. WHEELER & CO.,
Manufacturers and Dealers in
Machinists' Tools.
Lathes, Planers, Upright Drills, Milling Machines, Gear Cutters, Planer Centres, Chucks, Shafting, Pulleys, Hangers, Patterns, Models, &c., &c.

Fig.1

Length of Bed.	To plane in length.	To plane in width.	To plane in height.	Weight.	Price.
Feet. In.	Feet.	Inches.	Inches.	Pounds.	
5	3	18	18	1,600	$437
6 8	4	22	22	2,600	540
8 4	5	22	22	2,900	592
8 4	5	26	26	5,000	695
10	6	26	26	5,400	757
11 6	7	26	26	5,800	818
10	6	30	30	6,500	860
12 8	8	30	30	7,100	1004
16	10	30	30	7,700	1148
12 8	8	36	36	13,000	1133
16	10	36	36	13,800	1339
18	12	36	36	14,600	1545
21	14	36	36	15,400	1751
24	16	36	36	16,200	1957
30	20	36	36	17,800	2369
24	16	42	42	20,000	2111
30	20	42	42	23,000	2729
36	25	42	42	26,000	2347

Fig.2

Fig.3

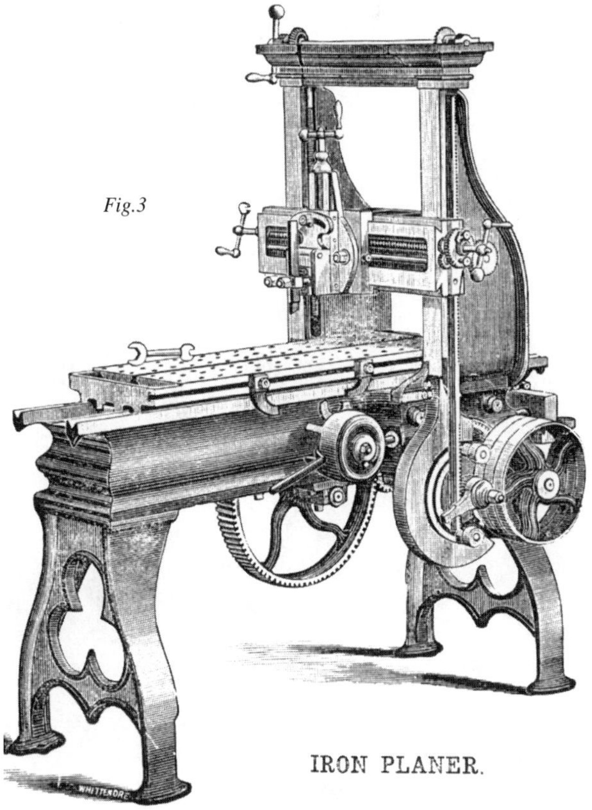

IRON PLANER.

WHEELER, WILLIAM A., Worcester, MA

Founded in 1823 when Wheeler established the first foundry in Worcester. In 1836, the firm employed 25 men, turning out 700,000 pounds of castings annually. Machine tool production began about 1835 and, by 1840, Wheeler had ten men building wooden bed, chain feed lathes. He is reported to have also made planers.

WHITCOMB & CO., C., Worcester, MA, later
WHITCOMB MFG. CO., Worcester, MA

A partnership of Carter Whitcomb and his brother Alonzo Whitcomb (1818-1900), formed in 1849 to build engine lathes and planers. Lathe production appears to have ceased prior to 1876 as the firm began to specialize in planers.

In 1881, Carter Whitcomb left and Alonzo Whitcomb merged the firm with Rice & Whitcomb to form the Whitcomb Mfg. Co. which, in 1882, employed 35 hands "building iron planers." Alonzo Whitcomb, Jr. (1862-1936) took over when his father died in 1900, operating the firm until 1905 when he merged with P. Blaisdell & Co. to form the Whitcomb-Blaisdell Machine Tool Co.

Planer production began with the Gothic style such as the 24" x 24" x 6 1/2' size offered in 1856 (Fig.1). By 1874, the Gothic styling was less pronounced and construction was heavier throughout (Fig.2) and, by 1880, the 17" crank planer was free of ornamentation (Fig.3). The 1893 catalog offered planers in 17" x 17" x 4', 22" x 22" x 5', 24" x 24" x 6' (Fig.4), 27" x 27" x 6', 30" x 30" x 8' (Fig.5), and 36" x 36" x 10'. *(continued next three pages)*

Fig.1

C. WHITCOMB & CO.,

MANUFACTURERS OF

Machinists' Tools

OF ALL KINDS. ALSO,

COPYING PRESSES OF ALL SIZES.

The Manufacture of Planing Machines for Working Metals a Specialty.

(Valuable Patents on Planers Secured.)

Fig.3

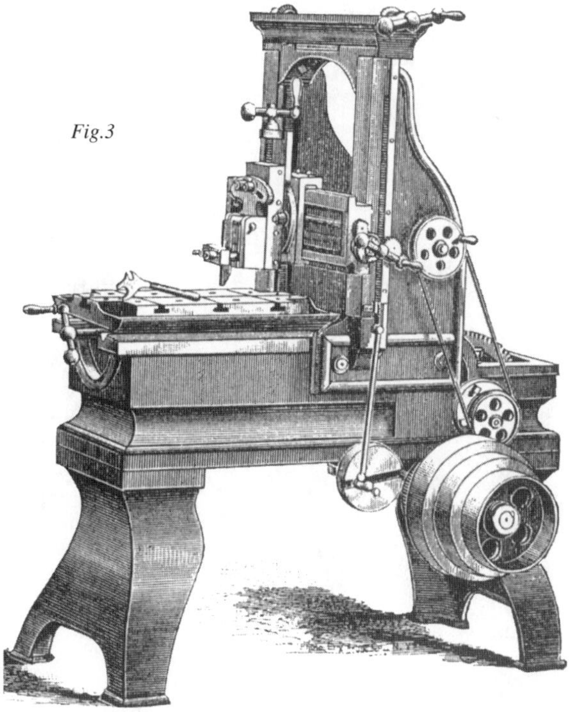

Fig.2

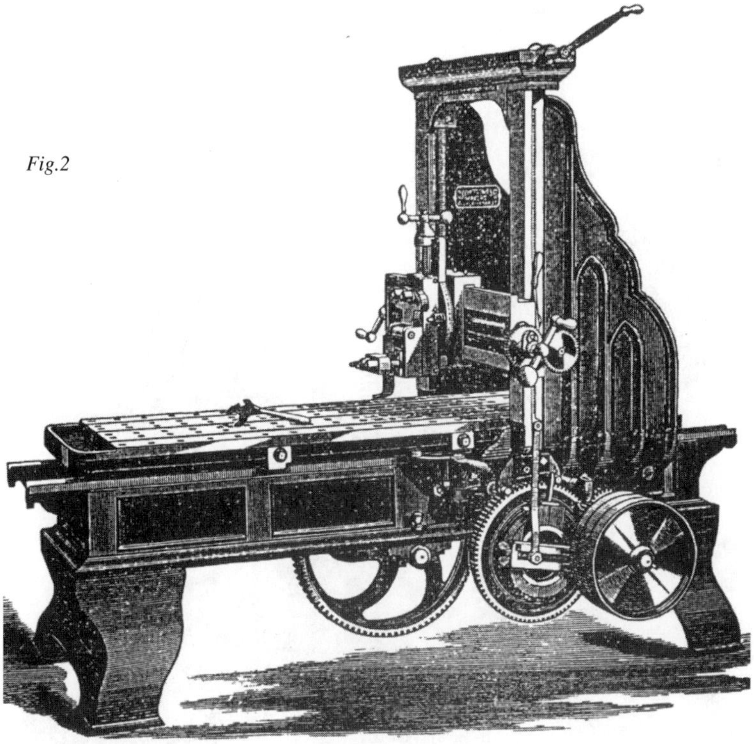

61 Jackson Street, corner of Railroad,

WORCESTER, MASS.

24 x 24 Inch Planers.

Fig.4

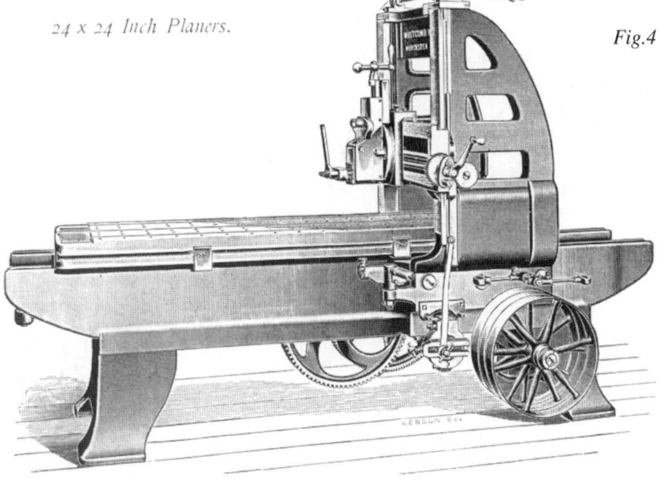

1900 production included 17" x 17" crank planers with stroke adjustable from 0" to 12" (Fig.6) and a line of improved planers from 17" to 48" size including 25" x 25" x 6' (Fig.7) and 42" x 42" x 10 (Fig.8). By 1903 the line, still available in 17" to 48" sizes, had been redesigned with a more rigid bed (Fig.9) and the Whitcomb "second belt" drive which replaced the first, and thus fastest, set of gears with a belt and was claimed to give "speeds that would soon ruin a geared planer" and to "run the machine without shock or jar."

30 x 30 Inch Planers.

Fig.5

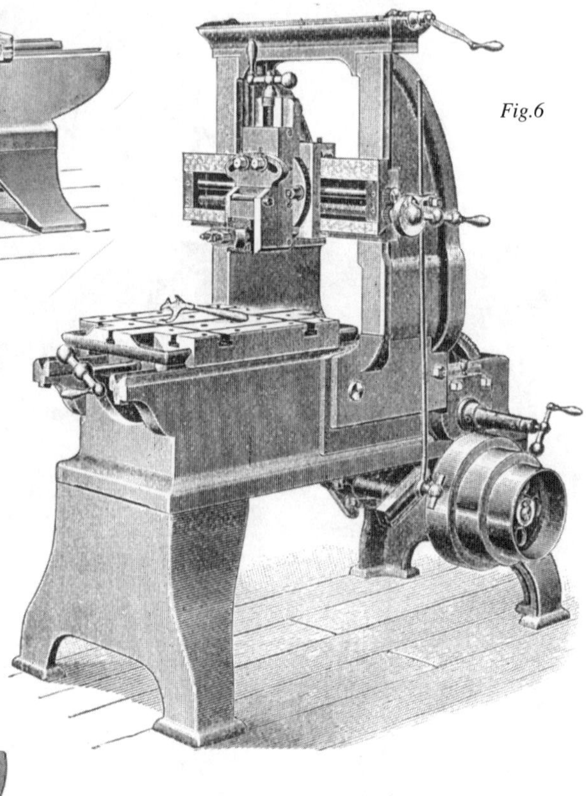

Fig.6

Fig.7

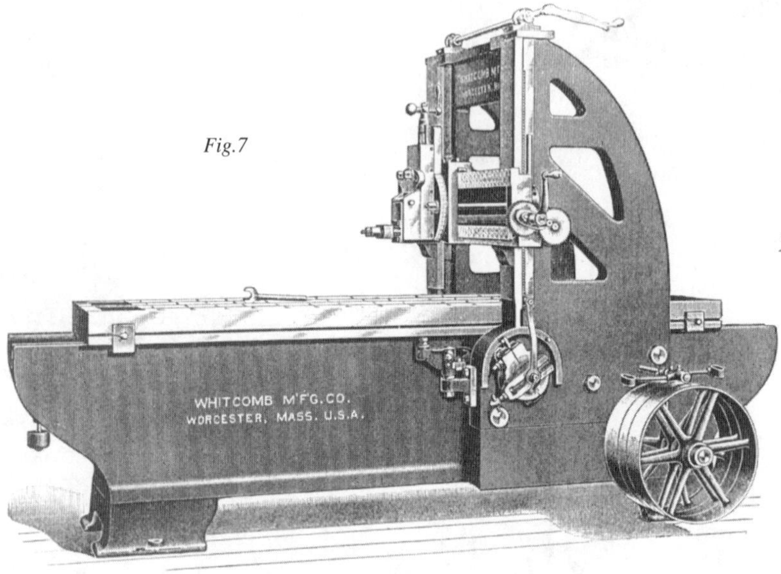

25 in. x 25 in. x 6 ft. Planer, with second-belt drive.

24-inch Whitcomb Planer

Fig.9

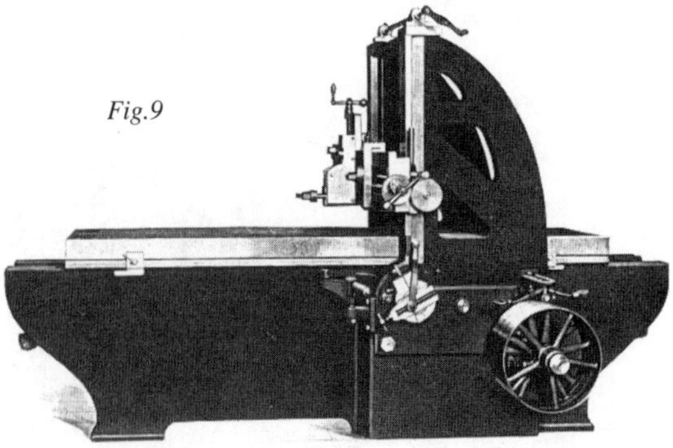

Whitcomb Mfg, Co.

Fig.8

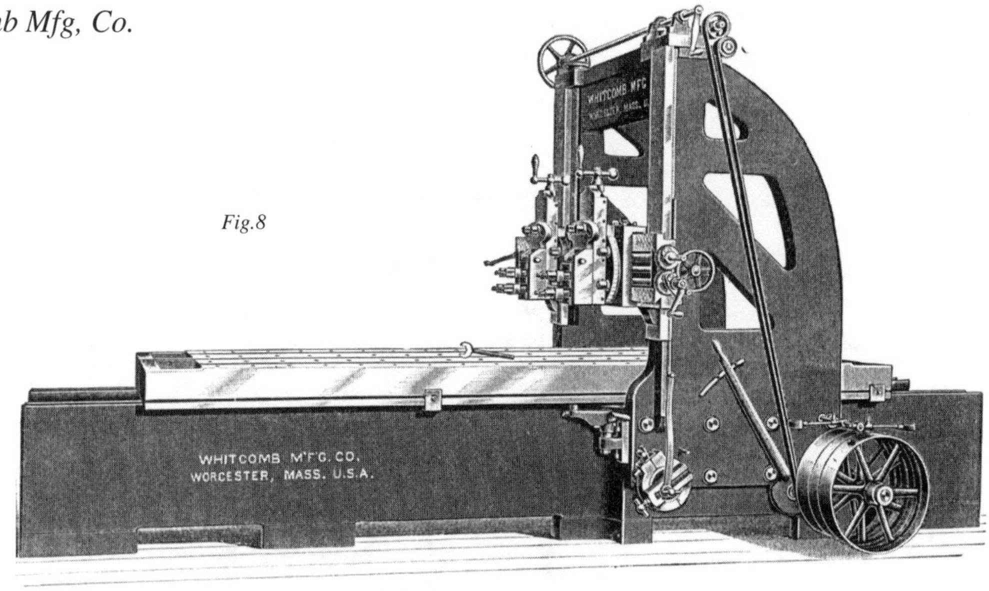

42 in. x 42 in. x 10 ft. Planer.

WHITCOMB-BLAISDELL MACHINE TOOL CO., Worcester, MA

Formed in 1905 by merger of the Whitcomb Mfg. Co. and P. Blaisdell & Co. Capital was $200,000; Alonzo W. Whitcomb was president.

Products built by the new firm included lathes and drilling machines previously made by P. Blaisdell and planers previously made by the Whitcomb Mfg. Co.

1910 planer production, right, was limited to four sizes; 22", 24", 26" and 30", all with the Whitcomb "second belt" planer drive.

WIGHT & POWELL, Worcester, MA

A partnership of Joseph H. Wight and Albert M. Powell formed March 1, 1881, to build engine lathes and 25" x 25" planers. Wight left the firm later in 1881 and Powell reorganized as A.M. Powell & Co.

WILKINSON & CO., A.J., Boston, MA

A partnership of Andrew J. Wilkinson and W.H. Wilkinson, the firm was a large Boston machine and tool dealership and supply house. It claimed to have been established in 1842.

Wilkinson also operated as a manufacturer of precision tools and small machinery. About 1880, Wilkinson began building a high quality hand and power planer. Weighing 375 pounds and planing 30" long, 12 1/2" wide and 8 1/2" high, this was one of the larger hand planers. The machine, shown on next page, was priced at $165 with a stand available for another $16. Production continued until about 1900.

A.J. Wilkinson & Co.

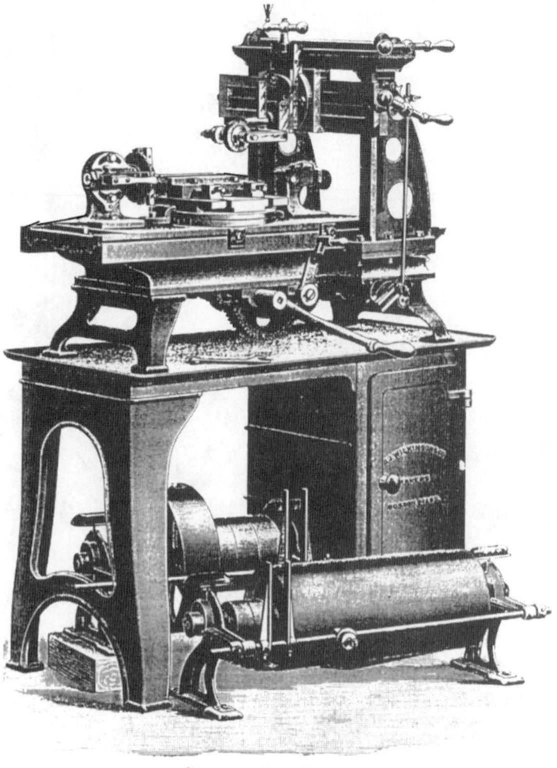

Power or Hand Planer.

WILSON & SHUGART, Philadelphia, PA

A partnership of Edgar Wilson and Charles H. Shugart formed in 1882 to build machine tools. Both were formerly with the American Machine Co.

WILSON, W.A., Rochester, NY, later
WILSON MACHINE CO. W.A., Rochester, NY

Formed in 1892 by William A. Wilson as successor to planer builder G.E. Brettell. Wilson bought out Brettell and continued the planer line with slight improvements (Fig.1).

In 1900, Wilson introduced a new line of spur geared planers, including a 24" model in lengths from 5 to 10 feet (Fig.2), 26" model from 5 to 10 feet, 30" model from 6 to 16 feet (Fig.3) and 36" model from 8 to 20 feet. All models had a forward speed of 20'/min. and reverse of 60'/min. *(continued next page)*

Fig.1

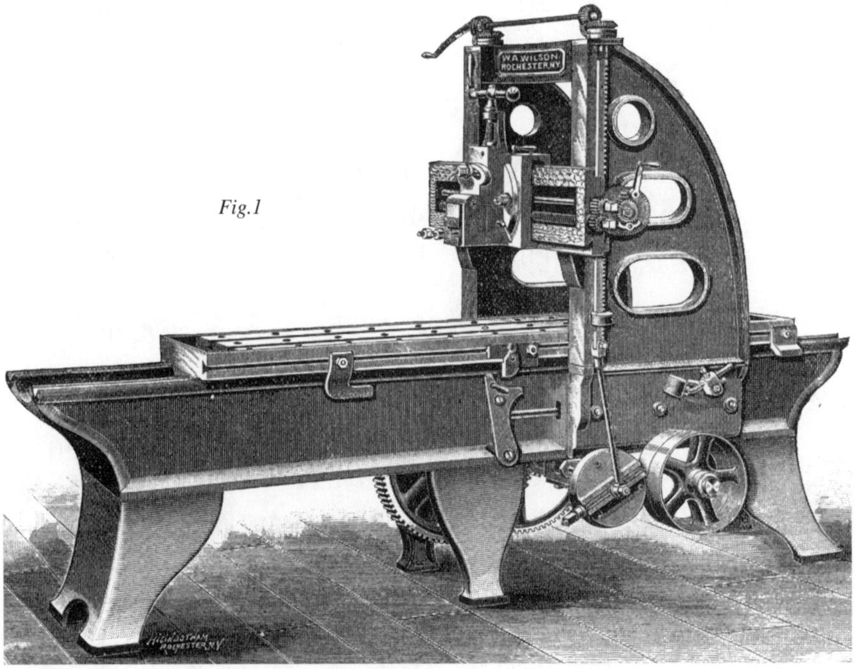

In 1901, the firm reorganized as the W.A. WILSON MACHINE CO. with Wilson as president and treasurer. Wilson died in 1917 and the company went out of business in 1920.

Fig.2

IMPROVED IRON PLANER

24-INCH SPUR GEARED PLANER

PLANES IN WIDTH	PLANES IN HEIGHT	PLANES IN LENGTH	WEIGHT ABOUT
24-in.	24-in.	5 feet	5,300 lbs.
24-in.	24-in.	6 feet	5,900 lbs.
24-in.	24-in.	7 feet	6,400 lbs.
24-in.	24-in.	8 feet	6,900 lbs.
24-in.	24-in.	9 feet	7,400 lbs.
24-in.	24-in.	10 feet	7,900 lbs.

Fig.3

IMPROVED IRON PLANER

30-INCH SPUR GEARED PLANER

PLANES IN WIDTH	PLANES IN HEIGHT	PLANES IN LENGTH	WEIGHT ABOUT
30-in.	30-in.	6 feet	8,200 lbs.
30-in.	30-in.	7 feet	8,900 lbs.
30-in.	30-in.	8 feet	9,600 lbs.
30-in.	30-in.	10 feet	11,000 lbs.
30-in.	30-in.	12 feet	12,400 lbs.
30-in.	30-in.	14 feet	13,800 lbs.
30-in.	30-in.	16 feet	15,200 lbs.

WINDSOR MFG. CO., Windsor, VT

Formed in 1865 by Ebenezer G. Lamson (1814-1892) and his son Eastborne E. Lamson as a reorganization of E.G. LAMSON & CO. Henry D. Stone continued as superintendent.

The firm built quarrying machinery and a variety of other machines, including, planers, turret lathes and engine lathes based on Frederick W. Howe and Henry D. Stone designs originally developed for ROBBINS & LAWRENCE and also made by E.G. Lamson & Co. An advertising broadsheet, issued in 1865, lists milling machines, drills, lathes and four sizes of iron planers identical to Robbins & Lawrence products.

In 1869, the firm reorganized as JONES, LAMSON & CO., with Russell L. Jones as the senior partner.

WOOD, CHARLES, Worcester, MA, later

WOOD & BALLARD, Worcester, MA

Formed in 1867 when Charles Wood left the partnership of Blaisdell & Wood. Wood operated alone until 1869 when he was joined by Charles M. Ballard and formed the partnership of WOOD & BALLARD.

Wood's products included engine lathes, hand lathes, crank planers, five sizes of upright drills, patented July 16, 1867, and other machine tools.

WOOD, JENNISON & CO., Worcester, MA

A partnership of Aurin Wood (1812-1896) and S.S. Jennison formed in 1880 as a reorganization of the WOOD & LIGHT MACHINE CO. The firm continued production of most Wood & Light products but soon specialized in shafting lathes only.

WOOD, LIGHT & CO., Worcester, MA, later

WOOD & LIGHT MACHINE CO., Worcester, MA

A partnership of Aurin Wood (1812-1896) and Joseph F. Light formed in 1852 as a reorganization of Woodburn, Light & Co.

The firm reorganized as a stock company, the WOOD & LIGHT MACHINE CO. in 1874. Light was replaced by S.S. Jennison in 1880 and the firm became WOOD, JENNISON & CO.

Production, c1860, included 24" x 48" planers (Fig.1), A unique double-acting planer (Fig.2), 60" wide, a table 11' long, with posts in the center of the bed and cross bar and head on both sides of the uprights. The machine could plane duplicate work, up to 60" long, on each end of the table, cutting in both directions. Nearly all planer builders tried to minimize the lost time when planers were reversing; Wood, Light & Co. appears to have offered the most effective solution, but also the most expensive.

Fig.1

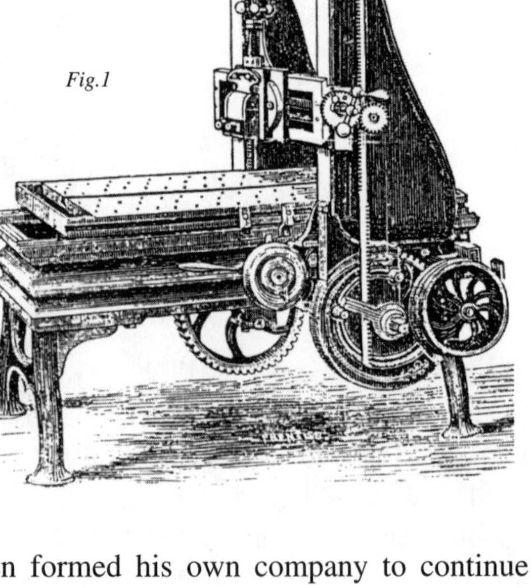

Crank planers, made under W.H. Warren's patent of January 14, 1868, (Fig.3) were offered in 1868.

Warren's patent (April 18, 1871) improved shaper (Fig.4), with 11" stroke and 24" traverse, was introduced in 1871. A traverse slotter version of the Warren shaper, patented August 6, 1872, (Fig.5) was offered in 1872.

In 1875, production included planers 24" x 23" x 4' (Fig.6) and 24" x 23" x 6'. Slotting machines, patented June 6, 1871, by W.H. Warren were introduced in 1871 (Fig.7).

When the Wood & Light Machine Co. failed in 1880, Warren formed his own company to continue production of shapers. *(continued next three pages)*

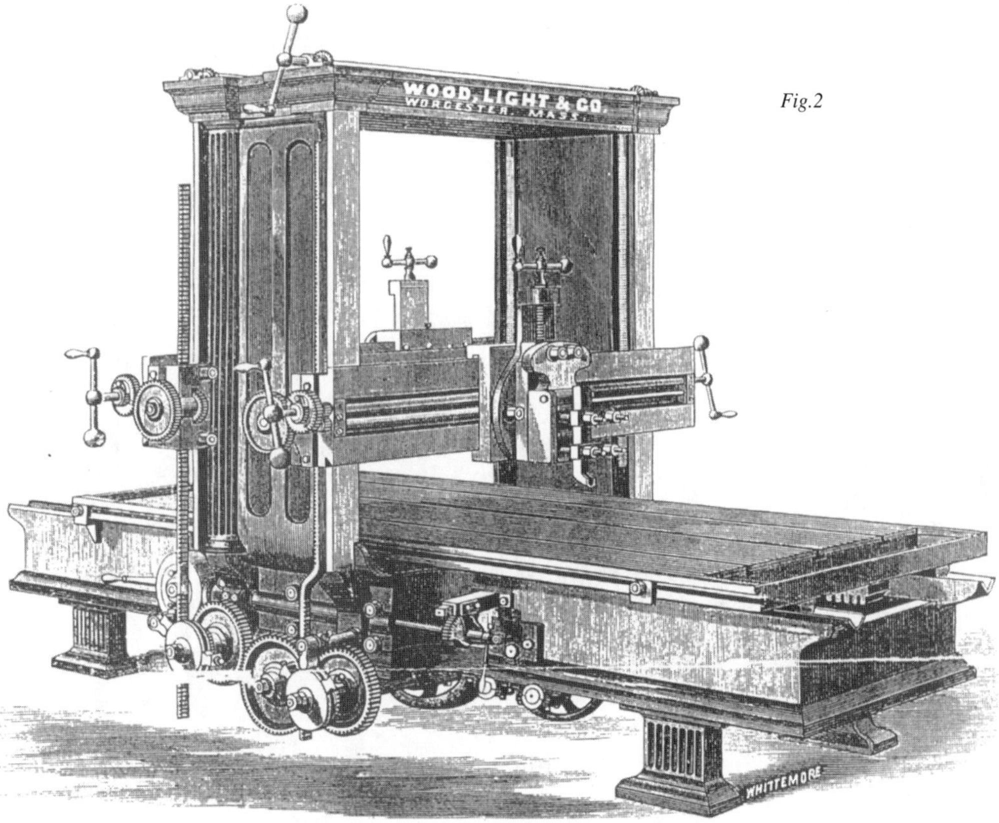

Fig.2

WOOD, LIGHT & CO.'S

DOUBLE-ACTING IRON PLANER

THIS Machine is 60 inches wide and table 11 feet long, with posts in center of bed, with cross bar and head upon each side. The tools when placed in the heads are 60 inches apart. The table runs same speed each way. For duplicate work, 60 inches and under in length, this Machine is well adapted. It will be seen, when placing one piece to be planed upon one end of Planer, and one upon the other end, that when the first piece has passed to the end, and the motion of the table reversed, the tool on the opposite side of post is ready to take a chip upon the second piece. This Machine takes no more power or room than a single acting planer, but will add a large per cent. to each day's work over the single acting planer.

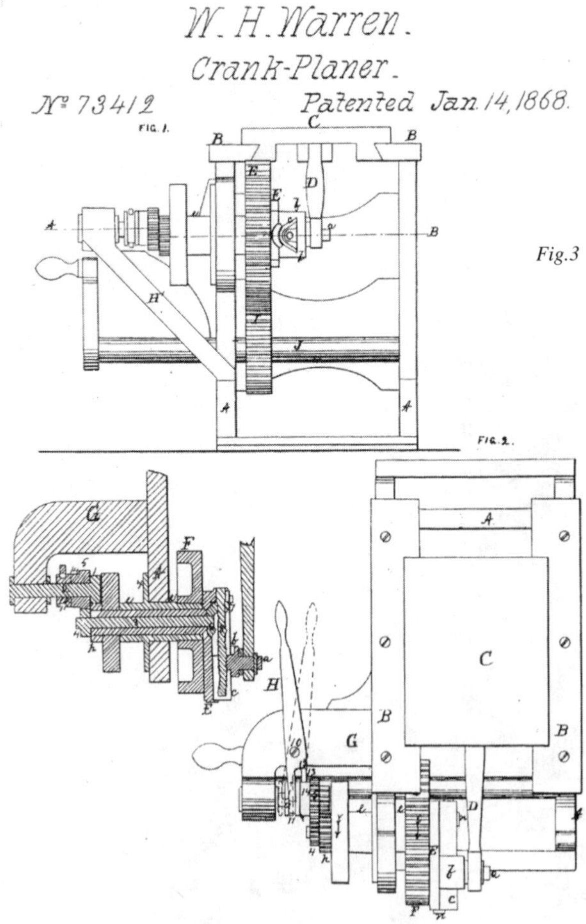

Fig.3

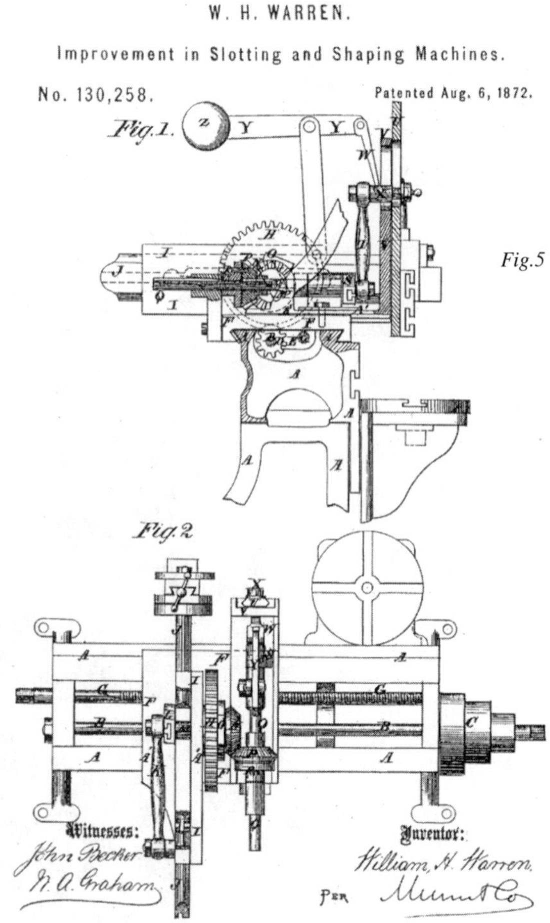

Fig.5

Fig.4

WARREN'S

PATENT IMPROVED SHAPER,

MANUFACTURED BY

WOOD, LIGHT & CO.,

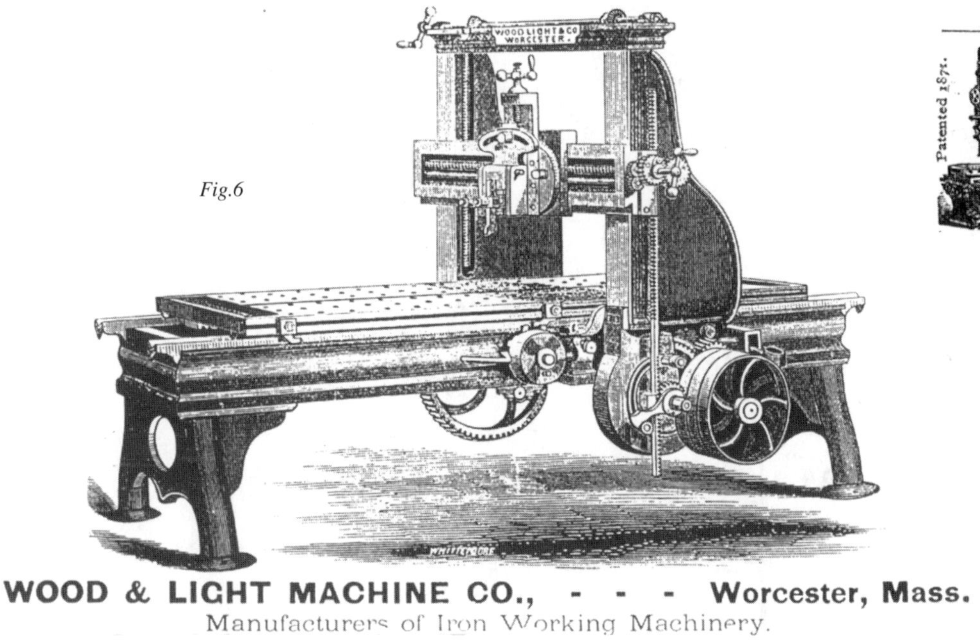

Fig.6

Fig.7

WOODBURN, LIGHT & CO., Worcester, MA

A partnership of Josiah Woodburn, Joseph Light, John Williams, and Charles Wood, formed in 1846 to build engine and hand lathes and planers "also screw cutting, iron planing and job work of every description at short notice." Woodburn left the firm in 1852 and was replaced by Aurin Wood. The firm was then reorganized as WOOD, LIGHT & CO.

WOODWARD & POWELL PLANER CO., Worcester, MA

Formed in 1899 as a reorganization of the POWELL PLANER CO. Edward M. Woodward (1846-1923) served as president until his death. Albert M. Powell served as vice president and secretary until selling out to Woodward in 1907.

Fig.1

1899 production (Fig.1) continued the Powell designs. By 1910, however, the line had been greatly expanded and the design was much heavier, more rigid (Fig.2) and included duplex planers which cut in both directions.

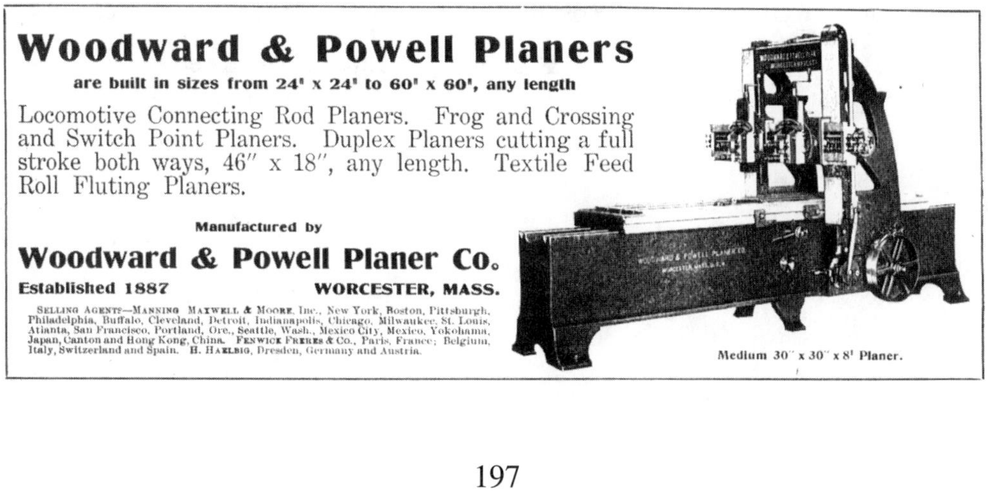

Fig.2

WORCESTER MACHINIST TOOL CO., Worcester, MA

Founded in 1856 and managed by Samuel Flagg who had previously operated SAMUEL FLAGG & CO. Other members of the firm were Dexter Flagg, Lemuel G. Mason, and Pierson Cowie. Operating through the civil war, the firm built planers and other machine tools such as shown in the 1856 ad below.

WORCESTER

MACHINIST TOOL COMPANY,

MAUFACTURERS OF

PLANING MACHINES FOR IRON,

ENGINE LATHES,

CHUCK AND HAND LATHES,

UPRIGHT DRILLS, &C.

THE PATTERNS OF THIS COMPANY
Are all new and of the most improved Style.

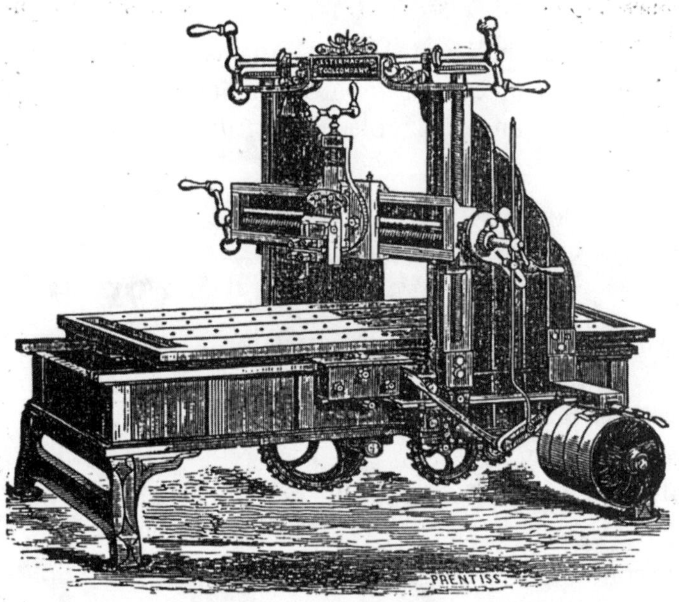

ALL WORK WILL BE WELL DONE
and at short notice, and ORDERS shall at all times
meet with prompt attention.

SHOP IN MERRIFIELD'S BUILDINGS,

Corner of Cypress and Foster Streets, - - Worcester, Mass.

SAMUEL FLAGG, Agent and Treasurer.

WORMWOOD, S.P., Boston and Watertown, MA

Builder, about 1885, of planer and milling machine chucks (Fig.1) and small power planers (Fig.2) that could plane 9" high, 6" wide and 24" long.

Fig.1

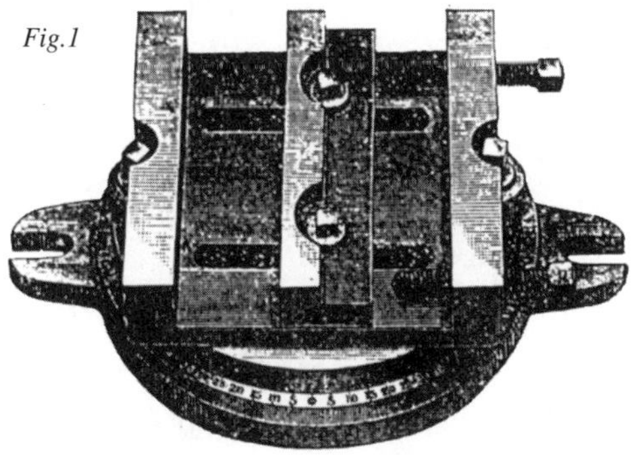

Fig.2

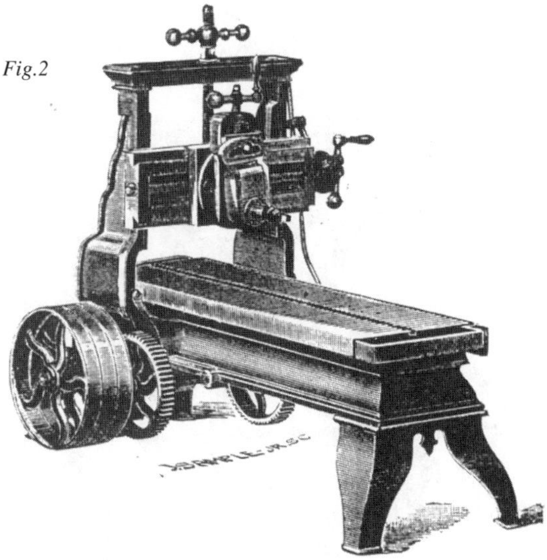

Planer, 24x9x6. Price, $110.00.

WRIGHT & CO., S.C., Fitchburg, MA

A partnership of Sylvester C. Wright (1816-1880) and his son-in-law James L. Chapman formed in May, 1864. In 1865, the firm offered "Machinists Tools Generally" which included lathes, planers and shapers.

On January 1, 1867, the partners reorganized as the FITCHBURG MACHINE CO., a stock company, with Wright as president.

WRIGHT, JOHN H., Bridgeport, CT

Builder of lathes and planers operating c1882-1883. He claimed to be using WOOD & LIGHT CO. patterns and to have been a contractor to Wood & Light. In 1883, Wright announced that he "recently brought out a new 24 x 23 inch friction planer and shaper combined. The capacity of the planer is 4 feet." No illustrations of the machine have been located.

WRIGHT & SONS, J.D., Brooklyn, NY

Builder, in 1890, of friction shapers (Fig.1) made with a worm and wheel drive, patented August 12, 1890, (Fig.2). The machines were equipped with a quick return stroke and tilting table for cutting angles.

Fig.1

Fig.2

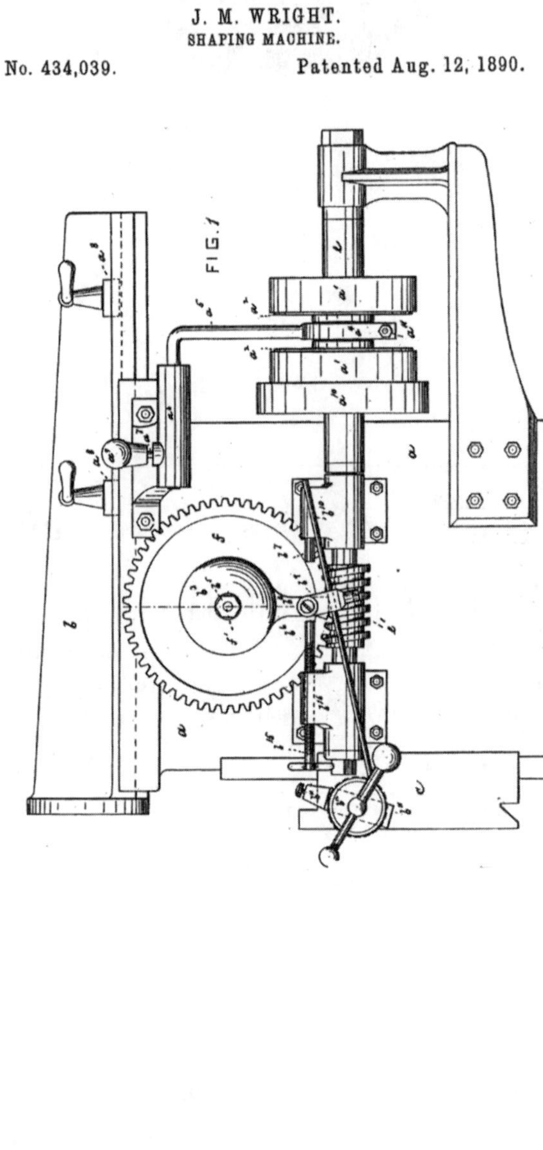